W9-ADZ-956

# SAMPLING THEORY

**McGRAW-HILL SERIES IN PROBABILITY AND STATISTICS**
**David Blackwell and Herbert Solomon,** Consulting Editors

# SAMPLING THEORY

**DES RAJ**
Sampling Expert, serving under the
United Nations Program of Technical Assistance

BRIAR CLIFF COLLEGE
LIBRARY
SIOUX CITY, IOWA

**McGRAW-HILL BOOK COMPANY**
New York     St. Louis     San Francisco     Toronto     London     Sydney

**Sampling Theory**

Copyright © 1968 by McGraw-Hill, Inc.   All Rights Reserved.
Printed in the United States of America.   No part of this
publication may be reproduced, stored in a retrieval system,
or transmitted, in any form or by any means, electronic,
mechanical, photocopying, recording, or otherwise, without
the prior written permission of the publisher.

*Library of Congress Catalog Card Number* 68-11618

51154

1234567890MAMM7543210698

QA
276.6
.R3

to **PUSHPA**

54925

# Foreword

We are living in a world in which most countries are making strenuous efforts to raise the living standards of their people. In order to achieve balanced development, carefully worked-out plans are drawn up and executed as far as possible. To formulate these plans in a scientific manner, it is essential to have basic facts in numerical terms for the various regions in the country and for the country as a whole.

It is beyond the resources of smaller countries to collect facts year after year from each person, establishment, or farm in the country. Fortunately, as we know now, it is not essential to enumerate each unit in the universe in order to arrive at an acceptable figure for the total. A carefully designed sample can provide the necessary information for guidelines that a country needs, at a cost the country may well afford.

The Statistical Office of the United Nations has been deeply concerned, since its organization in 1946, with ways and means to assist national governments to obtain the statistical data so indispensable for planning economic and social development, for checking on current implementation of programs, and for assessing results.

In this work, the United Nations has been assisted in two important ways. First, it has been aided by the United Nations Statistical Commission, which initiated and maintained a strong impetus toward the promotion and elaboration of sampling methods and toward the establishment of sampling offices in national governments. The Commission was greatly assisted in their efforts by the work of its Subcommission on Statistical Sampling, which recommended principles which could guide the development of suitable methodology in the developing countries. The composition of the Subcommission was enough to ensure the highest professional level of recommendations. Sir Ronald Fisher, Professor P. C. Mahalanobis, Dr. W. E. Deming, Dr. F. Yates, and Professor G. Darmois gave unstintingly of their time in elaborating the basic principles. In this work they were frequently joined by other distinguished experts.

Second, and this has been equally important in the development of national statistical systems, is the application of sampling methods to the practical problems encountered by developing countries. These countries generally had no long tradition of censuses, or similar periodic compilations, to use as a framework for sampling. The application of sampling methods that would produce acceptable results in such situations therefore required the utmost ingenuity.

Furthermore, the United Nations was fortunate in having the services of such experts as Dr. Des Raj under the auspices of the United Nations Technical Assistance Programs for practical field assignments. Dr. Des Raj has performed distinguished service in adapting theoretical principles to the practical conditions he found in one country in Southern Europe and one in Africa. At this writing he is continuing his service in another African country, especially oriented to training.

The book deals very competently with the application of sampling theory at an intermediate level; the operational conditions prevalent in many developing countries today are thoroughly considered. Taking into account the fact that most countries are now relying increasingly on sampling methods, the book bridges the gap between the highly theoretical material available and the application of methods in conditions that are far from optimum. This book is a very welcome addition to a literature which is far too scanty.

**W. R. Leonard,** Special Adviser
United Nations Institute
for Training and Research

**P. J. Loftus,** Director
Statistical Office
United Nations

# Preface

My objective in writing this book has been to provide an up-to-date account of sampling theory as it has been developed during the last three decades. The book is intended for students who want to learn sampling theory at an intermediate level and for research workers who need to be familiar with the latest developments in the subject. It should also serve as a reference work for the practicing statistician. The presentation is systematic and rigorous, and is based on the author's lectures to postgraduate students at the Indian Statistical Institute, Calcutta, and at Lucknow, Agra, Beirut, Athens, Addis Ababa, and Ibadan.

Probability theory forms the basis of sampling methods, and I have made no secret of this fact. A good working knowledge of algebra, calculus, and probability on the mathematical side, and of general statistical methods and elementary estimation theory on the statistical side is essential for a proper understanding of the rigorous development of sampling theory. Here and there, I have not hesitated to give an elegant proof which incorporates rather advanced mathematical tools. Most of the theory has been presented in the form of theorems, which are followed by remarks on the practical use of the results obtained and their interrelationships. Because sampling theory is meant to be used in practice, I have taken every opportunity to direct the reader's attention to the practical value of the results obtained.

I have started by proving a few theorems in mathematical expectation and some other results needed for developing the proofs in subsequent chapters. For a proper appreciation of sampling theory, Chapter 2 offers background information concerning the work of a sampling statistician in the field. Chapter 3 presents the three basic methods of sample selection—simple random sampling, systematic sampling, and sampling with probability proportionate to size. The use of auxiliary information by way of stratification and through ratio and regression estimation is explained in Chapters 4 and 5. Sampling and subsampling of clusters, double sampling procedures, and the problems peculiar to repetitive surveys form the subject matter of Chapters 6 and 7. How to plan the survey and analyze the data in the presence of response errors is discussed in Chapter 8. Developments not previously included, such as the stability of variance estimators, subpopulation analysis, etc., are discussed in Chapter 9. This is followed by a long exercises section, which forms an integral part of the book. The exercises carry the general theory beyond the stage reached in the text. They are based on about one hundred research papers published on the subject in different journals. The more difficult exercises are solved as they are presented. In all cases, references are given and the exact advance made is indicated.

In addition to the excellent books by Hansen et al., Cochran, Yates, Sukhatme, and Deming, there are a large number of research papers on sampling methods and theory. It is, therefore, difficult to make a detailed acknowledgement of all sources of material included in the book. Except for recent developments, no attempt has been made to trace the original sources of sampling theory.

This book could not have been written without the opportunity, made possible by the United Nations and the government of Greece, to use sampling methods on a variety of populations, for which I shall ever remain grateful. Also, thanks are due to Mrs. Kondouli-Baima for her patient help in typing.

**DES RAJ**

# Contents

SAMPLING THEORY

# CHAPTER ONE

# MATHEMATICAL PRELIMINARIES

## 1.1 INTRODUCTION

As the following chapters will show, probability forms the basis of sampling theory. Although some knowledge of probability theory is assumed on the part of the reader, we shall begin with a rapid review of the important concepts involved. A number of theorems will then be proved for subsequent use in the development of sampling theory. A few other useful results on the mathematical side, too, will be included in this chapter.

## 1.2 SAMPLE SPACE AND EVENTS

We shall be concerned with random experiments, the outcomes of which depend on chance. The results of a random experiment will be called sample points, and the aggregate of all sample points produced by the experiment will be called the sample space. Every outcome of the experiment is described by one, and only one, sample point. Any aggregate of the sample points will be called an event, which will be said to contain those points. We shall say that the event $H$ has occurred if the sample point representing the outcome of the experiment is contained in it. The event $\bar{H}$ consisting of all points not contained in $H$ will be called the complementary event. The totality of sample points contained in at least one of the two events $H_1$ and $H_2$ will be called the sum (or union) of $H_1$ and $H_2$ and will be denoted by $H_1 + H_2$. Further, the aggregate of sample points contained in both of the events $H_1$ and $H_2$ will be called the product (or intersection) of the two events and will be denoted by $H_1 H_2$. The events $H_1$ and $H_2$ are mutually exclusive if they have no points in common.

### 1.2.1 PROBABILITY

We shall be dealing with sample spaces in which the number of points is either finite or countably infinite (enumerable). Let the points of such a sample space be denoted by $E_1, E_2, \ldots$. With each point $E_i$ will be associated a nonnegative number, called the probability of $E_i$ (Feller, 1950) and denoted by $Pr(E_i)$ such that $\Sigma Pr(E_i) = 1$. The probability of an event $G$, denoted by $Pr(G)$, is then defined to be the sum of the probabilities of all sample points contained in it. For two events $G_1$ and $G_2$, it is easy to establish that

$$Pr(G_1 + G_2) = Pr(G_1) + Pr(G_2) - Pr(G_1 G_2) \qquad (1.1)$$

Further, it is convenient to express $Pr(G_1 G_2)$ as

$$Pr(G_1 G_2) = Pr(G_1) Pr(G_2 | G_1) \qquad (1.2)$$

where $Pr(G_2 | G_1)$ is called the conditional probability of the event $G_2$, given that the event $G_1$ has occurred. When $Pr(G_2 | G_1) = Pr(G_2)$, the event $G_2$ will be said to be independent of $G_1$. In this case we have

$$Pr(G_1 G_2) = Pr(G_1) P_r(G_2) \qquad (1.3)$$

### 1.2.2 RANDOM VARIABLES

Let there be a random experiment generating a sample space with its sample points $E_1, E_2, \ldots$ and the associated probabilities $Pr(E_1), Pr(E_2)$, $\ldots$. A function on this sample space will now be defined. Let there be a rule by which a number $U$ is associated with each point of the sample space. Following this rule, we assign real numbers $u_1, u_2, \ldots$ to the points $E_1, E_2, \ldots$, respectively. By collecting all points to which the number $u_i$ is attached, we form the event $U = u_i$, which will be interpreted to mean that "the random variable $U$ takes the value $u_i$." The set of relations:

$$Pr(U = u_i) = g(u_i) \qquad \Sigma g(u_i) = 1 \qquad (i = 1, 2, \ldots) \qquad (1.4)$$

defines the probability distribution of the random variable $U$.

Now let there be two random variables $U$ and $W$ defined on the same sample space. Let $U$ assume values $u_i$ $(i = 1, 2, \ldots)$ with probabilities $g(u_i)$ $(i = 1, 2, \ldots)$, and let $W$ assume the values $w_j$ with probabilities $h(w_j)$ $(j = 1, 2, \ldots)$. Then the set of relations:

$$Pr(U = u_i, W = w_j) = p(u_i, w_j) \qquad (i,j = 1, 2, \ldots) \qquad (1.5)$$
$$\Sigma\Sigma p(u_i, w_j) = 1$$

defines the joint probability distribution of $U$ and $W$.

The conditional probability of the event $W = w_j$, given that the event $U = u_i$ has occurred, will be defined as

$$Pr(W = w_j | U = u_i) = \frac{Pr(U = u_i, W = w_j)}{Pr(U = u_i)} = \frac{p(u_i, w_j)}{g(u_i)} \qquad (1.6)$$

In general this conditional probability will be different from the absolute probability $Pr(W = w_j)$, and the two random variables will be called dependent. In case

$$Pr(W = w_j | U = u_i) = Pr(W = w_j)$$

we have $\qquad Pr(U = u_i, W = w_j) = Pr(U = u_i)Pr(W = w_j)$

or $\qquad\qquad\qquad p(u_i, w_j) = g(u_i)h(w_j)$

If this equation holds for all combinations of $u_i, w_j$, the random variables $U$ and $W$ are called independent.

### 1.2.3  ILLUSTRATIONS

**1.**  There is a population (aggregate) of four units (objects) $A_1$, $A_2$, $A_3$, and $A_4$. If a pair of different units is to be selected, there will be six pairs in all, namely, $A_1A_2$, $A_1A_3$, $A_1A_4$, $A_2A_3$, $A_2A_4$, and $A_3A_4$. We agree to assign equal probabilities to all pairs so that each pair has a probability of $\frac{1}{6}$. Thus the random experiment consists in selecting two objects from a group of four. There are six outcomes of this experiment, giving six points in the sample space associated with this random experiment. Each point has a probability of $\frac{1}{6}$, the sum of probabilities of all the six points being unity. Consider the event $G_1$ that $A_3$ is included in the pair selected. There are three points in the sample space, namely, $A_1A_3$, $A_2A_3$ and $A_3A_4$, which give rise to the event $G_1$. Since each of these has a probability of $\frac{1}{6}$, the probability of the event $G_1$ or $Pr(G_1) = \frac{3}{6} = \frac{1}{2}$.

Consider another event $G_2$ in which $A_4$ is included in the pair selected.

Obviously, $Pr(G_2) = \frac{1}{2}$. The event $G_1G_2$ is said to occur when *both* $G_1$ and $G_2$ occur. Since there is only one sample point, $A_3A_4$, that gives rise to the joint appearance of $A_3$ and $A_4$, $Pr(G_1G_2) = \frac{1}{6}$. The event $G_1 + G_2$ that at least one of $G_1, G_2$ occurs contains the points $A_1A_3$, $A_1A_4$, $A_2A_3$, $A_2A_4$, and $A_3A_4$, and so $Pr(G_1 + G_2) = \frac{5}{6}$. Given that the event $G_1$ has occurred, the relevant sample points are $A_1A_3$, $A_2A_3$, and $A_3A_4$. In this part of the sample space the event $G_2$ has only one sample point, namely $A_3A_4$. To make the total probability unity on this part of the sample space, each point is given a probability of $\frac{1}{6} : \frac{1}{2} = \frac{1}{3}$. Thus $\frac{1}{3} = Pr(G_2|G_1)$, which is the conditional probability of $G_2$ given that $G_1$ has occurred. This is equivalent to saying that $Pr(G_2|G_1) = Pr(G_1G_2)/Pr(G_1)$ on the original sample space. Since $Pr(G_2|G_1) = \frac{1}{3} \neq \frac{1}{2} = Pr(G_2)$, the two events $G_1$ and $G_2$ are not independent. The absolute probability of $G_2$ is different from the conditional probability of $G_2$ given that $G_1$ has occurred.

**2.** Consider a collection of 16 different tickets, each bearing the pair $A_iA_j(i,j = 1, 2, 3, 4)$. The random experiment consists in selecting a ticket and noting down the pair on it. Then the sample space consists of the following 16 points:

| | | | | | | | |
|---|---|---|---|---|---|---|---|
| $A_1A_1$ | $A_1A_2$ | $A_1A_3$ | $A_1A_4$ | $A_2A_1$ | $A_2A_2$ | $A_2A_3$ | $A_2A_4$ |
| $A_3A_1$ | $A_3A_2$ | $A_3A_3$ | $A_3A_4$ | $A_4A_1$ | $A_4A_2$ | $A_4A_3$ | $A_4A_4$ |

Suppose that the eight sample points in the first row have a probability of $\frac{1}{24}$ each and that the other points have a probability of $\frac{1}{12}$ each. Consider the event $G_1$ in which $A_3$ is the first member of the pair selected. This event has four points, $A_3A_1$, $A_3A_2$, $A_3A_3$, $A_3A_4$ in it, and therefore $Pr(G_1) = \frac{1}{3}$. Similarly, the event $G_2$ in which $A_4$ is the second member of the pair has four points $A_1A_4$, $A_2A_4$, $A_3A_4$, $A_4A_4$, and so $Pr(G_2) = \frac{1}{4}$. The event $G_1G_2$, which consists of the joint occurrence of $G_1$ and $G_2$, has just one point in it and that is $A_3A_4$. Hence $Pr(G_1G_2) = \frac{1}{12}$. Given that $G_1$ has occurred, the only relevant sample points are $A_3A_1$, $A_3A_2$, $A_3A_3$, $A_3A_4$. In the sample space of this event, the event $G_2$ has one sample point, namely $A_3A_4$. Thus $Pr(G_2|G_1) = \frac{1}{4} = Pr(G_2)$. Whether or not we know that $G_1$ has occurred, the probability of $G_2$ is the same. The two events $G_1$ and $G_2$ are independent. We find that

$$Pr(G_1G_2) = Pr(G_1)Pr(G_2)$$

in this case. The event $G_1 + G_2$ that at least one of $G_1$ or $G_2$ occurs has seven points in it, from which we find that $Pr(G_1 + G_2) = \frac{1}{2}$.

3. Suppose a population consists of five families $F_1, F_2, F_3, F_4, F_5$, with incomes (measured on some scale) of 20, 60, 40, 20, and 60, respectively. The random experiment consists in selecting a pair of different families without regard to their order. Then the sample space has 10 points. Let each point have a probability of $\frac{1}{10}$. With each point we associate a value, for example, the mean income of the two families. We may define a random variable or random function $U$ on this space by saying that for any outcome (which will be a pair of families) of the experiment the random variable $U$ takes up the value associated with the point. Table 1.1 then gives the values of $U$ for different points of the sample space.

**Table 1.1  The random function $U$**

| Sample point | Pr | Value of $U$ | Sample point | Pr | Value of $U$ |
|---|---|---|---|---|---|
| $F_1,F_2$ | $\frac{1}{10}$ | 40 | $F_2,F_4$ | $\frac{1}{10}$ | 40 |
| $F_1,F_3$ | $\frac{1}{10}$ | 30 | $F_2,F_5$ | $\frac{1}{10}$ | 60 |
| $F_1,F_4$ | $\frac{1}{10}$ | 20 | $F_3,F_4$ | $\frac{1}{10}$ | 30 |
| $F_1,F_5$ | $\frac{1}{10}$ | 40 | $F_3,F_5$ | $\frac{1}{10}$ | 50 |
| $F_2,F_3$ | $\frac{1}{10}$ | 50 | $F_4,F_5$ | $\frac{1}{10}$ | 40 |

From this table we find that $Pr(U = 20) = \frac{1}{10}$, $Pr(U = 30) = \frac{2}{10}$, $Pr(U = 40) = \frac{4}{10}$, $Pr(U = 50) = \frac{2}{10}$, and $Pr(U = 60) = \frac{1}{10}$. Thus the random variable $U$ takes up the values 20, 30, 40, 50, and 60 with probabilities $\frac{1}{10}, \frac{2}{10}, \frac{4}{10}, \frac{2}{10}$, and $\frac{1}{10}$, respectively. This is called the probability distribution of the random variable $U$.

For the same population of the five families, consider another experiment, consisting of the selection of a pair of families; repetitions are included and due regard is paid to the order in which the families occur in the pair. The sample space then contains the 25 points:

| | | | | |
|---|---|---|---|---|
| $F_1,F_1$ | $F_2,F_1$ | $F_3,F_1$ | $F_4,F_1$ | $F_5,F_1$ |
| $F_1,F_2$ | $F_2,F_2$ | $F_3,F_2$ | $F_4,F_2$ | $F_5,F_2$ |
| $F_1,F_3$ | $F_2,F_3$ | $F_3,F_3$ | $F_4,F_3$ | $F_5,F_3$ |
| $F_1,F_4$ | $F_2,F_4$ | $F_3,F_4$ | $F_4,F_4$ | $F_5,F_4$ |
| $F_1,F_5$ | $F_2,F_5$ | $F_3,F_5$ | $F_4,F_5$ | $F_5,F_5$ |

and we agree to associate a probability of $\frac{1}{25}$ with each point. Consider a random variable $V$ which assumes a value equal to the income of the family occurring first in the pair. Similarly, the random variable $W$ takes on the value equal to the income of the second member of the pair.

The values of $V$ and $W$ for the 25 sample points are:

| $V,W$ | $V,W$ | $V,W$ | $V,W$ | $V,W$ |
|-------|-------|-------|-------|-------|
| 20,20 | 60,20 | 40,20 | 20,20 | 60,20 |
| 20,60 | 60,60 | 40,60 | 20,60 | 60,60 |
| 20,40 | 60,40 | 40,40 | 20,40 | 60,40 |
| 20,20 | 60,20 | 40,20 | 20,20 | 60,20 |
| 20,60 | 60,60 | 40,60 | 20,60 | 60,60 |

The joint probability that $V = 20$ and $W = 20$ is $\frac{4}{25}$, since there are four points involved. Similarly, $Pr(V = 40, W = 60) = \frac{2}{25}$. Such relations could be conveniently exhibited in the form of the two-way table (Table 1.2). The entries in the body of Table 1.2 are probabilities, such

**Table 1.2   Joint distribution of $V$ and $W$**

|   |   | | $W$ | | $Pr(V)$ |
|---|---|-----|-----|-----|---------|
|   |   | 20 | 40 | 60 |  |
| | 20 | $\frac{4}{25}$ | $\frac{2}{25}$ | $\frac{4}{25}$ | $\frac{2}{5}$ |
| $V$ | 40 | $\frac{2}{25}$ | $\frac{1}{25}$ | $\frac{2}{25}$ | $\frac{1}{5}$ |
| | 60 | $\frac{4}{25}$ | $\frac{2}{25}$ | $\frac{4}{25}$ | $\frac{2}{5}$ |
| | $Pr(W)$ | $\frac{2}{5}$ | $\frac{1}{5}$ | $\frac{2}{5}$ | $\frac{5}{5}$ |

as $Pr(V = v, W = w)$, and they specify the joint distribution of $V$ and $W$. The margins give the probability distributions of $V$ and $W$. It will be noted from Table 1.2 that $Pr(V = v, W = w) = Pr(V = v)Pr(W = w)$. Such random variables are called independent. Given that $V = 20$, the conditional probability that $W = 60$ is given by $\dfrac{\frac{4}{25}}{\frac{2}{5}} = \frac{2}{5}$ and we see that $Pr(W = 60|V = 20) = \frac{2}{5} = Pr(W = 60)$. It may also be noted that $V$ and $W$ have the same probability distribution.

For the same population of five families, consider now the selection of a pair of different families, order being considered. The sample space then contains 20 points. Suppose each point has a probability of $\frac{1}{20}$. Give random variables $X$ and $Y$ values equal to the income of the first family in the pair and the second family in the pair, respectively. Then their joint distribution is given by Table 1.3.

In this case $Pr(X = x, Y = y) \neq Pr(X = x)Pr(Y = y)$. The conditional probabilities are not the same as the absolute probabilities. The random variables $X$ and $Y$ are not independent.

**Table 1.3  Joint distribution of $X$ and $Y$**

| | | $Y$ | | |
| | 20 | 40 | 60 | $Pr(X)$ |
|---|---|---|---|---|
| **$X$**  20 | $\frac{2}{20}$ | $\frac{3}{20}$ | $\frac{4}{20}$ | $\frac{2}{5}$ |
| 40 | $\frac{2}{20}$ | $\frac{9}{20}$ | $\frac{2}{20}$ | $\frac{1}{5}$ |
| 60 | $\frac{4}{20}$ | $\frac{2}{20}$ | $\frac{2}{20}$ | $\frac{2}{5}$ |
| $Pr(Y)$ | $\frac{2}{5}$ | $\frac{1}{5}$ | $\frac{2}{5}$ | $\frac{5}{5}$ |

## 1.3  EXPECTED VALUE

With the background of Sec. 1.2, we prove a number of results in probability theory which will be used in the chapters that follow.  Let there be a random variable $U$ taking the values $u_i$ $(i = 1, \ldots , k)$ with probability $p_i$ $(i = 1, \ldots , k)$, $\Sigma p_i = 1$.  Then the expected value of $U$ is defined as

$$E(U) = \sum_i p_i u_i = \bar{U} \tag{1.7}$$

It follows that the expected value of $aU$ (where $a$ is a constant) is $E(aU) = aE(U)$, since the random variable $aU$ takes the values $au_i$ $(i = 1, \ldots , k)$ with probabilities $p_i$.  In the same way

$$E(aU + b) = aE(U) + b$$

where $b$ is a constant.  In general, let $\phi(U)$ be a function of $U$.  Then

$$E\phi(U) = \Sigma p_i \phi(u_i)$$

Let there be another random variable $W$ taking values $w_j$ $(j = 1, \ldots , l)$ with probabilities $p_j$, $\Sigma p_j = 1$.  Further, let the joint distribution of $U$ and $W$ be given by the relations

$$Pr(U = u_i, W = w_j) = p_{ij} \qquad \sum_i \sum_j p_{ij} = 1$$

Then, it is obvious that

$$p_i = Pr(U = u_i) = \sum_j p_{ij} \qquad p_j = Pr(W = w_j) = \sum_i p_{ij}$$

Consider now the random variable $Z = U + W$.  The expected value of $Z$ can be written down from first principles by listing the values that $Z$ can take up along with their probabilities.  But this can be done more conveniently by using the following theorem.

**Theorem 1.1**

*If U and W are two random variables,*

$$E(U + W) = E(U) + E(W) \qquad (1.8)$$

PROOF   By definition

$$E(U + W) = \sum_i \sum_j (u_i + w_j)p_{ij}$$
$$= \sum_i u_i \sum_j p_{ij} + \sum_j w_j \sum_i p_{ij}$$
$$= \sum p_i u_i + \sum p_j w_j = E(U) + E(W) \qquad \blacksquare$$

In words, the theorem states that the expected value of the sum of two random variables is the sum of the expected values of the random variables.   This theorem is remarkable in the sense that it holds whether or not the variables $U$ and $W$ are independent.

*Remark*   Theorem 1.1 can now be generalized to $n$ random variables

$$U_1, U_2, \ldots, U_n$$

It states that

$$E(U_1 + U_2 + \cdots + U_n) = \sum_{i=1}^{n} E(U_i) \qquad (1.9)$$

*Remark*   Given the constants $c_1, c_2, \ldots, c_n$, we have

$$E(\Sigma c_i U_i) = \Sigma c_i E(U_i)$$

In case the variables $U$ and $W$ are independent, we have

$$Pr(U = u_i, W = w_j) = Pr(U = u_i)Pr(W = w_j)$$

which means that

$$p_{ij} = p_i p_j$$

Then we prove the following result.

**Theorem 1.2**

*If U and W are independent*

$$E(UW) = E(U)E(W) \qquad (1.10)$$

PROOF

$$E(UW) = \Sigma\Sigma(u_i w_j)p_{ij} = \Sigma p_i u_i \Sigma p_j w_j = E(U)E(W) \qquad \blacksquare$$

**Corollary**

If $f_1(U)$ and $f_2(W)$ are any two functions of the independent random variables $U$ and $W$, we have

$$E[f_1(U)f_2(W)] = E[f_1(U)]E[f_2(W)]$$

Now let $U$ and $W$ be not necessarily independent. For a given value $u_i$ of $U$, the conditional expectation of $W$ would be $\left(\sum_j p_{ij}w_j\right)/p_i$, which we may call $E_2(W)$ for brevity. Then we prove the more general Theorem 1.3.

**Theorem 1.3**

$$E(UW) = E[UE(W|U)] = E[UE_2(W)]$$

where $E_2$ is the conditional expectation for a given value of $U$.

PROOF

$$E(UW) = \sum_i \sum_j u_i w_j p_{ij} = \sum_i u_i \sum_j p_{ij}w_j$$

$$= \sum_i p_i u_i \frac{\sum_j p_{ij}w_j}{p_i} = \sum_i p_i u_i E_2(W)$$

$$= \sum_i p_i E_2(UW) = E[UE_2(W)] \qquad \blacksquare$$

**Corollary**

If $U$ and $W$ are independent, $E(W|U) = E(W)$, and we get Theorem 1.2.

*Example* Consider the random variables $X$ and $Y$ having the joint distribution given in Table 1.3. We shall calculate $E(X)$, $E(Y)$, $E(X + Y)$, and $E(XY)$ in this case.

$$E(X) = 20 \times \tfrac{2}{5} + 40 \times \tfrac{1}{5} + 60 \times \tfrac{2}{5} = 40 = E(Y)$$
$$E(X + Y) = E(X) + E(Y) = 80$$

For $X = 20$, $40$, and $60$ the values of $E_2(XY)$ are $20 \times 45$, $40 \times 20$, and $60 \times 35$, respectively. Hence, $E(XY) = 1{,}360$.

**1.4 VARIANCE AND COVARIANCE**

Let there be a random variable $U$ with $E(U) = \bar{U}$. The variance of $U$ is defined as

$$V(U) = E(U - \bar{U})^2 = E(U)^2 - \bar{U}^2 = \sum_i p_i(u_i - \bar{U})^2 \qquad (1.11)$$

The positive square root of $V(U)$ is called the standard deviation of $U$ and is denoted by $\sigma(U)$. We note that if $V(U)$ is small, each term in the sum $\Sigma p_i(u_i - \bar{U})^2$ is small. This means that a value $u_i$ for which $|(u_i - \bar{U})|$ is large must have a small probability $p_i$. In other words, in case of small variance, large deviations of the random variable from its expected value are improbable. Consider now the variable $Z = aU + b$. We have $E(Z) = a\bar{U} + b$, $V(Z) = E(Z - \bar{Z})^2 = a^2E(U - \bar{U})^2$ or

$$V(aU + b) = a^2V(U)$$

Let there be another random variable $W$ defined on the same sample space as $U$. Let the joint distribution of $U$ and $W$ be specified by the relations

$$Pr(U = u_i, W = w_j) = p_{ij}$$

Then

$$E(W) = \Sigma p_j w_j = \bar{W} \qquad V(W) = E(W - \bar{W})^2 = \Sigma p_j(w_j - \bar{W})^2$$

We shall now introduce another concept, called the covariance of $U$ and $W$. It is defined as

$$\text{Cov } (U,W) = E[(U - \bar{U})(W - \bar{W})] = E(UW) - E(U)E(W) \quad (1.12)$$

Obviously, $\text{Cov } (U,U) = E(U - \bar{U})^2 = V(U)$. The covariance of $U$ and $W$ divided by the product of their standard deviations is called the correlation coefficient of $U$ and $W$ and is written as

$$\rho(U,W) = \frac{\text{Cov } (U,W)}{\sigma(U)\sigma(W)} \qquad (1.13)$$

If $U$ and $W$ are independent $E(UW) = E(U)E(W)$ by Theorem 1.2. Then $\text{Cov } (U,W)$ vanishes, and so does the correlation coefficient. In general we shall prove that $\rho$ lies between $-1$ and $+1$. This follows from the observation that the expected value of a random variable with non-negative values must be nonnegative.

Hence

$$E\left[\frac{U - \bar{U}}{\sigma(U)} \pm \frac{W - \bar{W}}{\sigma(W)}\right]^2 \geq 0$$

Expanding, we get

$$2[1 \pm \rho(U,W)] \geq 0$$

which proves that

$$|\rho(U,W)| \leq 1$$

A more general result is contained in Theorem 1.4.

### Theorem 1.4

*Let U and W be two random variables.   Then*

$$E(UW) \le [E(U^2)E(W^2)]^{1/2} \tag{1.14}$$

PROOF   For any real $t$ we have $E(U + tW)^2 \ge 0$.   Hence by Theorem 1.1, $f(t) = E(U^2) + t^2 E(W^2) + 2tE(UW) \ge 0$.   The function $f(t)$ is a quadratic in $t$.   Since $f(t) \ge 0$ for all $t$, its discriminant cannot be positive, which proves the theorem.                                    ∎

The following theorem is of the greatest importance in sampling theory.

### Theorem 1.5

*Let $U_i$ ($i = 1, \ldots, n$) be n random variables and $a_i$ ($i = 1, \ldots, n$) be n constants.   Then*

$$V\left(\sum a_i U_i\right) = \sum_i \sum_j a_i a_j \operatorname{Cov}(U_i, U_j) \tag{1.15}$$

PROOF   We have $E\left(\sum a_i U_i\right) = \sum a_i \bar{U}_i$ by Theorem 1.1.   By definition,

$$
\begin{aligned}
V\left(\sum a_i U_i\right) &= E\left[\sum a_i(U_i - \bar{U}_i)\right]^2 \\
&= E\sum_i \sum_j a_i a_j(U_i - \bar{U}_i)(U_j - \bar{U}_j) \\
&= \sum \sum a_i a_j E[(U_i - \bar{U}_i)(U_j - \bar{U}_j)] \\
&= \sum \sum a_i a_j \operatorname{Cov}(U_i, U_j) \qquad\qquad ∎
\end{aligned}
$$

***Remark***   Since $\operatorname{Cov}(U_i, U_i) = V(U_i)$, we can also state that

$$V\left(\sum a_i U_i\right) = \sum a_i^2 V(U_i) + 2\sum_i \sum_{j>i} a_i a_j \operatorname{Cov}(U_i, U_j) \tag{1.16}$$

or   $$V\left(\sum a_i U_i\right) = \sum a_i^2 V(U_i) + 2\sum_i \sum_{j>i} a_i a_j \rho_{ij}\sigma(U_i)\sigma(U_j)$$

where $\rho_{ij}$ is the correlation coefficient of $U_i$ and $U_j$.

***Remark***   If the random variables $U_i$ are mutually uncorrelated that is, $\rho_{ij} = 0$, we have

$$V(\Sigma a_i U_i) = \Sigma a_i^2 V(U_i)$$

A more general result, that is easy to prove, is contained in the following theorem.

### Theorem 1.6

*Let there be two linear functions of the sets of random variables* $(U_1, U_2,$
$\ldots, U_m), (W_1, W_2, \ldots, W_n)$, *namely,*

$$U = \sum_{i=1}^{m} a_i U_i \qquad W = \sum_{j=1}^{n} b_j W_j$$

Then

$$\mathrm{Cov}\ (U,W) = \sum_i \sum_j a_i b_j\ \mathrm{Cov}\ (U_i, W_j) \tag{1.17}$$

### 1.5  VARIANCE OF PRODUCTS

If $X$ and $Y$ are independent random variables, a simple expression can be
found (Goodman, 1960) for $V(XY)$ in terms of $E(X)$, $E(Y)$, $V(X)$, and
$V(Y)$.  Let $E(X) = \bar{X}, E(Y) = \bar{Y}, \delta x = (X - \bar{X})/\bar{X}, \delta y = (Y - \bar{Y})/\bar{Y}$.
Then $E(XY) = \bar{X}\bar{Y}$ by Theorem 1.2.  Also

$$X = \bar{X}\ (1 + \delta x) \qquad Y = \bar{Y}(1 + \delta y)$$

Now

$$V(XY) = E[XY - \bar{X}\bar{Y}]^2 = (\bar{X}\bar{Y})^2 E[\delta x + \delta y + \delta x \delta y]^2$$

$$= (\bar{X}\bar{Y})^2 \left[ \frac{V(X)}{\bar{X}^2} + \frac{V(Y)}{\bar{Y}^2} + \frac{V(X)V(Y)}{\bar{X}^2 \bar{Y}^2} \right]$$

Hence we get the important result

$$V(XY) = [E(Y)]^2 V(X) + [E(X)]^2 V(Y) + V(X)V(Y) \tag{1.18}$$

Further, let $Ev(X) = V(X), Ev(Y) = V(Y)$.  Then we shall prove that

$$E[X^2 v(Y) + Y^2 v(X) - v(X)v(Y)] = V(XY)$$

The proof follows from the observations that

$$E[X^2 v(Y)] = E(X^2) Ev(Y) = [\bar{X}^2 + V(X)]V(Y)$$
$$E[Y^2 v(X)] = [\bar{Y}^2 + V(Y)]V(X)$$

and

$$E[v(X)v(Y)] = V(X)V(Y)$$

***Further reading***   See Exercise 84 for an extension to the situation in
which the random variables are not necessarily independent.

### 1.6  CONDITIONAL EXPECTATION

As the subject of this book develops, it will be found that quite often
expectations and variances of random variables have been computed by

using the conditional argument, since it makes the derivation easier. In this section, two very important theorems involving conditional expectations will be proved. Survey statisticians have been using these results for a long time, but they first appeared in print in the book by Hansen, Hurwitz, and Madow (1953). Let $H_j$ $(j = 1, \ldots , n)$ be a set of mutually exclusive events $[Pr(H_k H_l) = 0]$ of which one necessarily occurs. Then any event can occur only in conjunction with some $H_j$. Thus the probability that a random variable $U$ take the value $u_i$ would be given by

$$Pr(U = u_i) = \sum_j Pr(U = u_i, H = H_j)$$
$$= \sum_j Pr(H_j)Pr(U = u_i | H_j)$$

Also, the conditional expected value of $U$ given $H_j$ would be

$$E(U | H_j) = \Sigma u_i Pr(U = u_i | H_j)$$

For convenience in writing we shall denote $E(U | H_j)$ by $E_2(U)$.

### Theorem 1.7

*The expected value of a random variable $U$ is given by*

$$E(U) = E[E(U | H_j)] \tag{1.19}$$

PROOF    We have

$$E(U) = \sum u_i Pr(U = u_i)$$
$$= \sum u_i \sum_j Pr(U = u_i, H = H_j) = \sum u_i \sum_j Pr(U = u_i | H_j)Pr(H_j)$$
$$= \sum_j Pr(H_j) \sum_i u_i Pr(U = u_i | H_j)$$
$$= \sum_j Pr(H_j)E(U | H_j) = \sum Pr(H_j)E_2(U)$$
$$= E[E_2(U)] \qquad \blacksquare$$

**Remark**    Symbolically we may write $E(U) = E_1 E_2(U)$, where $E_2(U)$ is the conditional expected value of $U$ given $H_j$ and $E_1$ stands for the subsequent procedure of taking the expectation (over the space of $H$).

### 1.6.1  CONDITIONAL VARIANCE AND COVARIANCE

With the help of Theorem 1.7 it is easy to obtain the covariance of two random variables in terms of conditional expectations. As before, we shall denote $E(U | H_j)$ by $E_2(U)$. Given $H_j$, the conditional covariance of $U$ and $W$ is $C_2(U, W) = E_2(UW) - E_2(U)E_2(W)$.

**Theorem 1.8**

$$\text{Cov } (U,W) = C(U,W) = E_1 C_2(U,W) + C_1(E_2 U, E_2 W).$$

PROOF    For simplicity, let

$$E_2(U) = x \qquad E_2(W) = y$$

$$\begin{aligned}
\text{Then} \quad \text{Cov } (U,W) &= E(UW) - E(U)E(W) \\
&= E_1 E_2(UW) - E_1(x)E_1(y) \\
&= E_1[E_2(UW) - xy] + E_1(xy) - E_1(x)E_1(y) \\
&= E_1 C_2(U,W) + C_1(E_2 U, E_2 W)
\end{aligned}$$  ∎

**Corollary**

$$\text{Cov } (U,U) = E_1 C_2(U,U) + C_1(E_2 U, E_2 U)$$
or
$$V(U) = E_1 V_2(U) + V_1 E_2(U) \tag{1.20}$$

Thus the variance of a random variable is the sum of the expected value of the conditional variance and the variance of the conditional expected value.


## 1.7  THE TCHEBYCHEFF INEQUALITY

The interpretation of the variance of a random variable as a measure of the degree of concentration around the expected value is made clear by the following inequality due to Tchebycheff. Let $U$ be a random variable with $E(U) = \bar{U}$. For any $t > 0$ we shall prove that

$$V(U) \geq t^2 Pr(|U - \bar{U}| \geq t) \tag{1.21}$$

We have

$$V(U) = \sum (u_i - \bar{U})^2 p_i = \sum_j (u_j - \bar{U})^2 p_j + \sum_k (u_k - \bar{U})^2 p_k$$

where the first summation runs over all $j$ for which $|U_j - \bar{U}| < t$, and the second summation runs over all $k$ for which $|U_k - \bar{U}| \geq t$. Now $V(U) \geq \sum_k (u_k - \bar{U})^2 p_k \geq t^2 \sum_k p_k = t^2 Pr(|U - \bar{U}| \geq t)$. From this it follows that

$$Pr(|U - \bar{U}| \geq t) \leq \frac{V(U)}{t^2}$$

Letting $t = \lambda \sigma(U)$, we have

$$Pr[|U - \bar{U}| \geq \lambda \sigma(U)] \leq \frac{1}{\lambda^2}$$

Thus the probability is at most $1/\lambda^2$ that the random variable differs from its expected value by more than $\lambda$ times its standard deviation.

## 1.8 AN EXAMPLE

An example will now be given to illustrate some of the theory presented. The result obtained will be put to good use in subsequent chapters. Suppose an urn contains balls of $k$ colors in proportions $p_h$ $(h = 1, \ldots, k)$, $\Sigma p_h = 1$. The random experiment consists in selecting one ball from the urn. We shall associate a probability of $p_h$ to the outcome that the ball is of color $h$. Suppose this experiment is repeated $n$ times; care is taken that the selected ball is always returned to the urn. Let $t_1$ denote the number of balls of one color (red) and $t_2$ the number of balls of another color (black) selected in the $n$ repetitions of the experiment. We define $U_i$ as a random variable which has the value 1 if the $i$th repetition gives a red ball and 0 otherwise. Similarly $W_i$ assumes the values of 1 or 0 according to whether the $i$th repetition produces or fails to produce a black ball. Obviously, then

$$t_1 = U_1 + U_2 + \cdots + U_n \qquad t_2 = W_1 + W_2 + \cdots + W_n$$

If $p_i$, $p_2$ are the probabilities of getting a red or black ball respectively at any selection, we have $E(U_i) = p_1$, $E(W_i) = p_2$. Again, $U_i^2$ has values 1 or 0 with probabilities $p_1$ and $1 - p_1$, respectively. Hence $E(U_i^2) = p_1$, and similarly $E(W_i^2) = p_2$. Since the variables $U_i$ and $U_j$ are independent, Theorem 1.2 gives $E(U_iU_j) = p_1^2$ for $i \neq j$. Similarly $E(W_iW_j) = p_2^2$ for $i \neq j$. And

$$V(U_i) = E(U_i^2) - E^2(U_i) = p_1(1 - p_1)$$
$$V(W_i) = p_2(1 - p_2)$$
$$\text{Cov } (U_i,U_j) = E(U_iU_j) - E(U_i)E(U_j) = 0$$
$$\text{Cov } (W_i,W_j) = 0$$

Since the $i$th selection can produce a ball of only one color, $U_i$ and $W_i$ cannot both take the value of 1 simultaneously, and so $E(U_iW_i) = 0$, which gives Cov $(U_iW_i) = -p_1p_2$. By the independence of $U_i$ and $W_j$ we get $E(U_iW_j) = p_1p_2$, Cov $(U_iW_j) = 0$. We are now in a position to calculate $E(t_1), E(t_2), V(t_1), V(t_2)$, and Cov $(t_1, t_2)$. By Theorem 1.1, $E(t_1) = np_1$ and $E(t_2) = np_2$. By Theorem 1.5, we have $V(t_1) = np_1(1 - p_1)$ and $V(t_2) = np_2(1 - p_2)$. Theorem 1.6 gives Cov $(t_1, t_2) = -np_1p_2$. These results may be stated in the form of the following theorem.

### Theorem 1.9

*A certain random experiment may produce any of $k$ mutually exclusive events $A_1, A_2, \ldots, A_k$, the probability of $A_i$ being $p_i > 0$ where $\Sigma p_i = 1$. In a* *series of n repetitions of the experiment let $A_i$ occur $t_i$ times.   Then*

$$E(t_i) = np_i$$
$$V(t_i) = np_i(1 - p_i)$$
$$\text{Cov } (t_i, t_j) = -np_i p_j$$

## 1.9  INTRACLASS CORRELATION COEFFICIENT

A population consists of $N$ families each having $M$ members.   To each member is attached a value measured on some scale (such as age in years). The random experiment consists in selecting a family and taking a pair of members from the family.   We assign the same probability to the selection of every pair.   Random variables $U$ and $W$ are defined which take up values associated with the first member and the second member forming the pair selected.   Obviously, the probability distributions of $U$ and $W$ are identical.   Thus $E(U) = E(W)$ and $V(U) = V(W)$.   The correlation coefficient of $U$ and $W$ is

$$\rho(U,W) = \frac{\text{Cov } (U,W)}{V(U)} = \frac{E[(U - \bar{U})(W - \bar{W})]}{E(U - \bar{U})^2}$$

This is called the intraclass (or intrafamily) correlation coefficient.   Let $y_{ij}$ be the value attached to the $j$th member of the $i$th family.   There will be $NM(M - 1)$ points in the sample space each having the same probability.   It is then easily seen that

$$E(U) = \frac{\sum_i \sum_j y_{ij}}{NM} = \bar{Y}$$

$$V(U) = \frac{\sum_i \sum_j (y_{ij} - \bar{Y})^2}{NM}$$

$$\text{Cov } (U,W) = \sum_{i=1}^{N} \sum_{j=1}^{M} \sum_{k \neq j} \frac{(y_{ij} - \bar{Y})(y_{ik} - \bar{Y})}{NM(M - 1)}$$

## 1.10  THE BEST WEIGHT FUNCTION

Another problem whose solution will be needed later is the following. There are a number of random variables $t_i$ $(i = 1, \ldots, p)$ with the same expected value $E(t_i) = \mu$ and Cov $(t_i, t_j) = a_{ij}$.   We want to find the weights $w_i$ $(i = 1, \ldots, p)$, $\Sigma w_i = 1$ such that $E(\Sigma w_i t_i) = \mu$ and $V(\Sigma w_i t_i)$ is a minimum.   By Theorem 1.5, $V(\Sigma w_i t_i) = \Sigma\Sigma w_i w_j$ Cov $(t_i, t_j)$.   Hence $V(\Sigma w_i t_i) = \Sigma\Sigma w_i w_j a_{ij} = wAw'$, where $A$ is the matrix $(a_{ij})$, $w$ is the vector $(w_1, w_2, \ldots, w_p)$, and $w'$ is the transpose of $w$.   Consider now Cauchy's inequality

$$(xy')^2 \leq (xMx')(yM^{-1}y') \tag{1.22}$$

where $M$ is symmetric positive definite. The sign of equality holds if and only if $xM = \lambda y$ where $\lambda \neq 0$ is a scalar. In this inequality we substitute $x = w$, $y = e$, the vector $e(1, 1, \ldots , 1)$, and $M = A = (a_{ij})$. We then have

$$(we')^2 \leq (wAw')(eA^{-1}e')$$

But $we' = \Sigma w_i = 1$. Hence $wAw' \geq 1/eA^{-1}e'$, there being equality if $wA = \lambda e$ or $w = \lambda eA^{-1}$ or $we' = \lambda eA^{-1}e'$. But $we' = 1$. Hence $\lambda = 1/eA^{-1}e'$ and so the best weight function is given by

$$w = \frac{eA^{-1}}{eA^{-1}e'} \tag{1.23}$$

and the minimum variance is $1/(eA^{-1}e')$. Now, $eA^{-1}e' = $ sum of all the elements in $A^{-1}$, the matrix inverse to $A$, and the $i$th component of $eA^{-1} = $ sum of the elements in the $i$th column of $A^{-1}$. Thus the best weights are calculable from the elements of the inverse matrix $A^{-1}$.

### 1.11 MINIMUM-VARIANCE UNBIASED ESTIMATION

The following theorem will be used in the sequel to find minimum-variance unbiased (MVU) estimators. An estimator $T$ is said to be unbiased for estimating the parameter $\theta$ if $E(T) = \theta$. And if $V(T) \leq V(T')$, where $T'$ is any other unbiased estimator of $\theta$, we shall call $T$ a MVU estimator.

#### Theorem 1.10

*A necessary and sufficient condition for $T_0$ to be the* MVU *estimator of a parameter is that* Cov $(T_0, z) = 0$ *for all $z$, where $z$ is a zero function, i.e., a function with expectation identically zero.*

PROOF   Let $T_0$ be MVU for the parameter. Then $V(T_0) \leq V(T_0 + \epsilon z)$ for all $\epsilon$. Thus

$$V(T_0) \leq V(T_0) + \epsilon^2 V(z) + 2\epsilon \text{ Cov } (T_0, z)$$

or $\quad\quad \epsilon[2 \text{ Cov } (T_0, z) + \epsilon V(z)] \geq 0$

Assume $\epsilon > 0$ and let $\epsilon \to 0$ through positive values. Then Cov $(T_0, z) \geq 0$. Again, assume $\epsilon < 0$ and let $\epsilon \to 0$ through negative values. Then Cov $(T_0, z) \leq 0$. Hence Cov $(T_0, z) = 0$. To prove that the condition is sufficient, let $T_1$ be any other unbiased estimator of the parameter. Then $T_1 = T_0 + (T_1 - T_0)$. Now

$$V(T_1) = V(T_0) + V(T_1 - T_0) + 2 \text{ Cov } (T_0, T_1 - T_0)$$

But Cov $(T_0, T_1 - T_0) = 0$, since $T_1 - T_0$ is a zero function.   Hence $V(T_1) \geq V(T_0)$, which proves that $T_0$ is MVU (Rao, 1952).            ■

### Corollary

If $T_0$ is MVU, Cov $(T_1 - T_0, T_0) = 0$ where $T_1$ is any unbiased estimator of the parameter.   Thus Cov $(T_1, T_0) = $ Cov $(T_0, T_0) = V(T_0)$.   This shows that the variance of a MVU estimator $T_0$ can be found by computing the covariance of $T_0$ and any other unbiased estimator of the parameter.

### 1.12  TWO LIMIT THEOREMS

We will conclude this chapter by stating two limit theorems in probability (Feller, 1950) which reveal a new aspect of the notion of the expectation of a random variable.

*Law of large numbers*   Let $\{X_k\}$ be a sequence of mutually independent random variables with a common distribution.   If the expectation $\bar{X} = E(X_k)$ exists, then for every $\epsilon > 0$ as $n \to \infty$

$$Pr\left(\left|\frac{1}{n}\sum_{i=1}^{n} X_i - \bar{X}\right| > \epsilon\right) \to 0 \tag{1.24}$$

Thus the probability that the average $\Sigma X_i/n$ will differ from the expectation by less than an arbitrarily prescribed $\epsilon$ tends to one.

*Central-limit theorem*   Let $\{X_k\}$ be a sequence of mutually independent random variables with a common distribution.   Suppose that $\bar{X} = E(X_k)$ and $\sigma^2 = V(X_k)$ exist.   Then for every fixed $a, b, (a < b) n \to \infty$

$$Pr\left(a < \frac{1}{\sigma n^{\frac{1}{2}}}\sum_{1}^{n} X_i - n\bar{X} < b\right) \to \Phi(b) - \Phi(a) \tag{1.25}$$

where $\Phi(x)$ is the probability that the standardized normal variable does not exceed $x$.

### REFERENCES

Feller, W. G. (1950).   "An introduction to probability theory and its applications."   John Wiley & Sons, Inc., New York.

Goodman, L. A. (1960).   On the exact variance of products.   *J. Am. Stat. Assoc.*, 55.

Hansen, M. H., W. N. Hurwitz, and W. G. Madow (1953).   "Sample survey methods and theory," vol. 2.   John Wiley & Sons, Inc., New York.

Rao, C. R. (1952).   Some theorems on minimum variance unbiased estimation.   *Sankhya*, 12.

# CHAPTER TWO

# SAMPLE SURVEY BACKGROUND

## 2.1 INTRODUCTION

The major aim of this book is to present sample survey theory. But theory by itself cannot be fully appreciated without an adequate knowledge of the type of problems in which it is to be used. It is therefore a matter of considerable importance that the reader have a good idea of the work a sampling statistician is called upon to do and the limitations under which he works. The purpose of the present chapter is to do just that.

## 2.2 THE MAIN PROBLEM

In its broadest sense the purpose of a sample survey is the collection of information to satisfy a definite need. The need to collect data arises in every conceivable sphere of human activity. Only a few examples will be given from selected fields.

*Population* Most governments nowadays collect information regularly about: the total population (number of persons); its distribution by area, sex, age, and other socioeconomic characteristics; the rate of growth of the population; internal migration, and so on. These data help in determining the future needs for such items as food, clothing, housing, education, and recreational facilities. Data on internal migration are used for assessing the social and economic problems when there are major shifts from the rural to the urban areas, for example. Broadly speaking, data on the nature and size of the population can be used for determining the demand for goods and services and the size and quality of the labor resources needed to produce these goods and services.

*Labor*   Since labor is a key resource in production, data are collected on the number of persons engaged in economic activity, the number of hours they work, and the average output per man-hour of work. The wages and salaries paid to labor determine living levels and the demand for goods and services. Data about the distribution of the labor force by branch of economic activity give a useful indication of the structure of production in the country. Classifications of the economically active by occupation can be used to study the capabilities of the labor force from the point of view of development projects. Detailed information on the unemployed persons is used to find out what type of work they are looking for, how long they have been in search of work, what type of training they have had, and other pertinent facts.

*Agriculture*   With rising populations, it is becoming more and more important to assess the agricultural resources of the country. The proportion of land under agriculture, areas under different crops, areas under pastures and forests, production of food—grains, fruits, etc.—and the number and quality of livestock are some of the items of information essential to any planned program of national development, especially in underdeveloped countries. Data on the number and area of farm holdings by size and type of tenure can be used to determine the extent to which these factors may be contributing to agricultural productivity as well as to devise remedies.

*Industry*   Collection of information in the industrial sector is no less important. The number of industrial undertakings and their kind, the number of persons engaged in them, the amount of raw materials consumed, the extent of production of goods and the value added by their manufacture are some of the data needed. Data on the capacity of power equipment installed in an industrial undertaking can be used to measure the extent of mechanization and to decide where efforts to increase capital equipment should be concentrated. Indices of industrial production, when regularly calculated, point to the success or failure in increasing production.

*Internal trade*   Commerce and related services form an important part of economic activity. Information is required on the role and char-

acter of the wholesale, retail, and service trades. The number of establishments engaged in each trade, by kind of business, the value of sales
of retail stores, and the value of inventories are some of the items on
which information is needed to assess business conditions. Figures on
sales of goods and services at retail can be used as indicators of the level of
personal consumption.

### 2.2.1 CHARACTERISTICS OF INTEREST

The foregoing discussion suggests that there is a variety of purposes for
which information is collected. Most frequently, however, interest has
centered on four characteristics of the universe or population under study.
These are: population total (e.g., the total number unemployed), population mean (the average number of persons engaged by an industrial
establishment), population proportion (proportion of cultivated area
devoted to cotton), and population ratio (the ratio of expenditure on foods
to that on rent). The populations considered are finite in the sense that
the number of objects contained in them (such as persons, farms, firms,
stores) is limited.

### 2.3 SAMPLE VERSUS COMPLETE ENUMERATION

Broadly speaking, information on a population may be collected in two
ways. Either every unit in the population is enumerated (called complete
enumeration, or census) or enumeration is limited to only a part or a
sample selected from the population (called sample enumeration or sample
survey). A sample survey will usually be less costly than a complete
census because the expense of covering all units would be greater than that
of covering only a sample fraction. Also, it will take less time to collect
and process data from a sample than from a census. But economy is not
the only consideration; the most important point is whether the accuracy
of the results would be adequate for the end in view. It is a curious fact
that the results from a carefully planned and well-executed sample survey
are expected to be more accurate (nearer to the aim of study) than those
from a complete census that can be taken. A complete census ordinarily
requires a huge and unwieldy organization and therefore many types of
errors creep in which cannot be controlled adequately. In a sample survey
the volume of work is reduced considerably, and it becomes possible to
employ persons of higher caliber, train them suitably, and supervise their
work adequately. In a properly designed sample survey it is also possible
to make a valid estimate of the margin of error and hence decide whether
the results are sufficiently accurate. A complete census does not reveal

by itself the margin of uncertainty to which it is subject. But there is not always a choice of one versus the other. For example, if data are required for every small administrative area in a country, no sample survey of a reasonable size will be able to deliver the desired information; only a complete census can do this.

## 2.4 THE ROLE OF THE SAMPLING METHOD

A sample survey has now come to be considered an organized fact-finding instrument. Its importance to modern civilization lies in the fact that it can be used to summarize, for the guidance of administration, facts which would otherwise be inaccessible owing to the remoteness and obscurity of the persons or other units concerned, or their numerousness. Sampling surveys allow decisions to be made which take into account the significant factors of the problems they are meant to solve. As a fact-finding agency a sample survey is not primarily concerned with the sociological or economic interpretation of the facts ascertained, although it should supply material adequate for such interpretation. Rather it is concerned with the accurate ascertainment of the individual facts recorded and with their compilation and summarization. How a sample survey is to be organized at different levels will depend upon the type of questions it is required to answer. There are, however, certain ingredients which are common to most large-scale surveys. We shall deal with some of these in the next section, providing occasional illustrations from the Greek Household Survey (GHS) of urban areas (National Statistical Service of Greece, 1963).

## 2.5 PLANNING AND EXECUTION OF SAMPLE SURVEYS

The following are some of the main steps involved in the planning and execution of large-scale sample surveys.

*Objectives* The first task is to lay down in concrete terms the objectives of the survey. It is generally found that the sponsoring agency itself does not know precisely what it wants and how it is going to use the results. The statistician's job is to hold discussions with the sponsors in order to make them start thinking in concrete terms. Failure to clarify the purpose of the survey will undermine its ultimate value; in the end it may be found that the results are not what was really wanted. (In the GHS the main purpose was to collect data on the pattern of expenditure of urban households to provide a reliable basis for the weighting of the planned index of consumer prices.)

*Population to be covered*  The objectives of the survey should define the population the survey is intended to cover.  But practical difficulties in handling certain segments of the population may point to their elimination from the scope of the survey.  For example, in a population survey it may be found extremely difficult to cover the transient population. In an agricultural inquiry in which the intention is to take in every small piece of land to determine what it grows, practical considerations may force the omission of such places as kitchen gardens.  In an industrial survey all plants employing less than two persons may have to be omitted if it is found that it would be extremely difficult to include them.  Thus the target population would generally be different from the population actually sampled.  The results obtained will apply to the population actually sampled.  Sometimes, information is collected in a different manner from the omitted sector.  This is done through procedures which are not entirely rigorous but which can throw some light on the subject matter of the survey.  The users of the data are provided with figures relating to both parts of the universe, along with a description of the limitations under which they were collected.  (The GHS had to be limited to urban areas only, and all institutional households, such as hotels, boarding houses, and hospitals, were excluded.)

*The frame*  In order to cover the population decided upon, there should be some list, map, or other acceptable material (called the frame) which serves as a guide to the universe to be covered.  The list or map must be examined to be sure that it is reasonably free from defects.  If it is out of date, consideration should be given to making it up to date.  It would be important to know how the list or the map had been made. (In the GHS the combined list of residential dwellings reported in the previous census and of residential dwellings erected since the census was used as the frame.)

*Sampling unit*  For purposes of sample selection, the population should be capable of being divided up into what may be called sampling units.  For example, a human population can be considered to be built up of villages, census enumeration districts, households, or persons.  The important point is that the division of the population into sampling units should be unambiguous.  Every element of the population should belong to just one sampling unit.  If, for example, the unit is a household, it should be so defined that a person does not belong to two different households nor should it leave out any persons belonging to the population. This is not an easy task, since borderline cases will always arise, and some arbitrary rules will have to be framed to handle these cases.  (In the GHS a private household was defined as a person living on his own in a dwelling, or a group of persons permanently sharing the same dwelling and having common arrangements for the provision of at least one principal meal a day. Persons temporarily absent for less than 6 months were included as members of the household, while temporary visitors sharing for less than 6 months were excluded.)

*Sample selection*   At this stage the question of the size of the sample, the manner of selecting the sample, and the estimation of population characteristics along with their margin of uncertainty are some of the technical problems that should receive the most careful attention. (Such questions form the contents of sampling theory, with which this book is primarily concerned.)

*The information to be collected*   The question of the kind of information to be collected should be considered at an early stage of planning the survey. Only data relevant to the purposes of the survey should be collected. If there are too many questions, the respondents begin to lose interest in answering them. On the other hand, it must be ensured that no important item is missing. A practical procedure is to prepare outlines of the tables that the survey should produce; this will eliminate irrelevant information and ensure that all essential items find a place. A major consideration would be the practicability of obtaining the information sought. Respondents may not be sufficiently informed to be capable of giving the right answers.

*Method of collecting information*   The method of collecting the information (whether by mail or by interview or otherwise) has to be decided, keeping in view the costs involved and the accuracy aimed at. Usually, one would prefer physical observation (if possible) to asking questions, interviewing respondents to mailing out questionnaires, etc. Mail surveys cost less, but there may be considerable nonresponse. Interviewers cost more and there are interviewer errors, but without interviewers the data collected may be worthless. The problem is a complex one, and a solution taking into account conditions pertaining to the particular survey must be found. In the annual industrial surveys in Greece, for example, questionnaires are mailed out to establishments, and nonrespondents are interviewed by a special staff recruited for this purpose. (In the Greek Household Survey there was no real choice in the method of collecting information. Interviewers who would make daily visits to the sample households in order to record expenditure incurred by all members had to be used.)

*Time reference and reference period*   A decision has to be made concerning the time reference (the period to which the results of the survey will relate) and the reference period (the period for which information is collected from sample units). For example, in the GHS the time reference was 1 year, but the reference period for most items was 1 week (each household was required to provide information for just 1 week). The sample was staggered over time (about one-twelfth of the total number of sample households was interviewed each month). The problem of the choice of the reference period is important. A shorter reference period may give more accurate data, but a larger sample is necessary with this method, and this means increased costs. A longer reference period may be cheaper, but the information collected may not be so accurate, owing to memory failure, etc.

*The questionnaire or schedule* The questionnaire (to be filled in by the respondent) or the schedule (to be completed by the interviewer) forms a very important part of the sample survey. Having decided upon the data to be collected, the problem of their presentation requires considerable skill. The questions should be clear, unambiguous, and to the point. Vague questions do not bring forth clear answers. Leading questions should be avoided. Since response may depend to some extent on the order in which questions are asked, the order of questions is another matter to be considered. A small pretest always helps to decide upon an effective method of asking the questions. All technical terms used should be properly defined.

*Training of interviewers and their supervision* The success of a survey using the interview method depends largely on the ability of the interviewers to elicit acceptable responses. Their selection and training is very important. Detailed instructions should be outlined for the proper training of interviewers in the methods of measurement. Observation by a supervisor during the course of an actual interview is valuable for maintaining standards and for studying the interviewer's adherence to procedures and tact in answering questions raised by respondents.

*Inspection of returns* An initial quality check should be instituted while the interviewers are in the field to supply missing entries and correct apparent inconsistencies. Later, the clerical staff should make a careful review of the questionnaires received.

*Nonrespondents* Procedures will have to be devised to deal with those who do not give information. The reason for nonresponse, as well as any other information which can be conveniently obtained from the sample unit, should be recorded. (In the GHS some basic data, such as size of household, were collected from households which refused to cooperate. This helped in assessing the effect of refusals on the characteristics of participating households.)

*Analysis of data* When the data are transferred to mechanical equipment for analysis, the errors involved should be kept under control. Since the machines, too, can make mistakes, machine tables must be checked. And finally a report must be written that gives the findings of the survey concerning those questions it was meant to answer.

## 2.6 JUDGMENT SAMPLING

For the collection of information on a sampling basis, certain procedures are rejected outright by the survey statistician. This happens when it is not possible to find an objective method of distinguishing one procedure from another. To give an example, information could be collected inexpensively by asking persons known as experts in the subject. These experts would no doubt differ from one another, and there is no objective method by which to distinguish the opinion of one expert from that of another. Another procedure belonging to this category consists of limiting the sample to units that appear to be representative of the population under consideration.[1] Information is collected on these units, and from these estimates of population characteristics are made. Here again the judgment of the person selecting the sample is significant, for different persons will judge differently. There is no objective method of preferring one judgment to another. We cannot predict the type or the distribution of the results produced by a large number of judgment samplers, nor can we predict the manner in which these will differ from the so-called "true" value aimed for. We do not know any objective method of measuring the confidence to be placed in the results obtained when the sample is selected by judgment. The reason is that with such methods the probability that a given unit will be selected into the sample is unknown. We are therefore unable to determine the frequency distribution of the estimates this procedure (of judgment sampling) will produce. In the absence of information on the manner in which different samples will differ from each other, the sampling error cannot be objectively determined.

## 2.7 PROBABILITY SAMPLING

The picture completely changes as soon as we begin using a sampling procedure in which every unit belonging to the population has a known and nonzero probability of being selected in the sample. With the help of probability theory we are then in a position to determine the frequency distribution of the estimates derivable from the sampling and estimation procedure. We can calculate the proportion of estimates that will fall in a specified interval around the so-called "true" value aimed for. We know what results the repeated use of a specific sampling procedure will produce, which enables us to distinguish one procedure from another. And, what is very important, a measure of the sampling variation (the

[1] An example is *quota sampling* in which interviewers are free to choose their respondents provided the sample shall contain so many men and so many women, so many persons of high income and so many of low income, and so on.

manner in which sample estimates will differ from the average) can be obtained objectively from the sample itself. The entire apparatus of probability theory and statistical inference (based on that) is available for drawing valid conclusions from the sample. Only procedures of probability sampling such as these will be considered henceforth in the book.

## 2.8 FORMATION OF ESTIMATORS

In the general estimation theory appropriate to infinite populations, linear estimators are of the form

$$c_1 y_1 + c_2 y_2 + \cdots + c_n y_n \tag{2.1}$$

The quantities $c_1, c_2, \ldots, c_n$ are constants attached to the observations made on the 1st, 2d, $\ldots$, $n$th selections (in the sample), respectively. In sampling theory dealing with finite populations in which the units are identifiable, linear estimators of a more general type can be considered. The coefficient to be attached to any selection may depend on the unit selected, the sample that produces this unit, and the order in which the unit appears in the sample. One may imagine the totality of ordered samples of size $n$ from a population of size $N$ and a coefficient attached to every unit in the population, depending upon the sample to which it belongs, and its position in the sample. The estimator (2.1) would be a particular case in which every sample has the same coefficient set attached to it.

## 2.9 UNBIASED ESTIMATION

Although any function of the observations could be used as an estimator of a population characteristic, only functions with some desirable properties will be considered. The trend in sample survey theory is to use unbiased estimators as much as possible. With such estimators the expected value is the same as that which could be obtained from a complete count or census using identical methods of measurements. That it is a useful requirement to place on estimators follows from a well-known theorem in probability (see Sec. 1.12) which states that in a long series of repetitions of the sampling procedure, the average of the different values assumed by the estimator will be close to its expected value. Working with finite populations as we do, the criterion of consistency will ordinarily mean that the sample estimate equals the census count when the sample size equals the population size. Another reason for preferring unbiased estimators is that in repetitive surveys where estimates are made regularly (say, every month), there is the problem of combining these estimates for getting, say, annual figures.   If the estimation procedure is biased, the bias accumulates faster than the sampling error, which can be a disadvantage of the estimation process.

## 2.10  PRECISION OF ESTIMATORS

The precision, or a measure of the closeness of the sample estimates to the census count taken under identical conditions,[1] is judged in sampling theory by the variance of the estimators concerned.   Here reliance is placed on the fact that with a small variance the probability of large deviations from the census count will be small.   The general principle is to use estimators which give the highest concentration of the sample estimates (in the sense of probability) around the value aimed for.   With unbiased estimators the measure used for judging the degree of concentration is the variance of the estimators.   If the distribution of the estimator is normal, there is an exact inverse relationship between the variance and the degree of concentration.   It is a part of good sampling practice to use procedures for which the distribution of the estimator approaches normality.   Here reliance is placed on the central-limit theorem (Sec. 1.12) in probability, by which the distribution of a sum approaches normality as the number of random variables gets large.   In sampling work the estimators generally are of the form of sums.

## 2.11  BIASED ESTIMATORS

We have no intention of suggesting that biased estimators should not be used at all.   In Fig. 2.1, the degree of concentration of the sample estimates around the value aimed at $(c_0)$ is higher for the distribution $B$ than

[1] On the other hand, *accuracy* refers to closeness to the true value.

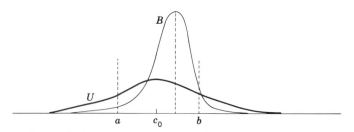

**Fig. 2.1.  Biased and unbiased estimators.**

for the distribution $U$, although $B$ does not center at $c_0$, and $U$ does. The probability that the sample estimates fall in the interval $(a,b)$ is much larger in the case of $B$ than with $U$. In such a situation the biased estimator is preferable to the unbiased one. As a matter of fact, biased estimators are extensively used in sampling work, for example, when the object is to estimate a population ratio. Now, two questions arise: (1) What criterion to use to distinguish one estimator from another? (2) How far do confidence statements remain valid when the distribution does not center at $c_0$? The variance is not a satisfactory criterion, since it measures deviations from the expected value of the estimator, which is not the same as $c_0$. It will be natural in such a situation to take deviations from $c_0$ itself and calculate the expected value of their squares. The quantity so obtained is called the mean square error (MSE). It is obvious that for any estimator $t$, the mean square error around the value $\mu$ would be

$$\begin{aligned}
\mathrm{MSE}(t) = E(t - \mu)^2 &= E[t - E(t)]^2 + [E(t) - \mu]^2 \\
&= V(t) + [B(t)]^2 \\
&= V(t) \left\{ 1 + \left[ \frac{B(t)}{\sigma(t)} \right]^2 \right\}
\end{aligned} \qquad (2.2)$$

where $V(t) = \sigma^2(t)$ and $B(t)$ stands for the bias associated with $t$. If $t$ is unbiased, the variance and the mean square error would coincide. Of two estimators $t_1$ and $t_2$, the one giving the smaller mean square error around the parameter to be estimated will be preferred. Another way of looking at it is to assume that the loss involved in using $t$ instead of $\mu$ is given by $(t - \mu)^2$. The average loss then is $E(t - \mu)^2$, the mean square error around $\mu$. An estimator giving a smaller average loss is preferred to another with which the average loss is higher.

### 2.11.1 CONFIDENCE INTERVALS

In order to estimate $\mu$, suppose a biased estimator $W$ is used with $E(W) = m$ so that $B(W) = m - \mu$ is the amount of bias present in $W$ for estimating $\mu$. Assuming the distribution of $W$ to be normal, the question raised in Sec. 2.11 is: What is the status of the confidence interval $\mathcal{I}$: $[W \pm 1.96\sigma(W)]$ based on the variance of $W$ although $W$ is subject to a bias of $B$? The answer lies in computing the exact probability $P_0$ that the interval $\mathcal{I}$ covers $\mu$. We have

$$\begin{aligned}
P_0 &= Pr[\mu - 1.96\sigma(W) < W < \mu + 1.96\sigma(W)] \\
&= Pr \left[ \frac{-B(W)}{\sigma(W)} - 1.96 < \frac{W - m}{\sigma(W)} < \frac{-B(W)}{\sigma(W)} + 1.96 \right]
\end{aligned} \qquad (2.3)$$

But $(W - m)/\sigma(W)$ is a normal variate with mean zero and variance unity. Hence $P_0$ can be calculated for each value of $B(W)/\sigma(W)$ using

the tables of the normal distribution.   A few calculations are presented
in Table 2.1.   When $W$ is unbiased, this probability is 0.95.   As the ratio

**Table 2.1  Probability of $\hat{g}$ covering $\mu$**

| $|B(W)|/\sigma(W)$ | $P_0$ | $|B(W)|/\sigma(W)$ | $P_0$ |
|---|---|---|---|
| 0.00 | 0.9500 | 0.10 | 0.9489 |
| 0.01 | 0.9500 | 0.30 | 0.9396 |
| 0.03 | 0.9499 | 0.50 | 0.9210 |
| 0.05 | 0.9497 | 0.70 | 0.8923 |
| 0.07 | 0.9494 | 0.90 | 0.8533 |
| 0.09 | 0.9491 | 1.00 | 0.8300 |

of bias to the standard deviation increases, this probability decreases.
Provided $|B(W)|/\sigma(W)$ remains less than 0.1, this probability does not
differ appreciably from 0.95.   Hence, if we can prove that the bias associated with an estimator as a fraction of its standard deviation is smaller
than 0.1, confidence statements can be made as if no bias were present.
In case the bias $B(W)$ is known, the exact 95 percent confidence interval
based on $\sigma(W)$ would be

$$W - B(W) \pm 1.96\sigma(W)$$

## 2.12  THE QUESTION OF COST

Sampling statisticians, dealing with problems in the real world as they do,
take a very practical attitude in the selection of their procedures.   Since
every operation means cost, an attempt is made to use simple, straight-
forward procedures, procedures which can be completed within the time
schedules, and which take into account all administrative requirements.
Modern sample surveys are becoming multipurpose in character in the
sense that information is collected on hundreds of items belonging to
different fields of enquiry and that the results must be made available
before they become out of date.   As a result, it is not practicable to use
many of the refined results in the general estimation theory.   There is no
time to examine the distribution followed by every item in the survey and
to calculate, as an example, maximum-likelihood estimates using the frequency distributions ascertained.   The sum and the sum of squares of
the observations in the sample are the only quantities which could possibly
be calculated in large-scale surveys.   An estimator with a larger variance,
but which is cheaper to handle, may be preferred to another which requires
heavier computations, although its variance is smaller.

## 2.13 THE FUNDAMENTAL PRINCIPLE OF SAMPLE DESIGN

With every sampling and estimation procedure is associated the cost of the survey and the precision (measured, say, in terms of the mean square error) of the estimates made. Only those procedures are considered from which an objective estimate of the precision attained can be made from the sample itself. And the procedures should be practical in the sense that it is possible to carry them through according to desired specifications. Out of all these procedures of sample selection and estimation (called sample design), the one to be preferred is that which gives the highest precision for a given cost of the survey or the minimum cost for a specified level of precision. This is the guiding principle of sample design.

## 2.14 SCOPE OF THIS BOOK

The scope of this book is limited to a description of sampling theory today. This theory does not point in a unique way to the best sample design for solving a particular problem. But it does provide a framework within which to think intelligently and produce effective methods. Not all the problems involved in the planning of sample surveys and their execution will be considered; it would be too ambitious to include them all here. Attention is restricted to different schemes of sample selection, formation of estimators of population characters, and an estimation of their variance from the sample itself. The situations under which one procedure is better than another are brought to the notice of the reader. The manner in which effective use can be made of all the relevant information is indicated. It is explained how to make order out of the chaos that results when the many types of errors that a sample investigation is subject to are taken into account.

## REFERENCE

National Statistical Service of Greece (1963). "Household survey of urban areas." Government of Greece, Athens.

# CHAPTER THREE

# BASIC METHODS OF SAMPLE SELECTION

### 3.1 SIMPLE RANDOM SAMPLING

This fundamental method of sample selection may be described thus. From a population of $N$ units select one by giving equal probability to all units. This is best done with the help of random numbers (see Appendix 3). Make a note of the unit selected and return it to the population. If this operation is performed $n$ times, we get a simple random sample of $n$ units, selected with replacement (wr). If, however, this procedure is continued till $n$ distinct (different) units are selected and all repetitions are ignored, a simple random sample of $n$ units, selected without replacement (wtr), is obtained. The latter procedure is exactly the same as retaining the unit (or units) selected and selecting a further unit with equal probability from the units that remain in the population. Denoting the units in the population by

$$U_1, U_2, \ldots, U_N$$

it is obvious that in wr sampling any selection produces

$$U_i \ (i = 1, 2, \ldots, N)$$

with probability $1/N$ for each unit. And all selections are independent, since the selected unit is restored to the population before making the next selection. In wtr sampling, the first selection can produce any $U_i$ with a probability of $1/N$. Given that the first selection is $U_j$, the conditional probability that the second selection will produce $U_i$ $(i \neq j)$ is $1/(N - 1)$. But the chance of getting $U_j$ at the first selection is $1/N$. Hence the absolute probability that $U_i$ is selected at the second draw (selection) is

$$\sum_{j \neq i} \frac{1}{N} \frac{1}{N - 1} = \frac{1}{N}$$

Similarly the absolute probability that a specified unit $U_i$ is selected at the third draw is $1/N$, and so on. Thus in wtr sampling, too, each selection can produce any unit $U_i$ with a probability of $1/N$. But the conditional probability that the $s$th selection produces $U_i$, when it is known that an earlier selection (say $r$th) has produced $U_j$ $(i \neq j)$, is $1/(N - 1)$. Hence the chance that selections $r$ and $s$ produce two units $U_i$ and $U_j$ (order of selection ignored) is $2/[N(N - 1)]$. A sample of $n$ units gives $\binom{n}{2}$ pairs of selections. Thus the probability $\pi_{ij}$ that units $U_i$ and $U_j$ will appear in the sample of size $n$ is given by $\pi_{ij} = n(n - 1)/[N(N - 1)]$. Also, the chance $\pi_i$ that unit $U_i$ will be selected in the sample would be $n/N$, since the chance that it is selected at any particular draw is $1/N$. The events "$U_i$ in sample" and "$U_j$ in sample" are not independent, since $\pi_{ij} \neq \pi_i \pi_j$. Again, given that units $U_{t1}, U_{t2}, \ldots, U_{tk}$ are selected in this order at the first $k$ draws, the conditional probability that a specified unit $U_s$ will be selected at the $(k + 1)$st draw is $1/(N - k)$. Following this argument the probability of a specified ordered sample of $n$ units is $1/[N(N - 1) \cdots (N - n + 1)]$. Hence the probability of a specified sample of $n$ units, ignoring order, is

$$\frac{n!}{[N(N - 1) \cdots (N - n + 1)]} = \frac{1}{\binom{N}{n}}$$

Thus all samples of size $n$ have the same probability of being selected.

## 3.2 ESTIMATION IN SIMPLE RANDOM SAMPLING

For simplicity of presentation we shall assume that to each unit $U_i$ in the population is attached a variate value $Y_i$ for the character $y$. The population total is $Y = \Sigma Y_i$, the mean being $\bar{Y} = \Sigma Y_i/N$. Let the $n$ units (selected in this order) in the simple random sample be $u_1, u_2, \ldots, u_n$, with variate values $y_1, y_2, \ldots, y_n$ respectively. We will prove the following theorem.

### Theorem 3.1

*In* wtr *simple random sampling, the sample mean*

$$\bar{y} = \frac{Sy_i}{n} \tag{3.1}$$

*is an unbiased estimator of $\bar{Y}$ and its variance is given by*

$$V(\bar{y}) = \frac{1}{n}\left(1 - \frac{n}{N}\right)S_y^2 = (1 - f)\frac{S_y^2}{n} \tag{3.2}$$

*where*

$$S_y^2 = \frac{\Sigma(Y_i - \bar{Y})^2}{N - 1} \tag{3.3}$$

*and f is the sampling fraction $n/N$.*

PROOF   The random variable $y_i$ attached to the $i$th selection can have any of the values $Y_i$ ($i = 1, 2, \ldots, N$), each with a probability of $1/N$ (Sec. 3.1).   Hence $E(y_i) = \Sigma Y_i/N = \bar{Y}$.   Using Theorem 1.1, which states that the expected value of the sum is the sum of expected values, we have

$$E(\bar{y}) = \frac{SE(y_i)}{n} = \bar{Y}$$

Thus the sample mean is an unbiased estimator of the population mean. The variance of $\bar{y}$ is given by

$$V(\bar{y}) = E(\bar{y} - \bar{Y})^2 = \frac{E[S(y_i - \bar{Y})]^2}{n^2} = \frac{E(Sz_i)^2}{n^2}$$

By Theorem 1.1, $E(Sz_i)^2 = SE(z_i^2) + 2S'E(z_iz_j)$ where $S'$ denotes summation over the $\binom{n}{2}$ different pairs in the sample.   Now,

$$E(z_i^2) = \frac{\Sigma z_i^2}{N} = \frac{(N - 1)S_y^2}{N}$$

Given $z_i$, the conditional expected value of $z_j$ would be

$$E_2(z_j) = \frac{\displaystyle\sum_{j \neq i} z_j}{N - 1} = \frac{-z_i}{N - 1}$$

since

$$\Sigma z_i = \Sigma(y_i - \bar{Y}) = 0$$

Hence, by Theorem 1.7,

$$E(z_i z_j) = -\frac{E_1(z_i^2)}{N-1} = -\frac{\Sigma z_i^2}{N(N-1)} = -\frac{S_y^2}{N}$$

Thus

$$V(\bar{y}) = \frac{1}{n}\frac{N-1}{N}S_y^2 - \frac{n-1}{n}\frac{1}{N}S_y^2 = \frac{1}{n}\left(1 - \frac{n}{N}\right)S_y^2 = (1-f)\frac{S_y^2}{n}$$

where $f = n/N$ is the sampling fraction, the fraction of the population taken into the sample.                                                                            ∎

### Corollary

An unbiased estimate of the population total $Y = N\bar{Y}$ is given by $\hat{Y} = N\bar{y}$ and $V(\hat{Y}) = N^2 V(\bar{y})$.

**Remark**   The variance of $y$ in the population is, by definition,

$$\sigma_y^2 = \frac{\Sigma(y_i - \bar{Y})^2}{N} \tag{3.4}$$

Thus the variance of the sample mean may be written as

$$V(\bar{y}) = [1 - (n-1)(N-1)^{-1}]\frac{\sigma_y^2}{n}$$

If the sampling fraction is very small so that $n/N$ and $(n-1)/(N-1)$ are negligible relative to unity, we have $V(\bar{y}) \doteq \sigma_y^2/n \doteq S_y^2/n$. Then the variance of $\bar{y}$ depends solely on the sample size and the population variance and not on the population size $N$.

**Remark**   The quantity $1 - (n-1)/(N-1)$ is called the finite population correction (fpc) and $N/n$ the raising, inflation, or expansion factor.

**Remark**   One may think of choosing a sample size such that the coefficient of variation $\sigma(\bar{y})/E(\bar{y})$ of $\bar{y}$ has a specified value $a_0$. (The coefficient of variation measures the precision of the estimator.)   In that case, and provided that a good guess can be made of $\bar{Y}$ and $S_y^2$, the sample size $n$ is calculated from the formula

$$\left(\frac{1}{n} - \frac{1}{N}\right)S_y^2 = a_0(\bar{Y})^2$$

***Further reading*** It is of interest to note that it always pays to possess information on some units in the population. If the variate value of a unit is known, a simple random sample of $n$ units from the remaining $(N-1)$ units gives a better estimate of the population total than a sample of $n$ taken from the $N$ (see Exercise 2).

## 3.3 ESTIMATION OF SAMPLING ERROR IN WTR SAMPLING

In order to obtain an estimate of $V(\bar{y})$, we prove the following theorem.

### Theorem 3.2

*In* wtr *simple random sampling*

$$E(s_y{}^2) = S_y{}^2 \tag{3.5}$$

*where*

$$s_y{}^2 = \frac{S(y_i - \bar{y})^2}{n-1} \tag{3.6}$$

PROOF We have $(n-1)s_y{}^2 = Sy_i{}^2 - n\bar{y}^2$. Since

$$V(\bar{y}) = E(\bar{y}^2) - [E(\bar{y})]^2$$

we get

$$E(\bar{y}^2) = V(\bar{y}) + \bar{Y}^2 = \bar{Y}^2 + (1-f)\frac{S_y{}^2}{n}$$

Also,

$$ESy_i{}^2 = \frac{n}{N}\sum Y_i{}^2$$

Hence,

$$(n-1)E(s_y{}^2) = \frac{n}{N}\sum Y_i{}^2 - (1-f)S_y{}^2 - n\bar{Y}^2$$

$$= \frac{n}{N}\left(\sum Y_i{}^2 - N\bar{Y}^2\right) - (1-f)S_y{}^2$$

$$= \frac{n}{N}(N-1)S_y{}^2 - \left(1 - \frac{n}{N}\right)S_y{}^2 = (n-1)S_y{}^2$$

which proves the theorem. ∎

### Corollary

Unbiased estimates of $V(\bar{y})$ and $V(\hat{Y})$ are given by $(1-f)\dfrac{s_y{}^2}{n}$ and $N^2(1-f)\dfrac{s_y{}^2}{n}$, respectively.

*Remark*    The simplicity of the result (3.5) is the reason for the definition of the quantity $S_y^2$ with the divisor $(N - 1)$.

*Remark*    We are dealing here with a case of probability sampling since any unit in the population has a known (nonzero) probability of $n/N$ of being selected in the sample.    It was stated in Sec. 2.7 that in probability sampling the sample itself provides an objective estimate of the variance. Theorem 3.2 is a demonstration of that statement.

*Further reading*    See Exercise 16 for an alternative method of estimating the variance.    See Exercises 82 and 83 as well.

### 3.4  SAMPLING WITH REPLACEMENT

If the sample of size $n$ is selected with replacement, we shall prove the following result.

### Theorem 3.3

*In* wr *simple random sampling*

$$E(\bar{y}) = \bar{Y} \qquad V(\bar{y}) = \frac{\sigma_y^2}{n} = \left(1 - \frac{1}{N}\right)\frac{S_y^2}{n} \qquad (3.7)$$

*and*         $$V(\bar{y}) \cong \frac{s_y^2}{n}$$

*where $\cong$ stands for "is estimated by."*

The proof of this theorem can be best given by first proving the more general Theorem 3.4.

### Theorem 3.4

*Let $u_i$ $(i = 1, 2, \ldots, m)$ be $m$ independent and identically distributed random variables with $E(u_i) = \mu$, $V(u_i) = \sigma^2$. Let $\bar{u} = \sum\limits_{i=1}^{m} u_i/m$. Then $E(\bar{u}) = \mu$, $V(\bar{u}) = \sigma^2/m$, and an unbiased estimator of $V(\bar{u})$ is given by*

$$V(\bar{u}) \cong \frac{\Sigma(u_i - \bar{u})^2}{m\,(m - 1)}$$

PROOF    By Theorem 1.1, $E(\bar{u}) = \Sigma E(u_i)/m = \mu$.    By Theorem 1.5, $V(\bar{u}) = \Sigma V(u_i)/m^2 = \sigma^2/m$, the terms such as Cov $(u_i, u_j)$ vanishing because of the independence of $u_i$ and $u_j$. Further,

$$E\Sigma(u_i - \bar{u})^2 = \Sigma E(u_i^2) - mE(\bar{u}^2)$$

Now, $\qquad E(u_i^2) = V(u_i) + [E(u_i)]^2 = \sigma^2 + \mu^2$

And, $\qquad E(\bar{u}^2) = V(\bar{u}) + [E(\bar{u})]^2 = \dfrac{\sigma^2}{m} + \mu^2$

Hence $\quad E\Sigma(u_i - \bar{u})^2 = m(\sigma^2 + \mu^2) - \sigma^2 - m\mu^2 = (m - 1)\sigma^2$

which proves the theorem. (This is a very powerful result, which can be used whenever the random variables are independent.) ■

In order to prove Theorem 3.3 we note that $y_1, y_2, \ldots, y_n$ are independently and identically distributed. The variable $y_i$ associated with the $i$th selection can have any of the values $Y_1, Y_2, \ldots, Y_N$, each with probability $1/N$. Hence $E(y_i) = \bar{Y}$, $V(y_i) = \sigma_y^2$. Setting $u_i = y_i$, $m = n$ in Theorem 3.4, we immediately prove Theorem 3.3.

*Remark* We note from Eqs. (3.2) and (3.7) that the variance of the mean in wtr sampling is smaller than the variance in wr sampling. Hence, if the estimator to be used is the mean of the values of all units in the sample, wtr sampling is preferable to wr sampling. But there is no appreciable difference if both $1/N$ and $n/N$ are negligible small as compared with unity.

### 3.5 A GENERAL PROCEDURE

A very general procedure of writing down the estimator and its variance will now be presented. This method will be used on several occasions in this book. Let $t_i$ be the number of times the $i$th unit $U_i$ (with variate value $Y_i$) in the population appears in the sample of size $n$, howsoever selected. In wr simple random sampling, we have from Theorem 1.9 (Sec. 1.8),

$$E(t_i) = np_i = \frac{n}{N} \qquad V(t_i) = \frac{n}{N}\left(1 - \frac{1}{N}\right) \qquad \text{Cov }(t_i, t_j) = \frac{-n}{N^2}$$

In wtr random sampling, $t_i$ is either zero or one. And

$$Pr(t_i = 1) = \pi_i = \frac{n}{N} \qquad Pr(t_i = 1, t_j = 1) = \pi_{ij} = \frac{n(n - 1)}{N(N - 1)}$$

Hence we get

$$E(t_i) = \frac{n}{N} = E(t_i^2) \qquad V(t_i) = E(t_i^2) - [E(t_i)]^2 = \frac{n}{N}\left(1 - \frac{n}{N}\right)$$

$$\text{Cov }(t_i, t_j) = E(t_i t_j) - E(t_i)E(t_j) = \frac{n(n - 1)}{N(N - 1)} - \frac{n^2}{N^2}$$

In either case, the estimator to use is

$$\bar{y} = \frac{\sum\limits_{i=1}^{N} t_i Y_i}{n} \tag{3.8}$$

where the summation is over all units in the population. The expected value of $\bar{y}$ is, by Theorem 1.1 (Sec. 1.3),

$$E(\bar{y}) = \frac{\Sigma E(t_i) Y_i}{n} \tag{3.9}$$

and its variance is given by (using Theorem 1.5)

$$V(\bar{y}) = \frac{1}{n^2} \left[ \sum Y_i^2 V(t_i) + 2 \sum_i \sum_{j>i} Y_i Y_j \, \mathrm{Cov} \, (t_i, t_j) \right] \tag{3.10}$$

Whether the sampling scheme is wtr or wr simple random sampling, we see from (3.9) that $\bar{y}$ is an unbiased estimator of $\bar{Y}$. Making relevant substitutions in (3.10) we can verify that the variance of $\bar{y}$ is given by (3.2) for wtr sampling and by (3.7) for wr sampling.

### 3.6 A BETTER ESTIMATOR IN WR SAMPLING

In order to estimate the population mean from a wr simple random sample, we have used the estimator based on all selections, including repetitions. It will now be proved that an estimator based on the distinct units only (Raj and Khamis, 1958) is superior. This is done in Theorem 3.5.

### Theorem 3.5

*Let there be u distinct units in a* wr *simple random sample of size n. Let $k_r$ be the frequency with which the rth distinct unit occurs in the sample. Then*

$$E(\bar{y}_u) = \bar{Y} \qquad V(\bar{y}_u) \le V(\bar{y}_n) \tag{3.11}$$

*where*
$$\bar{y}_u = \frac{\overset{u}{\underset{r=1}{S}} y_r}{u} \qquad \bar{y}_n = \frac{\overset{u}{\underset{r=1}{S}} k_r y_r}{n}$$

PROOF For a given number $u$ of distinct units, the sample of distinct units is a simple random sample selected without replacement. Hence,

$$E_2(\bar{y}_u | u) = \bar{Y}$$

and therefore

$$E(\bar{y}_u) = \bar{Y} \qquad \text{(Theorem 1.7)}$$

Again, for a given sample $A_u = (y_1, y_2, \ldots, y_u)$ of $u$ distinct units, the probability that a specified distinct unit $y_r$ will be selected at any selection (there being $n$ such selections) is $1/u$ and therefore $E_2(k_r|A_u) = n/u$. Hence,

$$E_2(\bar{y}_n|A_u) = (1/n)Sy_rE_2(k_r|A_u) = (1/u)Sy_r = \bar{y}_u$$

Now, by Theorem 1.8 on conditional variance, we have

$$V(\bar{y}_n) = E_1V_2(\bar{y}_n) + V_1E_2(\bar{y}_n)$$
$$= E_1V_2(\bar{y}_n) + V(\bar{y}_u) \geq V(\bar{y}_u)$$

which proves the theorem. ■

**Corollary**

By the same Theorem 1.8,

$$V(\bar{y}_u) = E_1V_2(\bar{y}_u) = E_1\left(\frac{1}{u} - \frac{1}{N}\right)S_y^2 = \left(E\frac{1}{u} - \frac{1}{N}\right)S_y^2$$

**Remark** In order to get an unbiased estimator of $V(\bar{y}_u)$, we note that for $u \geq 2$, an unbiased estimator of $S_y^2$ is provided by

$$s_u^2 = \frac{S(y_i - \bar{y}_u)^2}{u - 1}$$

Thus, considering

$$G_u = \left[\left(\frac{1}{u} - \frac{1}{N}\right) + N^{1-n}\left(1 - \frac{1}{u}\right)\right]s_u^2$$

we have

$$E[G_u|u \geq 2] = V(\bar{y}_u)$$

An alternative unbiased estimator is

$$G'_u = \left[\left(\frac{1}{u} - \frac{1}{N}\right) + (N - 1)(N^n - N)^{-1}\right]s^2$$

where $s^2 = S(y_i - \bar{y}_u)^2/(u - 1)$ for $u \geq 2$ and 0 for $u = 1$.

*Further reading*

*1.* For a realistic comparison between wtr and wr sampling schemes, see Exercise 17, in which the effective sample size (or total cost) is the same in both cases.

*2.* If sampling with replacement is continued till the sample contains $n$ distinct units, two estimators may be formed, one based on the distinct units only and the other based on all selections. For a comparison of the two estimators, see Exercises 1 and 95.

## 3.7 ESTIMATION OF PROPORTIONS

We now turn to the problem of estimating from a simple random sample the proportion $P$ of units of a population which belong to a class $A$ (like the proportion male, proportion unemployed, etc.). If we associate with $U_i$, the $i$th unit in the population, a variable $Y_i$ which takes up the value unity if the unit belongs to $A$ and zero otherwise, it is easy to see that the total number of units belonging to $A$ equals $\Sigma Y_i = Y$, and the proportion belonging to $A$ is $P = \Sigma Y_i/N = \bar{Y}$. Thus the problem of estimating a population proportion reduces to that of estimating a population mean by defining the variable $y$ as above. Hence no new principles are involved provided that we work with the new variate $y$ for purposes of making estimates from the sample. Denoting by $N_0$ and $n_0$ the number of units belonging to the class $A$ in the population and in the sample of size $n$ respectively, we have

$$\Sigma Y_i = N_0 = \Sigma Y_i^2 = NP \qquad Sy_i = n_0 = Sy_i^2 = np$$

where $p$ is the sample proportion. In simple random sampling, by Theorems 3.1 and 3.3, an unbiased estimate of the population proportion $P$ is given by

$$\hat{P} = \frac{1}{n} Sy_i = \frac{n_0}{n} = p \qquad (3.12)$$

In wtr sampling, the variance of $p$, by Theorem 3.1, is

$$V(p) = \frac{1}{n}(1-f)\,NP\,\frac{1-P}{N-1} \qquad (3.13)$$

since $\qquad S_y^2 = \dfrac{\Sigma Y_i^2 - (\Sigma Y_i)^2/N}{N-1} = \dfrac{[NP - (NP)^2/N]}{N-1}$

And further

$$V(p) \cong \frac{1}{n}(1-f)\,\frac{[Sy_i^2 - (1/n)(Sy_i)^2]}{(n-1)}$$

$$= \frac{1}{n}(1-f)\,\frac{np(1-p)}{n-1} = (1-f)\,\frac{p(1-p)}{(n-1)} \qquad (3.14)$$

In wr sampling, it is easy to see that

$$V(p) = \frac{P(1-P)}{n} \cong \frac{p(1-p)}{n-1}$$

**Remark** The estimate of $N_0 = NP$, the number of units belonging to the class $A$, is obtained by multiplying the sample proportion $p$ by $N$.

***Remark*** Provided the sampling fraction is negligible as compared with unity and $(N - 1)/N \doteq 1$, we have that $V(p) = P(1 - P)/n$ for wtr sampling. Thus the variance of $p$ depends on the population proportion $P$ and the sample size $n$. And $P(1 - P)$ is maximum for $P = \frac{1}{2}$, for which value of $P$ the variance of $p$ is $1/(4n)$. On the other hand, the coefficient of variation of $p$ is $[P(1 - P)/n]^{\frac{1}{2}}/P = [(1 - P)/nP]^{\frac{1}{2}}$. This decreases monotonically as $P$ increases from 0 to 1.

***Remark*** Suppose it is desired to estimate a population proportion with a coefficient of variation of $a_0$ or less. Then the sample size required to achieve this is given by the formula

$$(1 - P)^{\frac{1}{2}} \leq (nP)^{\frac{1}{2}} a_0 \qquad \text{or} \qquad n \geq \frac{1 - P}{P} \frac{1}{a_0^2}$$

If the value of $P$ is guessed as 0.05 and $a_0$ is 0.10, $n \geq 1900$. A very large sample size is needed if $P$ is very small, viz., the item is rare in the population.

## 3.8 SYSTEMATIC SAMPLING

A more convenient method of sample selection when the units are serially numbered from 1 to $N$ is the following. Suppose $N = nk$, where $n$ is the sample size desired and $k$ is an integer. A number is taken at random from the numbers 1 to $k$ (using a table of random numbers). Suppose the random number is $i$. Then the sample contains the $n$ units with serial numbers $i$, $i + k$, $i + 2k$, . . . , $i + (n - 1)k$. Thus the sample consists of the first unit selected at random and every $k$th unit thereafter. It is therefore called a systematic sample (with $k$ as the sampling interval), and the procedure of selection is known as systematic sampling. The convenience of selection lies in the fact that the selection of the first member of the sample determines the entire sample automatically. The first point to be noted about this procedure is that, for a given numbering of the units, we are in effect selecting with probability $1/k$ one group or cluster of units from the following $k$ clusters forming the entire population:

| Cluster | Composition of cluster |
|---------|------------------------|
| 1 | 1, $k + 1$, $2k + 1$, . . . , $(n - 1)k + 1$ |
| . . . | |
| $i$ | $i$, $k + i$, $2k + i$, . . . , $(n - 1)k + i$ |
| . . . | |
| $k$ | $k$, $2k$, $3k$, . . . , $nk$ |

Each unit $U_i$ in the population belongs to one and only one cluster. The probability of selecting a cluster is $1/k$, which is therefore the probability with which any member of the cluster is selected in the sample. Thus $\pi_i = 1/k$. This shows that systematic sampling is a probability sampling procedure. The chance that two units $U_i$ and $U_j$ belonging to the same cluster are in the sample is obviously given by $\pi_{ij} = 1/k$. However, $\pi_{ij} = 0$ when the two units referred to belong to different clusters. In case $N = nk + c$, $c < k$, some of the clusters will contain $n$ units while others will contain $n + 1$ units; i.e., cluster sizes will not be equal. But the probability that a given unit is selected into the sample (of size $n$ or $n + 1$) will still be $1/k$, since one cluster is picked up at random from the $k$.

### 3.9 ESTIMATION IN SYSTEMATIC SAMPLING

#### Theorem 3.6

*In systematic sampling with interval $k$, an unbiased estimator of the population total $Y$ is provided by*

$$\hat{Y} = k \underset{j}{S} y_{ij} = kG_i \tag{3.15}$$

*where $G_i = \underset{j}{S} y_{ij}$ is the total of the sample cluster. And*

$$V(\hat{Y}) = k \sum_{i=1}^{k} \left( G_i - \frac{Y}{k} \right)^2 \tag{3.16}$$

PROOF The random variable $kG_i$, attached to the sample cluster, takes up the values $kG_1$, $kG_2$, . . . , $kG_k$, each with probability $1/k$.

Hence
$$E(\hat{Y}) = \frac{1}{k} k \sum_i G_i = Y$$

Further, by the same argument,

$$V(\hat{Y}) = E(kG_i - Y)^2 = \frac{1}{k} \sum_i (kG_i - Y)^2 = k \sum \left( G_i - \frac{Y}{k} \right)^2 \quad \blacksquare$$

#### Corollary

The population mean will be estimated by $\hat{Y}/N$.

*Remark* In the derivation of Theorem 3.6 no assumption has been made that all clusters must contain the same number of units.

*Remark*  If the numbering of units in the population is changed, different clusters will be formed as a result of the selection procedure.   The cluster totals $G_i$ will be different, on which depends $V(\hat{Y})$.   Thus the variance associated with systematic sampling depends heavily on the manner in which the units are arranged in the population at the time of sample selection.   This is in marked contrast with simple random sampling, in which the arrangement of units had no part to play.

*Remark*  One cannot infer from Formula (3.16) that the variance in systematic sampling will surely decrease if the size of the sample is increased.   There is no guarantee that a larger sample will necessarily produce $G_i$ that are less variable.   This makes it clear that systematic sampling is a delicate tool if it is used solely for the purpose of achieving higher precision.

### 3.10  AN ALTERNATIVE EXPRESSION FOR THE VARIANCE

An alternative expression for the variance of the systematic sample estimate, which is more instructive, is given below.

#### Theorem 3.7

*In systematic sampling, with a sampling interval of $k$, from a population of size $N = nk$, the variance of*

$$\hat{Y} = N\bar{y}_i$$

*is given by*

$$V(\hat{Y}) = \frac{N(N-1)}{n} S_y{}^2[1 + (n-1)\rho] \tag{3.17}$$

*where $\bar{y}_i$ is the sample mean and*

$$\rho = \frac{E[(y_{ij} - \bar{Y})(y_{ik} - \bar{Y})]}{E(y_{ij} - \bar{Y})^2} \tag{3.18}$$

*is the intracluster correlation coefficient defined in Sec. 1.9.*

PROOF   From Theorem 3.6 we have

$$V(\hat{Y}) = k \sum_i (G_i - n\bar{Y})^2 = k \sum_i \left[ \sum_j (y_{ij} - \bar{Y}) \right]^2$$

$$= k \sum\sum (y_{ij} - \bar{Y})^2 + 2k \sum_i \sum_j \sum_{k>j} (y_{ij} - \bar{Y})(y_{ik} - \bar{Y})$$

$$= k(N-1)S_y{}^2 + k(n-1)(N-1)\rho S_y{}^2$$

$$= N(N-1)S_y{}^2 \frac{1 + \rho(n-1)}{n} \quad \blacksquare$$

### Corollary

The condition that $V(\hat{Y})$ in systematic sampling be smaller than $V(\hat{Y})$ in wtr simple random sampling is that

$$N(N-1)S_y^2 \frac{1+(n-1)\rho}{n} < N(N-n)\frac{S_y^2}{n}$$

or

$$\rho < -\frac{1}{N-1} \tag{3.19}$$

If $N$ is large, this requires that $\rho$ be negative if systematic sampling is to be superior to simple random sampling.

*Remark*   The quantity $\rho$ is the correlation coefficient between pairs of units in the same systematic sample.   Since there is no algebraic relationship between $n$ and $\rho$, the performance of systematic sampling, as $n$ is increased, becomes unpredictable.

*Remark*   If the ordering of the units in the population is essentially random, a sample of any $n$ predesignated positions will be a simple random sample.   Hence, systematic sampling in this situation coincides with wtr simple random sampling.   The same conclusion follows from the observation that $\rho = -1/(N-1)$ when the units are arranged at random.

### 3.11   ESTIMATION OF VARIANCE IN SYSTEMATIC SAMPLING

Since the variance of $\hat{Y}$ in systematic sampling is $k^2$ times the variance of $G_i$ (Sec. 3.9), an unbiased estimate of $V(\hat{Y})$ cannot be obtained by making just one observation on $G_i$, that is, by taking just one systematic sample.   If it is essential to have a rigorous estimate of the sampling variance, it can be best done by taking not one but $m$ independent systematic samples, each containing $n/m$ units to keep the total sample size the same.   Theorem 3.4 will then provide an unbiased estimate of $V(\hat{Y})$. In case the listing of units in the population can be considered to be random, the formulas for estimating the variance in the case of wtr simple random sampling will apply.   But quite often one would like to arrange the units in a particular pattern to achieve greater precision. For example, the city blocks may be arranged in a serpentine (geographically contiguous) fashion and a systematic sample of blocks taken to get a fair spread of the sample over the whole city.   This will have the effect of introducing negative correlation within systematic samples.   Since the units are deliberately ordered, the formulas for estimating the variance appropriate to simple random sampling will not apply. However, the position is not as bad as it looks. To anticipate matters, systematic sampling is generally used in large-scale surveys at the last stage of the sampling process (to select households, etc.) and the results of Chap. 6 will show that in this case rigorous estimates of the variance can be obtained.

### 3.12 SAMPLING WITH UNEQUAL PROBABILITIES

In the two schemes of sample selection discussed so far, every unit in the population had the same chance of being selected in the sample. The reader might get the impression that this is essential to the argument. It is not so. The only requirement is that the probabilities of inclusion should be known and should be nonzero. It can, in fact, be demonstrated that higher precision may be achieved by making the probabilities unequal. Now the question is: What is the procedure of selecting the sample with unequal probabilities? We shall take the concrete case of a population of $N$ agricultural holdings with areas $X_i$, $X_2$, . . . , $X_N$, the total area being $X = \Sigma X_i$. A sample of one holding is to be selected such that the chance that the $i$th holding will be selected is $X_i/X$. If the $X_i$ are integers, all we have to do is to assign the first $X_1$ natural numbers (1 to $X_1$) to the first holding, the next $X_2$ numbers ($X_1 + 1$ to $X_1 + X_2$) to the second holding, and so on. A number is then selected at random between 1 and $X$ (with the help of a table of random numbers) and the unit in whose range this random number falls is taken in the sample. It is evident that the probability that $U_i$ is selected is $X_i/X$. The $X_i$'s are called measures of size of the units, and the procedure is known as sampling with probability proportionate to size (pps). It may be noted that the measures of size can all be multiplied by a constant number to make them integral if they are not already so. This will not disturb the probabilities. If the above procedure of selection is repeated $n$ times with the precaution that the unit selected is restored to the population at every selection, we get a pps sample of size $n$ selected with replacement.

### 3.13 AN ALTERNATIVE SAMPLING PROCEDURE

In the method just described the measures of size $X_i$, of the units have to be cumulated progressively in order to assign them ranges of the type $X_1 + 1$ to $X_1 + X_2$. If $N$, the total number of units, is fairly large, the process of cumulation will become tedious. A procedure of selecting a pps sample has been devised by Lahiri (1951), in which no cumulations need be made. This consists in selecting a number at random between 1 and $N$ and noting down the unit selected provisionally. Another random number is then taken between 1 and $X_0$, where $X_0$ is the maximum (or something greater) of the $N$ measures of size. If the second random number is smaller than the size of the unit provisionally selected, this unit is finally taken into the sample. If not, the entire procedure (of selecting two random numbers) is repeated until a unit is finally selected. In order to prove that this procedure gives a pps sample of size one, we note that the chance that a trial (consisting in taking two random numbers) will end in no selection is given by $q = \sum_i (1/N)(1 - X_i/X_0) = 1 - \bar{X}/X_0$. (The probability of selecting $U_i$ provisionally is $1/N$, and the probability that the second random number exceeds $X_i$ is $1 - X_i/X_0$.) The chance that the unit $U_i$ is selected at a trial is $p_i = (1/N)X_i/X_0$. Hence the chance that the sample of one will finally end up in the selection of the unit $U_i$ is $p_i + qp_i + q^2p_i + \cdots = p_i/(1 - q) = X_i/X$.

### 3.14  ESTIMATION IN WR PPS SAMPLING

Let $p_j = X_j/X$ be the probability that the unit $U_j$ is selected in a sample of one. If $n$ independent selections are made and the value of $y$ for each selected unit is ascertained, we have the sample

$$\begin{pmatrix} y_i, \ y_2, \ \ldots \ , \ y_n \\ p_1, \ p_2, \ \ldots \ , \ p_n \end{pmatrix}$$

The random variable $y_i$ associated with the $i$th selection can have values $Y_1$, $Y_2, \ldots, Y_N$, with probabilities $p_1, p_2, \ldots, p_N$. Hence $E(y_i/p_i) = Y$ and $V(y_i/p_i) = \sum p_i \left( \dfrac{y_i}{p_i} - Y \right)^2$. Since the random variables $y_i/p_i$ $(i = 1, 2, \ldots, n)$ are independently and identically distributed, we can, by using Theorem 3.4, immediately prove the following theorem.

### Theorem 3.8

*In with-replacement pps sampling, an unbiased estimator of the population total $Y$ is given by*

$$\hat{Y} = \frac{1}{n} S \frac{y_i}{p_i} = \frac{1}{n} Sz_i = \bar{z} \tag{3.20}$$

*with*

$$V(\hat{Y}) = \frac{1}{n} \sum p_i \left( \frac{y_i}{p_i} - Y \right)^2 \tag{3.21}$$

*and*

$$V(\hat{Y}) \cong \frac{1}{n(n-1)} S(z_i - \bar{z})^2 \tag{3.22}$$

**Remark**   The expression for the variance of $\hat{Y}$ can be easily given by the following alternative form:

$$V(\hat{Y}) = \frac{1}{n} \sum' \left[ p_i p_j \left( \frac{y_i}{p_i} - \frac{y_j}{p_j} \right)^2 \right] \tag{3.23}$$

where $\sum'$ denotes summation over all different pairs of units in the population. Furthermore,

$$V(\hat{Y}) \cong S' \frac{(y_i/p_i - y_j/p_j)^2}{n^2(n-1)} \tag{3.24}$$

where $S'$ denotes summation over the different pairs in the sample.

### Corollary

We note from (3.21) or (3.23) that $V(\hat{Y}) = 0$ if $y_i/p_i$ is constant. This shows that the pps estimate will have zero variance if the measures of size are such that the variate $y$ is proportionate to $x$. It is on this proportionality or near-proportionality that the survey statistician relies when the method of pps sampling is decided upon. It is true that the values of $y$ are not known in advance. But if we have reason to believe that the measures of size chosen are such that $y/x$ is approximately constant, we have reason to expect from (3.21) that the variance of the estimate will be small.

**Remark**   The method of sampling with unequal probabilities is generally used for the selection of large units such as cities, villages, and blocks. The measures of size are usually based on information collected from censuses of population, agriculture, industry, etc.

**Remark**   Another way of writing the variance of $\hat{Y}$ is

$$V(\hat{Y}) = \frac{X}{n} \sum X_i \left( \frac{Y_i}{X_i} - R \right)^2 \qquad R = \frac{Y}{X}$$
$$= \frac{1}{n} \sum' \left[ X_i X_j \left( \frac{Y_i}{X_i} - \frac{Y_j}{X_j} \right)^2 \right] \tag{3.25}$$

**Further reading**   See Exercise 16 for another method of obtaining the variance estimator.

### 3.15 COMPARISON WITH SAMPLING WITH EQUAL PROBABILITIES

It must be stressed at this stage that the success of pps sampling depends heavily on the goodness of the measures of size. If these are poor, in the sense that near-proportionality does not exist, it may be no better than sampling with equal probabilities. In fact, a comparison of the variances

$$V_1(\hat{Y}) = \frac{X\Sigma Y_i^2/X_i - Y^2}{n} \qquad V_2(\hat{Y}) = \frac{N\Sigma Y_i^2 - Y^2}{n}$$

for pps and wr equal probability sampling, respectively, shows that the former will be superior if

$$\sum_i (X_i - \bar{X}) \frac{Y_i^2}{X_i} > 0 \tag{3.26}$$

that is, if $x$ and $y^2/x$ are positively correlated (Raj, 1954). The application of this criterion is difficult in practice. Another point to be borne in mind is that the correlation coefficient between $y$ and $x$ may be unity, and yet pps sampling may be worse than sampling with equal probabilities. This is brought out in the following theorem (Raj, 1954).

#### Theorem 3.9

*If for a finite population $y = a + bx$, so that there is perfect correlation between $y$ and $x$, pps sampling will be less precise than equal probability sampling if*

$$\frac{\bar{X} - \tilde{X}}{\tilde{X}\sigma_x^2} > \frac{b^2}{a^2} \qquad \tilde{X} = \frac{N}{\Sigma(1/X_i)} \tag{3.27}$$

The proof follows from the substitution of $y = a + bx$ in the inequality given by (3.26). If $a$ is large, the inequality (3.27) may be easily satisfied.

*Further reading* For a comparison between pps sampling and equal probability sampling when the finite population actually observed is assumed to be a random sample from an infinite superpopulation following a certain model, see Exercises 4 and 5.

### 3.16 SAMPLING WITHOUT REPLACEMENT WITH UNEQUAL PROBABILITIES

A natural generalization of the wr sampling scheme of Sec. 3.12 would be to select a pps sample of size unity as before and remove the selected unit from the population. From the units that remain another pps sample of size one is taken and the selected unit is removed from the population.    This procedure is continued till $n$ selections are made.    This will give a sample selected without replacement with unequal probabilities. If $n = 2$ and $X_i/X$ is denoted by $p_i$ $(i = 1, 2, \ldots, N)$, the probability that the unit $U_i$ is in the sample would be

$$\pi_i = p_i + \sum_{j \neq i} \frac{p_j p_i}{1 - p_j} = p_i \left[ 1 + \sum_{j \neq i} p_j (1 - p_j)^{-1} \right]$$

Further, the probability that units $U_i$ and $U_j$ are both in the sample is

$$\pi_{ij} = p_i p_j (1 - p_i)^{-1} + p_j p_i (1 - p_j)^{-1} = p_i p_j [(1 - p_i)^{-1} + (1 - p_j)^{-1}]$$

### 3.17  A MORE GENERAL SELECTION PROCEDURE

A more general sampling scheme is to start with some arbitrary proba-bilities $p_i$ $(i = 1, 2, \ldots, N)$ for drawing the first member of the sample. Depending upon the first selection, we can make an arbitrary assign-ment of probabilities for the remaining $(N - 1)$ units for making the second selection.    This will give rise to $\binom{N}{1}$ sets of conditional proba-bilities.    Similarly, for each pair of units selected in the first two selections we can specify arbitrary conditional probabilities for the remaining $(N - 2)$ units.    We will thus have $\binom{N}{2}$ sets of conditional probabilities for making the third selection, and so on.    Theoretically, the probability of every ordered sample $(U_1, U_2, \ldots, U_n)$ can be written down as the product of $Pr(U_1)$, $Pr(U_2|U_1)$, $Pr(U_3|U_1, U_2)$, $\ldots$, $Pr(U_n|U_1, \ldots, U_{n-1})$.    Consequently, the probability that any unit $U_i$ is selected in the sample can be obtained as the sum of the probabilities of all samples of size $n$ containing $U_i$.    Similarly, $\pi_{ij}$ is obtained as the sum of the proba-bilities of all samples containing both $U_i$ and $U_j$.

### 3.18  ANOTHER TYPE OF SELECTION PROCEDURE

A generalization can also be made about systematic sampling with equal probabilities.    We cumulate the measures of size of the units and assign them the ranges 1 to $X_1$, $X_1 + 1$ to $X_1 + X_2$, $X_1 + X_2 + 1$ to $X_1 + X_2 + X_3$, and so on, as in Sec. 3.12.    In order to select a sample of size $n$, a random number is taken between 1 and $k = X/n$.    The units in the sample are those in whose range lie the random number $i$ and all other numbers $i + k$, $i + 2k$, $\ldots$, obtained by adding $k$ successively to $i$.    If there is any unit whose measure of size $\geq X/n$, it is removed beforehand from the selection procedure and is taken into the sample with certainty. The probability that any unit $U_i$ is in the sample is obviously $X_i/(X/n) = np_i$. There is no simple formula to write down an expression for $\pi_{ij}$. For a specific arrangement of the units, this could be easily calculated by finding out which random numbers (from 1 to $X/n$) will select $U_i$ and $U_j$ simultaneously. If $m_{ij}$ is the number of such random numbers, $\pi_{ij} = nm_{ij}/X$.

### 3.19  ESTIMATION PROCEDURES

We thus find that there is no dearth of procedures for selecting the sample with unequal probabilities without replacement. (We shall study a few more later on.) Our next problem is that of estimation. Suppose we attach constants $c_1, c_2, \ldots, c_N$ to the units $U_1, U_2, \ldots, U_N$, respectively. A very general linear function of the sample values can then be written as

$$L(s) = \sum_i t_i c_i Y_i \tag{3.28}$$

where $t_i$'s are random variables defined as $t_i = 1$ if $U_i$ occurs in the sample and 0 otherwise. Obviously, $E(t_i) = \pi_i$ (the probability that $U_i$ occurs in the sample) and $E(t_i t_j) = \pi_{ij}$ (the probability that $U_i$ and $U_j$ both occur in the sample).

Thus $\quad V(t_i) = \pi_i - \pi_i^2 = \pi_i(1 - \pi_i) \qquad \text{Cov}\,(t_i, t_j) = \pi_{ij} - \pi_i \pi_j$

Now, $\qquad\qquad\qquad EL(s) = \Sigma c_i Y_i E(t_i) = \Sigma \pi_i c_i Y_i$

In order that $L(s)$ be an unbiased estimator of $Y$, we must have

$$EL(s) = \Sigma Y_i$$

which gives $c_i = 1/\pi_i$. Thus

$$\hat{Y} = \sum \frac{t_i Y_i}{\pi_i} = S \frac{y_i}{\pi_i} \tag{3.29}$$

and

$$V(\hat{Y}) = \sum \frac{Y_i^2}{\pi_i^2} V(t_i) + \sum_i \sum_{j \neq i} \frac{Y_i}{\pi_i} \frac{Y_j}{\pi_j} \text{Cov}\,(t_i, t_j)$$

$$= \sum \frac{\pi_i(1 - \pi_i) Y_i^2}{\pi_i^2} + \sum_i \sum_{j \neq i} \frac{(\pi_{ij} - \pi_i \pi_j) Y_i Y_j}{\pi_i \pi_j} \tag{3.30}$$

This expression for the variance is due to Horvitz and Thompson (1952).

**Remark** The variance of $\hat{Y}$ depends solely on the quantities $\pi_{ij}$ and

$\pi_i$ calculated from the sampling procedure adopted. This is the reason that these probabilities were determined for the various selection procedures proposed in the preceding sections.

**Remark**  If the selection procedure is such that $\pi_i \propto Y_i$, the estimator (3.29) reduces to a constant, and thus has zero variance. Hence, in practice, we search for measures of size $X_i \propto Y_i$ and try to have a selection procedure based on the $X_i$ such that $\pi_i \propto X_i$.

**Further reading**  When the number of units within the population is small, it may be possible to determine the $\pi_{ij}$ so that the variance of the estimator (3.29) is minimized. This is the subject matter of Exercise 8.

### 3.20  ESTIMATION OF VARIANCE

Let $f(y)$ be a function of $y$. We shall define $L_1(s)$ and $L_2(s)$ as

$$
\begin{aligned}
L_1(s) &= Sc_i f(y_i) = \Sigma t_i c_i f(y_i) \\
L_2(s) &= S' c_{ij} f(y_i) f(y_j) = \sum t_{ij} c_{ij} f(y_i) f(y_j)
\end{aligned}
\tag{3.31}
$$

where $c_{ij}$'s are determined beforehand for all pairs in the population, and $t_{ij} = 1$ if both $U_i$ and $U_j$ are in the sample, and 0 otherwise. By the argument given in Sec. 3.19, we have

$$
EL_1(s) = \sum \pi_i c_i f(y_i)
\tag{3.32}
$$

$$
EL_2(s) = \sum \pi_{ij} c_i c_j f(y_i) f(y_j)
\tag{3.33}
$$

This shows that the expected value of any random function of the type $L_1(s)$ is obtained by multiplying by $\pi_i$ and summing over all units in the population. And the expected value of a function such as $L_2(s)$ is obtained by multiplying by $\pi_{ij}$ and adding over all pairs of units in the population. Now we are in a position to estimate $V(\hat{Y})$ of Eq. (3.30). The first part is estimated by $Sy_i{}^2(1 - \pi_i)/\pi_i{}^2$ and the second part by

$$
2S'(\pi_{ij} - \pi_i \pi_j)(\pi_{ij})^{-1} \frac{y_i}{\pi_i} \frac{y_j}{\pi_j}
$$

Adding, we have an unbiased estimator as

$$
\hat{V}(\hat{Y}) = S \frac{1 - \pi_i}{\pi_i{}^2} y_i{}^2 + 2S' \frac{\pi_{ij} - \pi_i \pi_j}{\pi_{ij}} \frac{y_i}{\pi_i} \frac{y_j}{\pi_j}
\tag{3.34}
$$

This estimator is due to Horvitz and Thompson (1952).

*Remark*   In order to obtain an unbiased estimator of the variance, the sampling scheme must be such that all $\pi_{ij} > 0$.

### 3.21  TWO USEFUL RELATIONS

The quantities $\pi_i$ and $\pi_{ij}$ are probabilities, and so they lie between 0 and 1. They are subject to the following further relations

$$\sum \pi_i = n \qquad \sum_{j \neq i} \pi_{ij} = (n - 1)\pi_i \qquad (3.35)$$

The proof is simple. For the totality of samples $s$ of size $n$, $\Sigma Pr(s) = 1$. Now $\Sigma \pi_i$ is the sum of the probabilities of all samples containing $U_1$, of all samples containing $U_2$, and so on. Thus every $Pr(s)$ occurs $n$ times in this sum, once as a sample containing the first member in it, then as a sample containing the second member in it, and so on. Hence $\Sigma \pi_i = n$. In the same way $\sum\limits_{j \neq 1} \pi_{1j}$ is the sum of the probabilities of all samples containing $U_1$ and $U_2$, $U_1$ and $U_3$, $U_1$ and $U_4$, and so on. Thus every $Pr(s)$ containing $U_1$ occurs $(n - 1)$ times in this sum as the sample has $(n - 1)$ other members in it, and it occurs once for each of these members. Hence $\sum\limits_{j \neq 1} \pi_{1j} = (n - 1)\,\pi_1$. In general, $\sum\limits_{j \neq i} \pi_{ij} = (n - 1)\,\pi_i$.

### 3.22  AN ALTERNATIVE EXPRESSION FOR THE VARIANCE

We shall now exhibit the variance of the estimator (3.29) in wtr sampling in a form similar to (3.23) obtained for wr sampling. We have

$$V(\hat{Y}) = \sum \left[ \frac{y_i^2(1 - \pi_i)}{\pi_i} \right] + 2 \sum\nolimits' \left[ (\pi_{ij} - \pi_i\pi_j) \frac{y_i\, y_j}{\pi_i\, \pi_j} \right]$$

Now, 
$$\sum\nolimits' \left[ (\pi_i\pi_j - \pi_{ij}) \left( \frac{y_i^2}{\pi_i^2} + \frac{y_j^2}{\pi_j^2} \right) \right] = \sum_i \sum_{j \neq i} \left[ (\pi_i\pi_j - \pi_{ij}) \frac{y_i^2}{\pi_i^2} \right]$$

$$= \sum_i \frac{y_i^2}{\pi_i} \sum_{j \neq i} \pi_j - \sum \frac{y_i^2}{\pi_i^2} \sum_{j \neq i} \pi_{ij} = \sum \left[ \frac{y_i^2}{\pi_i} (n - \pi_i) \right]$$

$$- (n - 1) \sum \frac{y_i^2}{\pi_i} = \sum \left[ \frac{y_i^2}{\pi_i} (1 - \pi_i) \right]$$

Hence

$$V(\hat{Y}) = \sum\nolimits' \left[ (\pi_i\pi_j - \pi_{ij}) \left( \frac{y_i}{\pi_i} - \frac{y_j}{\pi_j} \right)^2 \right] \qquad (3.36)$$

Using the relation (3.33), an unbiased estimator of $V(\hat{Y})$ is given by

$$\hat{V}(\hat{Y}) = S'\left[\frac{\pi_i\pi_j - \pi_{ij}}{\pi_{ij}}\left(\frac{y_i}{\pi_i} - \frac{y_j}{\pi_j}\right)^2\right] \qquad (3.37)$$

This expression was first given by Yates and Grundy (1953).

**Remark**   In the case of with-replacement pps sampling, it is clear from (3.23) that all pairs of units in the population make a positive contribution to the variance.   This is not necessarily so in the case of without-replacement pps sampling, as is evident from (3.36).   All those pairs for which $\pi_i\pi_j < \pi_{ij}$ will make a negative contribution to $V(\hat{Y})$.   As a result, the estimator of variance (3.37) or (3.34) may assume negative values for some samples.

**Remark**   When sampling is carried out without replacement with equal probabilities, $\pi_{ij} = n(n - 1)/[N(N - 1)]$, $\pi_i = n/N$.   Substituting these in formulas (3.29), (3.30), (3.36), and (3.37), we derive the customary population-total estimator, its variance, and its variance estimator.   In this case $\pi_i\pi_j - \pi_{ij} > 0$, and all pairs make a positive contribution to the variance.

**Further reading**

**1.**   It may be of some interest to use the simpler variance estimator (3.22) in place of (3.34) or (3.37).   The status of this estimator in wtr sampling is discussed in Exercise 6.
**2.**   Some well-known situations in which the variance estimator (3.37) must be positive are presented in Exercises 7 and 9.

**3.23   COMPARISON OF WTR AND WR SCHEMES**

When is wtr sampling superior to wr sampling with unequal probabilities? An answer to this question will now be attempted.   We start with a set of probabilities $p_i$ $(i = 1, 2, \ldots , N)$, $\Sigma p_i = 1$, with which a pps sample of size $n$ is selected with replacement.   Let there be a wtr sampling scheme for which $\pi_i = np_i$ (this could be achieved, for example, by the method of Sec. 3.18).   Then we prove the following theorem (Raj, 1966).

**Theorem 3.10**

*A sufficient condition for the* wtr *estimator* $S(y_i/\pi_i)$ *to have smaller variance than the* wr *estimator* $n^{-1}S(y_i/p_i)$ *with* $\pi_i = np_i$, *independently of the y's is that*

$$\pi_{ij} > \frac{(n-1)}{n} \pi_i \pi_j \qquad \text{for all } i,j \tag{3.38}$$

PROOF

$$V\left(S\frac{y_i}{\pi_i}\right) = \sum' \left[ (\pi_i \pi_j - \pi_{ij}) \left(\frac{y_i}{\pi_i} - \frac{y_j}{\pi_j}\right)^2 \right]$$

$$V\left[ n^{-1}S\frac{y_i}{p_i} \right] = \sum' n^{-1} \left[ \pi_i \pi_j \left(\frac{y_i}{\pi_i} - \frac{y_j}{\pi_j}\right)^2 \right]$$

since $\pi_i = np_i$. Hence, if

$$\pi_i \pi_j - \pi_{ij} < \frac{\pi_i \pi_j}{n}$$

sampling without replacement will be superior. This leads to the condition

$$\pi_{ij} > (n-1)\frac{\pi_i \pi_j}{n} \qquad \text{for all } i,j \qquad \blacksquare$$

### Corollary

In sampling without replacement with equal probabilities

$$\pi_{ij} = n(n-1)[N(N-1)]^{-1} \qquad \pi_i = \pi_j = \frac{n}{N}$$

Now $\pi_{ij}[(n-1)\pi_i \pi_j/n]^{-1} = N/(N-1) > 1$. This proves that the associated wr scheme is inferior.

A necessary condition for wtr sampling to be superior to wr sampling is obtained (Narain, 1951) in Theorem 3.11.

### Theorem 3.11

*A necessary condition for the* wtr *estimator* $S(y_i/\pi_i)$ *to be better than the* wr *estimator* $n^{-1}S(y_i/p_i)$ *with* $\pi_i = np_i$, *independently of the y's, is*

$$\pi_{ij} \leq \frac{2(n-1)\pi_i \pi_j}{n} \tag{3.39}$$

PROOF   Let

$$V\left(S\frac{y_i}{\pi_i}\right) \leq V\left(\frac{1}{n}S\frac{y_i}{p_i}\right)$$

Then
$$\sum \frac{y_i^2}{\pi_i} + 2 \sum' \left( \pi_{ij} \frac{y_i \, y_j}{\pi_i \, \pi_j} \right) - Y^2 \le \sum \frac{y_i^2}{\pi_i} - \frac{Y^2}{n}$$

or
$$2 \sum' \left( \pi_{ij} \frac{y_i \, y_j}{\pi_i \, \pi_j} \right) \le n^{-1}(n-1) \left( \sum y_i^2 + 2 \sum' y_i y_j \right)$$

or
$$\sum y_i^2 + \sum_i \sum_{j \neq i} \lambda_{ij} y_i y_j \ge 0 \qquad \lambda_{ij} = 1 - n\pi_{ij}[(n-1)\pi_i \pi_j]^{-1}$$

It follows then that the principal minors of the matrix $A = (\lambda_{ij})$ with $\lambda_{ii} = 1$ are nonnegative. Thus $1 - \lambda_{ij}^2 \ge 0$, which leads to (3.39). ∎

### Corollary

In samples of size $n = 2$ the estimator of variance (3.37) will be positive if wtr sampling is superior to with-replacement pps sampling independently of the $y$'s.

*Further reading* A wtr sampling scheme which is definitely superior to the associated wr sampling scheme from the point of view of variance is presented in Exercise 10.[1]

### 3.24 ANOTHER PROCEDURE OF ESTIMATION IN WTR SAMPLING

For the more general wtr sampling scheme of Sec. 3.17, in which conditional probabilities are specified for each selection, an alternative estimation procedure consists in making direct use of conditional probabilities without calculating $\pi_i$ and $\pi_{ij}$, which may be difficult to compute for some sampling schemes. In this procedure the expectations are calculated by making use of the conditional argument. As an example, suppose two units are selected from a population in the following manner. The first selection is made with probabilities $p_i$ $(i = 1, 2, \ldots, N)$ based on $X_i$, and the second selection is made with probabilities proportionate to the sizes of the remaining units. In this situation, the conditional probability that $U_j$ is selected when it is known that $U_i$ is the first selection is given by $p_j/(1 - p_i)$. We form the estimators

$$t_1 = \frac{y_1}{p_1} \qquad t_2 = y_1 + y_2 \frac{1 - p_1}{p_2}$$

where $y_1$, $y_2$ are the variate values associated with the first and second selections and $p_1$, $p_2$ are the corresponding initial probabilities. Now $E(t_1) = \Sigma(y_1/p_1)p_1 = Y$, $E_2(t_2|t_1) = y_1 + (Y - y_1) = Y$, so that $E(t_2) = Y$.

[1] Some other procedures of selecting a sample of two different units from a universe such that $\pi_i \propto x_i$ are outlined in Exercise 102.

Thus $t_1$ and $t_2$ are unbiased estimators of $Y$. Again, we have

$$V(t_1) = \sum{}' \left[ x_i x_j \left( \frac{y_i}{x_i} - \frac{y_j}{x_j} \right)^2 \right] \quad \text{from (3.25)}$$

And $V(t_2) = E_1 V_2(t_2) + V_1 E_2(t_2)$ by Theorem 1.8. As $E_2(t_2) = Y$, $V_1 E_2(t_2) = 0$. Hence we have $V(t_2) = E_1 \sum_k{}' [x_i x_j (y_i/x_i - y_j/x_j)^2]$, where $\sum_k{}'$ runs over the $\binom{N-1}{2}$ pairs formed out of the $(N-1)$ units eliminating $U_k$, the one selected at the first selection. Thus

$$V(t_2) = E_1 \sum_k{}' a_{ij} = \frac{x_1}{X} \sum_1{}' a_{ij} + \frac{x_2}{X} \sum_2{}' a_{ij} + \cdots$$

$$= \sum{}' \left[ \frac{X - x_i - x_j}{X} x_i x_j \left( \frac{y_i}{x_i} - \frac{y_j}{x_j} \right)^2 \right]$$

$$= \sum{}' \left[ \left( 1 - \frac{x_i + x_j}{X} \right) x_i x_j \left( \frac{y_i}{x_i} - \frac{y_j}{x_j} \right)^2 \right] < V(t_1)$$

Further $\qquad\qquad E(t_1 t_2) = E_1[t_1 E_2(t_2|t_1)] = Y^2$

so that $t_1$ and $t_2$ are uncorrelated. Hence $t = (t_1 + t_2)/2$ is an unbiased estimator of $Y$ and

$$V(t) = \frac{V(t_1) + V(t_2)}{4} < \frac{V(t_1)}{2}$$

$$= \frac{1}{2} \sum{}' \left[ x_i x_j \left( \frac{y_i}{x_i} - \frac{y_j}{x_j} \right)^2 \right] = V \left( 2^{-1} S \frac{y_i}{p_i} \right)$$

We have then proved the following (Raj, 1966) Theorem 3.12.

### Theorem 3.12

*In samples of size two, let the first selection be made with probabilities proportionate to $X_i$ $(i = 1, 2, \ldots, N)$ and the second, with pp to the remaining $X_i$. Let*

$$t_1 = \frac{y_1}{p_1} \qquad t_2 = y_1 + y_2 \frac{1 - p_1}{p_2} \qquad t = \frac{t_1 + t_2}{2}$$

*Then $E(t_1) = E(t_2) = E(t) = Y$,*

$$V(t_2) < V(t_1) \qquad V(t) < V \left( 2^{-1} S \frac{y_i}{p_i} \right)$$

This theorem provides immediately an example of a situation in which without-replacement pps sampling is superior to with-replacement pps sampling. This result can be extended to any sample size $n$.

## Theorem 3.13

*Suppose a sample of size $n$ is selected in the manner of Theorem 3.12, that is, the $i$th selection is made with probabilities proportionate to the sizes of the remaining $N - i + 1$ units. Define $t_1 = y_1/p_1$,*

$$t_\lambda = y_1 + y_2 + \cdots + y_{\lambda-1} + y_\lambda \frac{1 - \sum_{j=1}^{\lambda-1} p_j}{p_\lambda} \qquad (\lambda = 2, \ldots, n)$$

*Then* $\qquad E(t_\lambda) = Y \qquad E(t_\lambda t_\mu) = Y^2 \qquad V(t_\lambda) < V(t_{\lambda-1})$

PROOF Given the units selected at the first $(\lambda - 1)$ selections, the conditional expectation of $t_\lambda$ is

$$y_1 + y_2 + \cdots + y_{\lambda-1} + (Y - y_1 - y_2 - \cdots - y_{\lambda-1}) = Y$$

so that $t_\lambda$ is an unbiased estimator of $Y$. If $\lambda < \mu$, given the first $(\mu - 1)$ selections, $E(t_\mu) = Y$ so that $E(t_\lambda t_\mu) = Y^2$, which proves that $t_\lambda$ and $t_\mu$ are uncorrelated. Further, given the units selected at the first $(\lambda - 2)$ selections, it is proved from Theorem 3.12 that the conditional variance of $t_\lambda$ is smaller than that of $t_{\lambda-1}$, and hence $V(t_\lambda) < V(t_{\lambda-1})$. ∎

## Corollary

We have $V(t_n) < V(t_{n-1}) < \cdots < V(t_1)$. Defining

$$t = \frac{(t_1 + t_2 + \cdots + t_n)}{n}$$

we get $\qquad V(t) = (1/n^2)\Sigma V(t_i) < (1/n)V(t_1) = V\left(n^{-1}S\frac{y_i}{p_i}\right)$

This proves that the wtr scheme is superior to the wr scheme.

## Further reading

**1.** Refer to Exercise 18, in which an equivalent procedure of sample selection is considered. In this method sampling with pps is continued till the sample contains $(n + 1)$ different units. The last unit is rejected, and the sample consists of the $n$ different units selected. A comparison of the two situations is made in Exercise 19.

**2.** For an alternative method of forming estimators when sampling is done without replacement with unequal probabilities, see Exercise 12.

**3.** The estimator $t$ is an example of an ordered estimator, making use of the order in which the units are selected in the sample. It is proved in Exercise 13 that an unordered estimator is superior to an ordered one.

## 3.25 ESTIMATION OF VARIANCE

An unbiased estimator of the variance of $t = \Sigma t_i/n$ is proved by the following general theorem.

### Theorem 3.14

*Let $t_1, t_2, \ldots, t_n$ be uncorrelated random variables with the same expectation $E(t) = \mu$. Let $t$ be defined as $t = (t_1 + t_2 + \cdots + t_n)/n$. Then $E(t) = \mu$ and an unbiased estimator of $V(t)$ is given by*

$$\hat{V}(t) = \Sigma(t_i - t)^2/[n(n - 1)]$$

PROOF   It is obvious that $E(t) = \mu$. As $t_i$ and $t_j$ are uncorrelated, $E(t_it_j) = \mu^2$, and hence $\displaystyle\sum_i \sum_{j>i} t_it_j/[n(n - 1)/2]$ is an unbiased estimator of $\mu^2$. Now

$$V(t) = E(t^2) - \mu^2$$

Hence   $\displaystyle \hat{V}(t) = t^2 - 2\,\frac{\sum_i \sum_{j>i} t_it_j}{n(n - 1)} = \frac{(\Sigma t_i)^2}{n^2} - 2\,\frac{\Sigma\Sigma t_it_j}{n(n - 1)} = \frac{\Sigma(t_i - t)^2}{n(n - 1)}$   ∎

**Remark**   The proof of this theorem shows that it is not necessary to assume in Theorem 3.4 that the variances of the random variables $U_i$ are the same and that the variables are necessarily independent, if all that is wanted is an unbiased estimator of the variance.

## REFERENCES

Horvitz, D. G. and D. J. Thompson (1952).   A generalization of sampling without replacement from a finite universe.   *J. Am. Stat. Assoc.*, 47.

Lahiri, D. B. (1951).   A method of sample selection providing unbiased ratio estimates.   *Bull. Intern. Stat. Inst.*, 33.

Narain, R. D. (1951).   On sampling without replacement with varying probabilities.   *J. Ind. Soc. Agr. Stat.*, 3.

Raj, D. (1954).   On sampling with probabilities proportionate to size.   *Ganita*, 5.

——— (1966).   On a method of sampling with unequal probabilities.   *Ganita*, 17.

——— and S. H. Khamis (1958).   Some remarks on sampling with replacement. *Ann. Math. Stat.*, 29.

Yates, F. and P. M. Grundy (1953).   Selection without replacement from within strata with probability proportionate to size.   *J. Roy. Stat. Soc.*, B15.

# CHAPTER FOUR

# STRATIFICATION

## 4.1 INTRODUCTION

It has been seen that in simple random sampling the variance of the estimate (say, of the population mean $\bar{Y}$) depends, apart from the sample size, on the variability of the character $y$ in the population. If the population is very heterogeneous and considerations of cost limit the size of the sample, it may be found impossible to get a sufficiently precise estimate by taking a simple random sample from the entire population. And populations encountered in practice are generally very heterogeneous. In surveys of manufacturing establishments, for example, it can be found that some establishments are very large, that is, they employ 1,000 or more persons, but there are many others which have only two or three persons on their rolls. Any estimate made from a direct random sample taken from the totality of such establishments would be subject to exceedingly large sampling fluctuations. But suppose it is possible to divide this population into parts (or strata) on the basis of, say, employment, thereby separating the very large ones, the medium-sized ones, and the smaller ones. If a random sample of establishments is now taken from each stratum, it should be possible to make a better estimate of the strata averages, which in turn should help in producing a better estimate of the population average. Similarly, if a sample is selected with probability proportionate to $x$ from the entire population, the variance of the population-total estimate may be very high because the ratio of $y$ to $x$ varies considerably over the population. If a way can be found of subdividing the population so that the variation of the ratio of $y$ to $x$ is considerably reduced within the subdivisions (or strata), a better estimate of the population total can be made. This is the basic consideration involved in the use of stratification for improving the precision of estimation. There are, however, other considerations. For example, it is advisable to treat certain parts of the population as strata if estimates are wanted separately for them. If the main purpose of stratification is to achieve higher precision, a number of questions arise for which answers must be found. How should the strata be made and how many of them should be made? How should the total sample be allocated to the strata? How should data be analyzed (estimates made and their variances calculated) from a stratified design? We shall answer these questions in inverse order.

## 4.2 ESTIMATION IN STRATIFIED SAMPLING

We shall begin by proving the following basic result.

### Theorem 4.1

*Let a population of $N$ units be divided up into $L$ strata, the $h$th stratum containing $N_h$ units with a total of $Y_h$ for the character $y$. Within each stratum a probability sample is selected, sampling in one stratum being independent of that within another. Let $\hat{Y}_h$ be an unbiased estimate of $Y_h$, based on a sample of size $n_h$ taken from the stratum. Further, let $\hat{V}(\hat{Y}_h)$ be an unbiased estimate of $V(\hat{Y}_h)$. Then*

$$\hat{Y} = \Sigma \hat{Y}_h \qquad V(\hat{Y}) = \Sigma V(\hat{Y}_h) \triangleq \Sigma \hat{V}(\hat{Y}_h) \qquad (4.1)$$

PROOF  We have $E(\hat{Y}_h) = Y_h$. By Theorem 1.1 then,

$$E(\hat{Y}) = \Sigma E(\hat{Y}_h) = \Sigma Y_h = Y$$

Since sampling in one stratum is independent of sampling in another, the random variables $\hat{Y}_h$ ($h = 1, 2, \ldots, L$) are mutually independent. Hence by Theorem 1.5 we have $V(\hat{Y}) = \Sigma V(\hat{Y}_h)$. By the same argument, $E\Sigma \hat{V}(\hat{Y}_h) = \Sigma V(\hat{Y}_h)$. ∎

Theorem 4.1 states that the population-total estimate is the sum of the estimates of individual strata totals. The variances add up, and so do the estimates of variances. Thus no new principles are involved in analyzing the data provided that the estimation problem can be solved within a stratum. But we have already studied in Chap. 3 how estimates are to be made within a stratum. Thus we have proved the following results.

### Theorem 4.2

*In wtr simple random samples of size $n_h$, $\Sigma n_h = n$, within strata, an unbiased estimate of the population total is provided by*

$$\hat{Y} = \Sigma N_h \bar{y}_h$$

*with a variance of*

$$V(\hat{Y}) = \sum N_h{}^2 \frac{1}{n_h}(1 - f_h)S_{yh}{}^2$$

*and*

$$\hat{V}(\hat{Y}) = \sum N_h{}^2 \frac{1 - f_h}{n_h} s_{yh}{}^2$$

*where $f_h = n_h/N_h$ is the sampling fraction in the hth stratum, the variance being $S_{yh}{}^2 = \Sigma(Y_{ih} - \bar{Y}_h)^2/(N_h - 1)$ and*

$$s_{yh}{}^2 = \frac{1}{n_h - 1}\underset{i}{S}(y_{ih} - \bar{y}_h)^2$$

### Corollary

The population mean $\bar{Y} = Y/N$ is estimated by $\hat{Y}/N$.

*Remark*  If the units within strata are similar with respect to $y$, the strata variances $S_{yh}{}^2$ are small, which will produce a small value of $V(\hat{Y})$.

*Remark*  The chance that a unit belonging to stratum $h$ will be selected in the sample would be $n_h/N_h$. The chance that two units belonging to the same stratum will both be in the sample is $n_h(n_h - 1)/[N_h(N_h - 1)]$. If the two units belong to different strata (say, strata $h$ and $k$), the chance of their joint appearance is $n_h n_k/[N_h N_k]$. All this is very different from taking a direct random sample from the entire population.

### Theorem 4.3

*In wtr simple random samples of size $n_h$, $\Sigma n_h = n$, within strata, an unbiased estimate of the population proportion $P$ is given by*

$$\hat{P} = \Sigma N_h p_h/N = \Sigma W_h p_h$$

*with a variance of*

$$V(\hat{P}) = \sum \left[ W_h{}^2 \frac{1 - f_h}{n_h} \frac{N_h P_h(1 - P_h)}{N_h - 1} \right]$$

*and*
$$\hat{V}(\hat{P}) = \sum \left[ W_h{}^2(1 - f_h) \frac{p_h(1 - p_h)}{n_h - 1} \right]$$

*where $p_h$ is the sample proportion in the hth stratum, and $W_h$ is the stratum weight.*

### Corollary

If $N_h/(N_h - 1)$ can be taken as unity, we get

$$V(\hat{P}) \doteq \sum W_h{}^2 \frac{1 - f_h}{n_h} P_h(1 - P_h)$$

**Remark**   The variance of $\hat{P}$ depends on the product of $P_h$ and $1 - P_h$ within strata.   The product is small if $P_h$ is near to zero or to unity. Thus higher precision will be achieved if the strata can be formed so that units belonging to the given class (for which the proportion is sought) can be allocated to the same stratum.

### Theorem 4.4

*If the units within strata are selected with replacement with probabilities $p_{jh}$, $\Sigma p_{jh} = 1$, based on a character $x$, an unbiased estimate of the population total would be*

$$\hat{Y} = \sum_h \frac{1}{n_h} S \frac{y_{jh}}{p_{jh}} = \sum_h \frac{1}{n_h} S z_{jh} = \sum_h \bar{z}_h$$

*and*    $$V(\hat{Y}) = \sum_h \frac{1}{n_h} \sum_j p_{jh}(z_{jh} - Y_h)^2 \,\hat{=}\, \sum \frac{1}{n_h(n_h - 1)} S(z_{jh} - \bar{z}_h)^2$$

### Corollary

If $y_{jh}$ is reasonably proportional to $x_{jh}$ within strata, the variance of $\hat{Y}$ is expected to be small.

**Remark**   If we have any prior knowledge that the ratio of $y$ to $x$ for some units would be very much different from the rest, such units should be segregated and allocated to a separate stratum.

## 4.3 ALLOCATION OF SAMPLE TO STRATA

The question of how the sample numbers $n_h$ could best be determined will be answered now. The principle, of course, is that the sample be distributed among the strata such that for a given cost of the survey the variance of the estimate be a minimum (Sec. 2.13). Let $c_h$ be the cost of collecting information from a unit in stratum $h$. (These costs can differ substantially between strata. For example, information from large manufacturing establishments can be obtained cheaply if we mail them a questionnaire, whereas small establishments may have to be visited personally in order to get acceptable data.) Let

$$C = c_0 + \Sigma c_h n_h \tag{4.2}$$

be the total cost of the survey. The variance of $\hat{Y}$ will be of the form (Stuart, 1954)

$$V(\hat{Y}) = \Sigma A_h/n_h \tag{4.3}$$

where the component independent of $n_h$ is ignored, since it is not relevant to the problem of determining the best $n_h$. Now, by Cauchy's inequality $(\Sigma a_i^2)(\Sigma b_i^2) \geq (\Sigma a_i b_i)^2$, we have

$$(\Sigma A_h/n_h)(\Sigma c_h n_h) \geq (\Sigma \sqrt{A_h c_h})^2$$

there being equality if and only if $b_i$ is proportional to $a_i$, that is,

$$\frac{c_h n_h}{A_h/n_h} = \text{const}$$

or

$$n_h \propto \frac{\sqrt{A_h}}{\sqrt{c_h}} \tag{4.4}$$

Thus the product of the variance $V(\hat{Y})$ and the cost $C$ is a minimum when relation (4.4) is satisfied. This amounts to minimizing $V(\hat{Y})$ for a fixed $C$ or vice versa. From this it follows that $n_h$ will be small if the cost of collecting information from stratum $h$ is large. An application of (4.4) to some stratified sampling schemes will now be made.

## 4.4 ALLOCATION IN SIMPLE RANDOM SAMPLING

In case sampling within strata is simple random, we find from Theorem 4.2 that $A_h = N_h^2 S_{yh}^2$. By (4.4) the best sample sizes within strata are given by

$$n_h = n \frac{N_h S_{yh}}{\sqrt{c_h}} \left( \sum_h \frac{N_h S_{yh}}{\sqrt{c_h}} \right)^{-1} \tag{4.5}$$

This means that the sample size in a stratum should be larger if the stratum contains more units ($N_h$ is higher), or is more variable for $y$ ($S_{yh}$ is bigger), or cheaper to investigate ($c_h$ is smaller). This allocation of the total sample size to strata is called optimum or minimum-variance allocation and is due to Neyman (1934). This is appropriate when the cost function given by (4.2) holds. Substituting in (4.2) the value of $n_h$ from (4.5) we get

$$C - c_0 = n\Sigma N_h S_{yh} \sqrt{c_h}(\Sigma N_h S_{yh}/\sqrt{c_h})^{-1} \tag{4.6}$$

which gives the value of $n$ when the total cost is fixed. Equations (4.5) and (4.6) will provide the best values of $n_h$, for which $V(\hat{Y})$ would be a minimum for fixed cost. In case the object is to minimize the cost of the survey for a specified value of $V(\hat{Y})$, namely, when

$$V(\hat{Y}) = \Sigma N_h^2 S_{yh}^2/n_h - \Sigma N_h S_{yh}^2 = V_0 \tag{4.7}$$

the value of $n$ will be calculated from (4.7) instead of from (4.6). In case $c_h = c$, it is easy to see that the minimum variance would be given by

$$V_{\min} = \frac{1}{n}\left(\sum N_h S_{yh}\right)^2 - \sum N_h S_{yh}^2 \tag{4.8}$$

In order to achieve this minimum variance the standard deviations $S_{yh}$ in formula (4.5) should be known or stable estimates of them from previous surveys on the population should be available. When information on strata variances is not available, one may decide to use the allocation

$$n_h = nN_h/N \tag{4.9}$$

which will be called $N$-proportional allocation. With this allocation the variance of $\hat{Y}$ in wtr simple random sampling within strata would be

$$V_{\text{prop}} = \frac{N}{n}\left(1 - \frac{n}{N}\right)\sum N_h S_{yh}^2 = \frac{1-f}{f}\sum N_h S_{yh}^2 \tag{4.10}$$

The corresponding results for wr simple random sampling are:

$$V_{\min} = \frac{1}{n}\left(\sum N_h \sigma_{yh}\right)^2 \qquad V_{\text{prop}} = \frac{N}{n}\sum N_h \sigma_{yh}^2 \tag{4.11}$$

In this case, it is possible to show that $V_{\text{prop}}$ is smaller than $N^2\sigma_y^2/n$, which is the variance for a wr simple random sample taken from the entire population (without stratifying it). The proof follows from the observation that

$$\frac{N^2}{n}\sigma_y{}^2 = \frac{N^2}{n}\frac{1}{N}\sum_h\sum_i (y_{ih} - \bar{Y})^2 = \frac{N}{n}\sum\sum (y_{ih} - \bar{Y}_h + \bar{Y}_h - \bar{Y})^2$$

$$= \frac{N}{n}\sum N_h\sigma_{yh}{}^2 + \frac{N}{n}\sum N_h(\bar{Y}_h - \bar{Y})^2$$

$$\geq \frac{N}{n}\sum N_h\sigma_{yh}{}^2 = V_{\text{prop}}$$

This shows that proportional allocation will be very beneficial if the strata averages $\bar{Y}_h$ differ considerably from each other. If the strata made are such that their means are about the same, stratification (along with proportional allocation) will bring about only slight reduction in the variance. Another advantage of proportional allocation is that the estimator $\hat{Y}$ assumes the simple form $\hat{Y} = N\sum_h\sum_i S\, y_{ih}/n$, which does not require the use of strata weights. Such an estimator is said to be self weighting.

**Further reading** See Exercise 23, in which it is shown that moderate departures of the actual allocation from the optimum do not lead to any appreciable increase in the variance.

### 4.4.1 X-PROPORTIONAL ALLOCATION

In case measures of size $x_{ih}$ are available for all units in the population, the sample sizes $n_h$ may be found as a proportion of $X_h$ (aggregate measure of size of stratum $h$) rather than of $N_h$. This allocation will be called $X$-proportional. In this case

$$n_h = \frac{nX_h}{X} \tag{4.12}$$

and the variance of $\hat{Y}$, for wr simple random sampling, will be

$$V_{X\text{-prop}} = \frac{N}{n}\sum_h \frac{N_h\sigma_{yh}{}^2}{\bar{X}_h/\bar{X}} \tag{4.13}$$

whereas N-proportional allocation will give a variance of

$$V_{N\text{-prop}} = \frac{N}{n}\sum N_h\sigma_{yh}{}^2 \tag{4.14}$$

Consider now skew populations in which a small proportion of the units accounts for a large proportion of the total (of $y$). Examples are employment in manufacturing industries and income of individuals. The stratum containing the very large units will be found to be many times more variable than other strata. In the case of $N$-proportional allocation the contribution of this stratum to the total variance will be very considerable, as is evident from formula (4.14). But since its average $\bar{X}_h$ will be many times greater than the general average $\bar{X}$, the factor $\bar{X}_h/\bar{X}$ in the denominator of (4.13) will exert a damping effect on the variance if $X$-proportional allocation is used. This analysis shows how important it is to use $X$-proportional and not $N$-proportional allocation when the problem is to estimate totals or means of populations which are very skew in nature.

**Further reading** For a skew population it may be considered desirable to take the $m$ largest units into the sample with certainty and select a sample from the rest. How to determine the point of cutoff (beyond which to include all units with certainty) is discussed in Exercise 98.

### 4.4.2  ESTIMATION OF PROPORTIONS

Before concluding this subject, some comments will be made on the problem of sample allocation when the object is to estimate a population proportion $P$. By Theorem 4.3, we have for wtr simple random sampling

$$V(\hat{P}) \doteq \sum W_h{}^2 \frac{1 - f_h}{n_h} P_h(1 - P_h)$$

With $N$-proportional allocation, $V_{N\text{-prop}} = \left(\frac{1}{n} - \frac{1}{N}\right) \sum W_h P_h(1 - P_h)$.

If the optimum allocation can be used, $n_h$ will be chosen proportional to $N_h \sqrt{P_h(1 - P_h)}$. This allocation will differ substantially from proportional allocation only if the quantities $\sqrt{P_h(1 - P_h)}$ differ considerably from stratum to stratum. For example, let the $P_h$ lie between 0.3 and 0.7, in which case $P_h(1 - P_h)$ will lie between 0.46 and 0.50. In this situation the optimum allocation will not be preferred to proportional allocation when the simplicity of the computations involved is another factor to be taken into account.

### 4.5  ALLOCATION IN UNEQUAL PROBABILITY SAMPLING

If units within strata are selected with replacement with probabilities proportionate to $x$, the variance of $\hat{Y}$ by Theorem 4.4 is given by

$$V(\hat{Y}) = \sum_h \frac{X_h}{n_h} \sum_j x_{jh} \left(\frac{y_{jh}}{x_{jh}} - R_h\right)^2 = \sum \frac{A_h}{n_h} \tag{4.15}$$

where $R_h = Y_h/X_h$. The formula for the optimum allocation of the total sample size to the strata is apparent, although difficult to apply. On the other hand, the so called $X$-proportional allocation namely, $n_h = nX_h/X$ is easy to handle. In this case (Raj, 1963) the variance of $\hat{Y}$ would be

$$V_{X\text{-prop}} = \frac{X}{n} \sum_h \sum_j \frac{y_{jh}^2}{x_{jh}} - \frac{X}{n} \sum \frac{Y_h^2}{X_h} = V_1 \qquad (4.16)$$

If no stratification be made and a wr pps sample of $n$ units is taken from the unstratified population, we have

$$V_{\text{unst}} = \frac{X}{n} \sum_h \sum_j \frac{y_{jh}^2}{x_{jh}} - \frac{Y^2}{n} = V_2 \qquad (4.17)$$

Hence

$$V_2 = V_1 + \frac{X}{n} \sum X_h (R_h - R)^2 \qquad (4.18)$$

which shows that stratification with $X$-proportional allocation will be always superior to unstratified sampling. But the gains from stratification will be considerable only when the strata ratios $R_h$ differ considerably from each other.

*Further reading* For a comparison of the unstratified pps sampling scheme with stratified simple random sampling under a certain model, see Exercise 27.

### 4.6 FORMATION OF STRATA

The question of how strata are made will now be considered. As noted earlier, the basic consideration involved in the formation of strata is that the strata should be internally homogeneous. For example, if units are to be selected at random from within strata, strata variances for the character under estimation should be as small as possible. This can be achieved by allocating units believed to be similar to the same stratum. Thus all prior knowledge, personal intuition, and judgment can be brought into play to bring about similarity within strata. The ideal situation is that in which the distribution of $y$ is available. Then the strata would be created by cutting this distribution at suitable points. In the absence of this information, a search will be made for the distribution of $y$ as obtained at a recent census or that of a character $x$ highly correlated with $y$. We are going to pursue this problem when the distribution of $y$ is known. Although it is not a practical situation and the results obtained could not be used directly as such, the discussion is given in the hope that it will offer some guidance in practice. Let the distribution of $y$ be continuous with the density function $f(y)$, $a \leq y \leq b$. In order to make $L$ strata, the range of $y$ is to be cut up at points $y_1 < y_2 < \cdots < y_{L-1}$. The relative frequency $W_h$, the mean $M_h$, and the variance $\sigma_h{}^2$ of the $h$th stratum are given by

$$W_h = \int_{y_{h-1}}^{y_h} f(t)\, dt$$

$$W_h M_h = \int_{y_{h-1}}^{y_h} t f(t)\, dt \qquad (4.19)$$

$$W_h \sigma_h{}^2 = \int_{y_{h-1}}^{y_h} t^2 f(t)\, dt - W_h M_h{}^2$$

The population mean is $M = \Sigma W_h M_h$, and its estimate obtained from a stratified random sample is $\hat{M} = \Sigma W_h \bar{y}_h$ with a variance of

$$V(\hat{M}) = \sum W_h{}^2 \frac{\sigma_h{}^2}{n_h} \qquad (4.20)$$

Obviously, $V(\hat{M})$ is a function of the strata boundaries $y_1, \ldots, y_{L-1}$. The problem is to determine the best values of $y_i$ for which $V(\hat{M})$ becomes a minimum for a given allocation of the $n_h$ (Dalenius, 1950).

### 4.6.1 PROPORTIONAL ALLOCATION

If $n_h = n W_h$, we have

$$V(\hat{M}) = \frac{1}{n} \sum W_h \sigma_h{}^2 \qquad (4.21)$$

To determine the best values of $y_h$, we differentiate $\Sigma W_h \sigma_h{}^2$ with respect to $y_h$ and equate the expression thus obtained to zero. The expression in $\Sigma W_h \sigma_h{}^2$ involving $y_h$ is

$$A = -\frac{(W_h M_h)^2}{W_h} - \frac{(W_{h+1} M_{h+1})^2}{W_{h+1}}$$

Now $\dfrac{\partial W_h}{\partial y_h} = f(y_h)$  $\dfrac{\partial}{\partial y_h} W_{h+1} = -f(y_h)$  $\dfrac{\partial}{\partial y_h}(W_h M_h)^2 = 2 W_h M_h y_h f(y_h)$

and $\dfrac{\partial}{\partial y_h}(W_{h+1} M_{h+1})^2 = -2 W_{h+1} M_{h+1} y_h f(y_h)$

Hence, $\partial A / \partial y_h = 0$ gives

$$y_h = \tfrac{1}{2}(M_h + M_{h+1}) \qquad (4.22)$$

This shows that the best $y_h$ is the average of the two strata means which it separates.   The points $y_h$ $(h = 1, 2, \ldots, L - 1)$ will have to be found by iterative procedures, since the $M_h$ depend on $y_h$.

*Further reading*   For an extension of stratification problems to two dimensions, see Exercise 29.

### 4.6.2   EQUAL ALLOCATION

This is a situation of considerable practical interest.   For reasons of administrative convenience or otherwise, it is often found desirable to take the same sample size from each stratum.   In this case the best $y_h$ are to be obtained by minimizing

$$V(\hat{M}) = \frac{L}{n} \sum W_h{}^2 \sigma_h{}^2 \tag{4.23}$$

Differentiating the relevant terms with respect to $y_h$ and equating the resulting expression to zero, it will be found that the best points of stratification are those for which

$$W_h[\sigma_h{}^2 + (y_h - M_h)^2] - W_{h+1}[\sigma_{h+1}^2 + (y_h - M_{h+1})^2] = 0$$
$$h = 1, 2, \ldots, L - 1 \tag{4.24}$$

Iterative procedures will have to be used to get these points.

### 4.6.3   OPTIMUM ALLOCATION

In this allocation

$$n_h = \frac{n W_h \sigma_h}{\Sigma W_h \sigma_h} \qquad V(\hat{M}) = \frac{1}{n} \left( \sum W_h \sigma_h \right)^2 \tag{4.25}$$

Then the best values of $y_h$ will be obtained by minimizing

$$B = W_h \sigma_h + W_{h+1} \sigma_{h+1} \qquad \text{for variations in } y_h$$

From (4.19), we have

$$\frac{\partial}{\partial y_h} (W_h \sigma_h{}^2) = \sigma_h{}^2 \frac{\partial}{\partial y_h} W_h + 2 W_h \sigma_h \frac{\partial}{\partial y_h} \sigma_h$$

$$= f(y_h) \sigma_h{}^2 + 2 W_h \sigma_h \frac{\partial}{\partial y_h} \sigma_h$$

$$= f(y_h)(y_h - M_h)^2$$

and hence    $$W_h \frac{\partial}{\partial y_h} \sigma_h = (2\sigma_h)^{-1} f(y_h)[(y_h - M_h)^2 - \sigma_h{}^2]$$

Then $\quad \dfrac{\partial}{\partial y_h} (W_h \sigma_h) = \sigma_h \dfrac{\partial}{\partial y_h} W_h + \left( \dfrac{\partial}{\partial y_h} \sigma_h \right) W_h$

$$= (2\sigma_h)^{-1} f(y_h)[(y_h - M_h)^2 + \sigma_h^2]$$

Similarly $\quad \dfrac{\partial}{\partial y_h} (W_{h+1} \sigma_{h+1}) = (2\sigma_{h+1})^{-1} f(y_h)[(y_h - M_{h+1})^2 + \sigma_{h+1}^2]$

Hence $\partial B / \partial y_h = 0$ gives the equations

$$\frac{(y_h - M_h)^2 + \sigma_h^2}{\sigma_h} - \frac{(y_h - M_{h+1})^2 + \sigma_{h+1}^2}{\sigma_{h+1}} = 0 \qquad h = 1, 2, \ldots, L - 1$$

$$(4.26)$$

These equations for the $y_h$ are difficult to solve, since the quantities $M_h$, $\sigma_h^2$ themselves depend upon $y_h$. For this reason, approximate rules have been found by which $V(\hat{M})$ in (4.25) can be directly made small. Probably the best approximate solution has been given by Dalenius and Hodges (1959). The basic argument used by them is that the distribution of $y$ within strata can be assumed to be rectangular if the number of strata is large. In that case

$$W_h \doteq (y_h - y_{h-1}) f_h \qquad \sigma_h = \frac{y_h - y_{h-1}}{\sqrt{12}} \qquad f(y_h) = f_h$$

so that $\quad \sqrt{12}\, \Sigma W_h \sigma_h = \Sigma f_h (y_h - y_{h-1})^2 = \Sigma [\sqrt{f_h}\, (y_h - y_{h-1})]^2$

Defining $G(h) = \displaystyle\int_a^{y_h} \sqrt{f(t)}\, dt$

we have $\quad G(h) - G(h - 1) = \displaystyle\int_{y_{h-1}}^{y_h} \sqrt{f(t)}\, dt \doteq \sqrt{f_h}\, (y_h - y_{h-1})$

Hence $\quad \sqrt{12}\, \Sigma W_h \sigma_h \doteq \Sigma [G(h) - G(h - 1)]^2$

But $\Sigma [G(h) - G(h - 1)]$ is a constant and hence $\Sigma W_h \sigma_h$ will be a minimum when $G(h) - G(h - 1)$ is a constant. This means that the points $y_h$ are to be obtained by taking equal intervals on the cumulatives of $\sqrt{f(y)}$.

**Remark** Among the other approximate rules suggested is the one by Ayoma (1954) in which it is recommended to make strata of equal width $y_h - y_{h-1}$. There is another device, by Ekman (1959), in which $W_h(y_h - y_{h-1})$ is made constant. Cochran (1961) used these rules on a number of actual populations that are skew and found that the rule given by Dalenius and Hodges (1959) worked best.

### 4.6.4 STRATA OF EQUAL AGGREGATE SIZE

Another rule widely used in practice is to make strata which have the same aggregate size $W_h M_h$. This rule is considered to be particularly useful when a constant sample number is to be taken from each stratum. The suggestion came originally from Mahalanobis (1952). Raj (1964) tested this rule on four theoretical distributions to find out how it compared with the optimum (Sec. 4.6.2) for constant sample numbers within strata. The distributions considered were:

$$(2/\pi)^{1/2} \exp(-y^2/2) \quad y \geq 0 \qquad \exp(-y) \quad y \geq 0$$
$$y \exp(-y) \quad y \geq 0 \qquad 2(1-y) \quad 0 \leq y \leq 1$$

For these distributions the rule was found to give poorer results as the number of strata increased. It was not optimum or near-optimum for large $L$. An explanation found was that the lowest stratum created by this rule was highly variable.

*Further reading*   See Exercise 25 for an illustration.

### 4.7 THE NUMBER OF STRATA

The question that now remains to be answered relates to the number of strata to have. It has already been noted in Secs. 4.4 and 4.5 that stratification along with proportionate allocation always produces a smaller variance than unstratified sampling.[1] This shows that given a population divided up into $k$ strata, we can always improve upon this situation by further subdivision of the strata. In fact, stratification can be carried to the point that only one unit is selected from each stratum, thus making the number of strata as large as the number of units to be selected. And, provided that self-weighting estimators are used, multiplicity of strata will cause no inconvenience so far as calculations are concerned. This is one reason that the survey statistician favors the use of a large number of strata. But it is also recognized that, beyond a reasonable number of strata, doubling the number (of strata) does not bring about a proportionate reduction in the variance when stratification for $y$ is made on the basis of another character $x$. How this occurs may be demonstrated with the help of a simple model. Let $x$ be a rectangular variate in the range 0 to $a$. Further, let $y = x + e$ where $e$ and $x$ are uncorrelated. Then $\sigma_y^2 = \sigma_x^2 + \sigma_e^2$. Let $g$ strata of equal width be formed. Then

$$\sigma_{xh}^2 = \frac{a^2}{12g^2} \qquad W_h = \frac{N_h}{N} = \frac{1}{g}$$

If sample allocation is equal, the variance of the estimate of the popu-

[1] When selection is made with replacement.

lation mean will be

$$\frac{g}{n} \Sigma W_h{}^2 \sigma_{yh}{}^2 = \frac{a^2}{12ng^2} + \frac{\sigma_e{}^2}{n}$$

If the number of strata be increased to $\lambda g$, the variance based on $\lambda g$ strata will be

$$\frac{1}{\lambda^2} \frac{a^2}{12ng^2} + \frac{\sigma_e{}^2}{n}$$

The first component of the variance has decreased by increasing the number of strata but the second has not. Thus a point will soon be reached when the second component begins to dominate the variance and any further increase in the number of strata will not be accompanied by a worthwhile gain in precision. (See Exercise 24.)

### 4.8 SOME PRACTICAL SITUATIONS

A number of practical problems encountered in stratified sampling will now be discussed.

### 4.8.1 THE METHOD OF COLLAPSED STRATA

As stated in Sec. 4.7, in order to achieve greater homogeneity, stratification may be carried to the point that only one unit is selected from each stratum. Suppose selection within strata is with probability proportionate to $x$. Then

$$\hat{Y} = \sum_{h=1}^{L} \hat{Y}_h = \sum \frac{y_{jh}}{p_{jh}} \qquad V(\hat{Y}) = \sum V(\hat{Y}_h)$$

Since only one unit is selected from a stratum, it is not possible to make a rigorous estimate of $V(\hat{Y})$. But suppose that the strata are grouped (or collapsed) into pairs and we calculate

$$b = \sum_{j=1}^{L/2} (\hat{Y}_{j1} - \hat{Y}_{j2})^2 \qquad (4.27)$$

where $\hat{Y}_{j1}$, $\hat{Y}_{j2}$ are the estimates of the totals of the two strata forming the $j$th pair. It is easy to see that

$$E(b) = \sum_j [(Y_{j1} - Y_{j2})^2 + V(\hat{Y}_{j1}) + V(\hat{Y}_{j2})]$$
$$= V(\hat{Y}) + \sum_j (Y_{j1} - Y_{j2})^2$$

This shows that the quantity $b$, used as an estimate of the variance, will overstate the true variance of $\hat{Y}$, the overstatement depending upon the extent to which strata forming the same pair differ with respect to their totals. If the pairing could be so arranged (before the collection of data) that the strata forming the pair are about equal in size (total of $y$), the overstatement will not be serious. It may be remarked that by substituting $1/N_h$ for $p_{jh}$, we obtain results appropriate to simple random sampling.

### 4.8.2 ESTIMATION OF GAIN DUE TO STRATIFICATION

It is of interest to determine from a survey, carried out according to a particular stratification, how useful the mode of stratification has been. A comparison can be made with the situation in which no stratification is used by estimating from the stratified sample the variance of the estimate in case of unstratified sampling. If sampling within strata is with probability proportional to $x$, we have for wr sampling

$$\hat{Y} = \sum_h \hat{Y}_h \qquad V(\hat{Y}) = \sum V(\hat{Y}_h) = \sum_h \frac{X_h}{n_h} \sum_j x_{jh} \left(\frac{y_{jh}}{x_{jh}} - R_h\right)^2$$

and

$$V(\hat{Y}) \cong \sum \frac{1}{n_h(n_h - 1)} S_j \left(\frac{y_{jh}}{p_{jh}} - \hat{Y}_h\right)^2 = \sum \hat{V}(\hat{Y}_h) \qquad (4.28)$$

If a pps sample of size $n = \Sigma n_h$ is selected directly from the entire population without using any stratification, the variance of $\hat{Y}$ will be

$$V_1 = V(\hat{Y}_{\text{unst}}) = \frac{X}{n} \sum_h \sum_j x_{jh} \left(\frac{y_{jh}}{x_{jh}} - R\right)^2$$

$$= \frac{X}{n} \sum \sum x_{jh} \left(\frac{y_{jh}}{x_{jh}} - R_h + R_h - R\right)^2$$

$$= \frac{X}{n} \sum_h \frac{n_h}{X_h} V(\hat{Y}_h) + \frac{X}{n} \sum X_h (R_h - R)^2 \qquad (4.29)$$

where $R = \Sigma Y_h / \Sigma X_h$. An unbiased estimate of the first term in (4.29) can be immediately made from (4.28). In order to estimate the second part, we try $\Sigma X_h (\hat{R}_h - \hat{R})^2$, where $\hat{R}_h = \hat{Y}_h/X_h$, $\hat{R} = \Sigma \hat{Y}_h/X$. We have

$$E \sum X_h (\hat{R}_h - \hat{R})^2 = \sum X_h (R_h - R)^2 + \sum X_h V(\hat{R}_h - \hat{R})$$

$$= \sum X_h (R_h - R)^2 + \sum \left(\frac{1}{X_h} - \frac{1}{X}\right) V(\hat{Y}_h)$$

Hence $\displaystyle\sum X_h (R_h - R)^2 \cong \sum X_h (\hat{R}_h - \hat{R})^2 - \sum \left(\frac{1}{X_h} - \frac{1}{X}\right) \hat{V}(\hat{Y}_h)$

Thus an unbiased estimate of $V_1$ is provided by

$$V_1 \cong \frac{X}{n} \sum_h \left( \frac{n_h - 1}{X_h} + \frac{1}{X} \right) \hat{V}(\hat{Y}_h) + \frac{X}{n} \sum X_h (\hat{R}_h - \hat{R})^2 \quad (4.30)$$

Equations (4.28) and (4.30) provide a comparison between the two variances based on the stratified sample.

### 4.8.3 DEPENDENT SELECTION

In all applications considered so far, selection within one stratum is independent of that within another. There may be situations, however, in which it is considered desirable that certain combinations of units (belonging to different strata) be given a higher probability of selection at the expense of other combinations. This procedure is called controlled selection (Goodman and Kish, 1950). Thus the selection is not made independently but in a dependent manner. As an example, let there be two strata; a sample of one unit is to be selected from each stratum with probabilities $p_i$ $(i = 1, 2, \ldots, N_1)$ and $p_j$ $(j = 1, 2, \ldots, N_2)$ from the two strata, respectively. Let $p_{ij}$ be the joint probability of selecting unit $U_i$ from the first stratum and unit $U_j$ from the second. An actual example is provided in Table 4.1, in which the probabilities $p_{ij}$ (to be obtained by dividing by 100) are given in the body of the table. The

**Table 4.1  Probabilities of selecting
two units, one from each stratum**

|  |  | *Stratum 1* | | | | | | |
|  |  | $A$ | $B$ | $C$ | $D$ | $E$ | $F$ | $p_j$ |
|---|---|---|---|---|---|---|---|---|
|  | $a$ | 15 |  |  |  |  |  | 15 |
|  | $b$ |  | 10 | 20 |  |  |  | 30 |
| *Stratum* | $c$ |  |  |  | 10 |  |  | 10 |
| *2* | $d$ |  |  |  |  | 20 | 5 | 25 |
|  | $e$ |  |  |  |  |  | 20 | 20 |
|  | $p_i$ | 15 | 10 | 20 | 10 | 20 | 25 | 100 |

preferred combinations of units have higher probabilities of selection, and the nonpreferred ones have a lower (mostly zero) chance of selection. Yet, the probabilities $p_i$, $p_j$ of the units are preserved. An unbiased estimate of the total of the two strata is

$$\hat{Y} = \frac{y_i}{p_i} + \frac{y_j}{p_j}$$

But the variance of $\hat{Y}$ is given by

$$V(\hat{Y}) = E(\hat{Y}^2) - Y^2 = \sum \frac{y_i^2}{p_i} + \sum \frac{y_j^2}{p_j} + 2 \sum \sum p_{ij} \frac{y_i}{p_i} \frac{y_j}{p_j} - Y^2 \quad (4.31)$$

If selection within strata is made independently, the variance will be $\Sigma(y_i^2/p_i) + \Sigma(y_j^2/p_j) - (Y_1^2 + Y_2^2)$. (See Sec. 9.5.)

### 4.8.4  ESTIMATING SEVERAL PARAMETRIC FUNCTIONS

Instead of estimating just one function $Y = \Sigma N_h \bar{Y}_h$ of the strata means, we may be interested in providing estimates for several of them. For example, we may want to estimate the area under food crops not only for the province as a whole but also for a particular group of strata within the province. For each linear function there is one best allocation of the total sample size, and these allocations may not agree. The problem to be considered is how to arrive at a single allocation of the total sample to be used in the survey. The same problem arises when there are a number of items to be estimated from the same survey, but only one allocation can be used. The answer to these problems will depend on (Raj, 1957) what the sample is supposed to achieve. We shall consider some approaches to the problem.

*Minimization of cost plus loss*  If the results obtained from the sample are going to form the basis of some practical action, we may be able to calculate in monetary terms the loss that will be incurred in a decision through an error of amount $d$ in the estimate. For example, if this loss be $\mu d^2$ (Yates, 1949), and the estimate is unbiased, the average loss in a series of samples of the same type and size will be $\mu_i V(\hat{L}_i)$ for the $i$th linear function $L_i = \sum_h l_{ih} \bar{Y}_h$. The purpose in taking the sample may be to diminish the sum of the total expected loss

$$L = \Sigma \mu_i V(\hat{L}_i) = \Sigma \mu_i \Sigma l_{ih}^2 S_h^2 \left( \frac{1}{n_h} - \frac{1}{N_h} \right)$$

and the total cost $C = \sum_h c_h n_h{}^g$, where the cost function used is more general than the usual one. Thus the best values of the $n_h$ can be found by calculus methods. (See Exercise 21, where this is done.)

*Minimization of cost*  As an alternative approach to the problem, we may consider the survey to be useful if the parametric functions $L_i$ are estimated with some desired variances $a_i$. In such a case the total sample size is to be allocated to the different strata in such a way that the cost of the survey is made a minimum. The problem then reduces to the minimization of

$$f(n_i, n_2, \ldots, n_k) = \Sigma c_h n_h{}^g$$

subject to the conditions

$$\phi_i = V(\hat{L}_i) \leq a_i$$

*Minimization of variances*    Another type of requirement may be that the relative precisions of the different estimates be in some assigned ratios. As a particular case, it may be desired that the coefficients of variation of different estimates be all equal, the common value being necessarily dependent on the cost of the survey.   In such a case the variance of one of the estimates will be minimized for fixed cost and for stipulated relations between the variances.

If the relative precisions of the estimates are governed by

$$V(\hat{L}_1) = a_2 V(\hat{L}_2) = \cdots = a_r V(\hat{L}_r)$$

and the cost function is $C = \Sigma c_h n_h{}^g$, the best values of the $n_h$ can be obtained by calculus methods.

**Further reading**    The problem of sample allocation to strata when several items are to be estimated from the survey is considered in Exercise 30.

### 4.9 THE STRATUM OF NONRESPONDENTS

Another problem, though not directly related to the contents of this chapter, will be presented now.   The reason for its inclusion here is that its solution is facilitated by the idea that a population can be considered to be divided up into strata even if we have no lists of the units falling into the strata and their sizes are unknown.   The problem arises this way.   A random sample of units is selected and questionnaires are mailed to get information on some items of interest.   No response is received from a number of units.   It is not proper to base the results of the survey on the respondents alone, since the nonrespondents may be different from the respondents.   On the other hand, it is very expensive to hold a personal interview with each nonrespondent.   This situation may be tackled by assuming that the entire population is divided up into two strata: the first is made up of those who would respond to the questionnaire under the conditions of the survey, and the second is made up of those who would not.   The respondents of the survey give a random sample from the first stratum, and the nonrespondents form a random sample taken from the second stratum.   Let $n_1$ and $n_2$, $\Sigma n_i = n$, be the sample sizes observed in the two strata.   In order to collect information from the second stratum, a subsample of a convenient size $u = n_2/k$ is taken, and information is collected by personal interview from these units. The two samples are then pooled to get an estimate for the entire population. How this can be done will be evident from the following (Hansen and Hurwitz, 1946) theorem.

### Theorem 4.5

*Let a random sample of n units contain $n_1$ units from the response stratum and $n_2$ from the nonresponse stratum. If information can be collected on a sample of $u = n_2/k$ units from the second stratum, an unbiased estimate of the population average for y is given by*

$$\hat{M} = \frac{n_1\bar{y}_{n_1} + n_2\bar{y}_u}{n} \tag{4.32}$$

*with a variance of*

$$V(\hat{M}) = \frac{k-1}{n} W_2 S_{y2}^2 + \left(\frac{1}{n} - \frac{1}{N}\right) S_y^2 \tag{4.33}$$

*where $W_2$, $S_{y2}^2$ represent, respectively, the weight and variance of the second stratum.*

PROOF   Given the sample of $n$ units, $E_2(\bar{y}_u) = \bar{y}_{n_2}$ so that

$$E(\hat{M}) = \frac{1}{n} E_1(n_1\bar{y}_{n_1} + n_2\bar{y}_{n_2}) = E_1(\bar{y}_n) = \bar{Y}$$

Again, given the sample of $n$ units, the conditional variance of $\hat{M}$ would be

$$V_2(\hat{M}) = \frac{n_2^2}{n^2}\left(\frac{1}{u} - \frac{1}{n_2}\right) S_{n_2}^2 = \frac{k-1}{n^2} n_2 S_{n_2}^2$$

where $S_{n_2}^2$ represents the variance for the sample of $n_2$ units. By Theorem 1.8, we have

$$V(\hat{M}) = E_1 V_2(\hat{M}) + V_1 E_2(\hat{M}) = E_1\left(\frac{k-1}{n^2} n_2 S_{n_2}^2\right) + V_1(\bar{y}_n)$$

Now, given that the sample of $n$ gives $n_2$ nonrespondents,

$$E(S_{n_2}^2) = S_{y_2}^2 = \text{the variance of } y$$

in the nonresponse stratum. And $E(n_2) = nW_2$. Hence, by Theorem 1.7, we get

$$V(\hat{M}) = \frac{k-1}{n} W_2 S_{y2}^2 + \left(\frac{1}{n} - \frac{1}{N}\right) S_y^2 \qquad \blacksquare$$

*Remark*   The first term in (4.33) represents the contribution to the variance due to the fact that only a fraction of the nonrespondents were contacted for collecting information.   This term would vanish for $k = 1$.

*Remark*   Let $c_0$ be the cost per questionnaire of mailing, $c_1$ be the cost per questionnaire of processing the completed questionnaires, and $c_2$ be the cost (per questionnaire) both of enumerating and of processing returns obtained from the nonrespondents.   Since $E(n_1) = nW_1$,

$$E(u) = E\left(\frac{n_2}{k}\right) = \frac{nW_2}{k}$$

the expected cost of the survey will be given by

$$C = c_0 + nW_1c_1 + \frac{nW_2c_2}{k} \tag{4.34}$$

The problem is to choose the initial sample size $n$ and the subsampling rate $k$ such that the expected cost is minimized for a given value $V_0$ of the variance of $\hat{M}$.   It can be easily shown that

$$k^2 = \frac{c_2(S_y{}^2 - W_2S_{y2}{}^2)}{S_{y2}{}^2(c_0 + c_1W_1)} \tag{4.35}$$

and

$$n = \frac{N[S_y{}^2 + (k - 1)W_2S_{y2}{}^2]}{NV_0 + S_y{}^2} \tag{4.36}$$

*Remark*   In order to use formulas (4.35) and (4.36) in practice, we may assume that $S_{y2}{}^2 = S_y{}^2$ and that an advance estimate of $W_2$, the rate of nonresponse, is available.   In such a situation the formulas become

$$k^2 = \frac{c_2W_1}{c_0 + c_1W_1} \qquad n = n_0[1 + (k - 1)W_2] \tag{4.37}$$

where $n_0$ is the sample size that would be required to achieve a variance of $V_0$ if there were no nonresponse.

*Remark*   In a survey conducted in Greece for estimating wages and salaries in manufacturing establishments, the information collected showed $W_2 = 40$ percent, $c_0 = 1$, $c_1 = 5$, $c_2 = 15$.   In this case $k = 1.5$ and $n = 1.2(n_0)$.   If $n_0$ is 100, questionnaires will be mailed to 120 establishments and two-thirds of the nonrespondents will be interviewed.

## 4.10  LATIN SQUARE STRATIFICATION[1]

Suppose there are two important criteria, $A$ and $B$, of stratification such that $p$ strata can be constructed from the $A$ criterion and within each of these, $p$ from the $B$ criterion, giving in all $p^2$ substrata, or cells.  As an example, the $A$ criterion may be altitude of locality, there being $p$ altitude groups.  The $B$ criterion may be the size (population) of the locality, there being $p$ size groups.  It is considered very desirable to introduce this stratification into the survey, but the number of units that can be taken into the sample is small and not all the $p^2$ substrata can be sampled. (The problem is more relevant when the units are the psu's of Chap. 6.) We shall consider the situation when just $p$ units can be taken into the sample, and each substratum or cell in the population contains $M$ units. In order that each altitude group and each population group be represented in the sample, the Latin square design (see Table 4.2) is the obvious choice, the rows of the Latin square representing the population groups and the columns the altitude groups.  The selection proceeds this way.  Select one cell at random from the first row and delete from the population the $p - 1$ cells occurring in the column to which the selected

Table 4.2   Latin square selection

|       | $c_1$ | $c_2$ | $c_3$ | $c_4$ | $c_5$ |
|-------|-------|-------|-------|-------|-------|
| $r_1$ |       |       | $\times$ |       |       |
| $r_2$ |       |       |       |       | $\times$ |
| $r_3$ |       | $\times$ |       |       |       |
| $r_4$ |       |       |       | $\times$ |       |
| $r_5$ | $\times$ |       |       |       |       |

cell belongs.  From the second row select one cell at random from the $p - 1$ that remain and delete from the population the $p - 1$ cells that occur in the column to which the second selection belongs, and so on. This gives a sample of $p$ cells.  Within each selected cell select one unit at random from the $M$.  Let $y_{rc}$ be the observation on the unit in the sample cell occurring in the $r$th row and the $c$th column.  It is easy to verify that the unconditional probability that a cell is selected in the sample is $1/p$ and the unconditional probability that two specified cells (not in the same row or column) are selected is $1/[p(p - 1)]$.  The expected value of $Y_{1i}$ (the selection in the first row) is $(1/p) \sum_{i=1}^{p} Y_{1i} = G_{r1}/p$, where

[1] To be read with Sec. 9.6.

$G_{r1}$ refers to the total of the first row. The variance of $Y_{1i}$ is $\Sigma Y_{1i}{}^2/p$ $- (G_{r1}/p)^2$. Also

$$E(Y_{1i}Y_{2j}) = \frac{1}{p(p-1)} \sum_{i \neq j} Y_{1i}Y_{2j} = \frac{1}{p(p-1)} [Y_{11}(G_{r2} - Y_{21}) + \cdots]$$

$$= \frac{G_{r1}G_{r2} - \sum_i Y_{1i}Y_{2i}}{p(p-1)}$$

With this background, we shall prove Theorem 4.6.

### Theorem 4.6

*In the $p \times p$ Latin square design in which one unit is selected from the M contained in the selected cell, an unbiased estimate of the population total is given by*

$$\hat{Y} = pM \sum_r y_{rc} \qquad (4.38)$$

*with a variance of*

$$V(\hat{Y}) = \frac{p^4}{p-1} \left( \sigma^2 - \frac{\sigma_r{}^2 + \sigma_c{}^2}{p^2} \right) + pM^2 \sum \sum \sigma_{rc}{}^2 \qquad (4.39)$$

*where*

$$p^2\sigma^2 = \Sigma\Sigma Y_{rc}{}^2 - \frac{Y^2}{p^2}$$

$$p\sigma_r{}^2 = \Sigma G_r{}^2 - \frac{Y^2}{p}$$

$$p\sigma_c{}^2 = \Sigma G_c{}^2 - \frac{Y^2}{p}$$

$\sigma_{rc}{}^2 = $ *variance of y in $(r,c)$ cell*

PROOF  Given the selected cell, $E_2(y_{rc}) = \bar{Y}_{rc}$, $V_2(y_{rc}) = \sigma_{rc}{}^2$.

Hence $\qquad E_2(\hat{Y}) = p \sum_r Y_{rc} \qquad V_2(\hat{Y}) = p^2M^2 \sum_r \sigma_{rc}{}^2$

Thus $\qquad\qquad E(\hat{Y}) = p \frac{1}{p} \sum_r G_r = Y$

And $\qquad\qquad E_1V_2(\hat{Y}) = pM^2 \sum_r \sum_c \sigma_{rc}{}^2$

Now $\quad V_1E_2(\hat{Y}) = p^2 \sum_r \left[ \dfrac{\sum_c Y_{rc}^2}{p} - \left(\dfrac{G_r}{p}\right)^2 \right]$

$+ p^2 \sum_r \sum_{r' \neq r} \left[ \dfrac{G_rG_{r'} - \sum_l Y_{rl}Y_{r'l}}{p(p-1)} - \dfrac{G_rG_{r'}}{p^2} \right] = p \sum_r \sum_c Y_{rc}^2 - \sum_r G_r^2$

$+ \dfrac{p}{p-1} \sum \sum G_rG_{r'} - \dfrac{p}{p-1} \sum_r \sum_{r'} \sum_l Y_{rl}Y_{r'l} - \sum_r \sum_{r'} G_rG_{r'}$

But

$\sum \sum G_rG_{r'} = Y^2 - \sum G_r^2 \qquad \sum_r \sum_{r'} \sum_l Y_{rl}Y_{r'l} = \sum G_c^2 - \sum \sum Y_{rc}^2$

Hence,

$V_1E_2(\hat{Y}) = p \sum \sum Y_{rc}^2 - \sum G_r^2 + \dfrac{1}{p-1}\left( Y^2 - \sum G_r^2 \right)$

$\qquad\qquad\qquad - \dfrac{p}{p-1}\left( \sum G_c^2 - \sum \sum Y_{rc}^2 \right)$

$= \dfrac{p^2}{p-1} \sum \sum Y_{rc}^2 - \dfrac{p}{p-1} \sum G_r^2 + \dfrac{1}{p-1} Y^2 - \dfrac{p}{p-1} \sum G_c^2$

$= \dfrac{1}{p-1}\left[ p^2\left(\sum \sum Y_{rc}^2 - \dfrac{Y^2}{p^2}\right) - p\left(\sum G_r^2 - \dfrac{Y^2}{p}\right) - p\left(\sum G_c^2 - \dfrac{Y^2}{p}\right) \right]$

$\qquad\quad = \dfrac{1}{p-1}(p^4\sigma^2 - p^2\sigma_r^2 - p^2\sigma_c^2) = \dfrac{p^4}{p-1}\left( \sigma^2 - \dfrac{\sigma_r^2 + \sigma_c^2}{p^2} \right)$

This proves the theorem, which is due to Cornfield and Evans (Hansen et al., 1953). ∎

**Remark** If only the rows of the Latin square are used as strata and one cell is selected at random from each row without regard to the columns, an unbiased estimate of the population total is given by $\hat{Y} = pM \sum_r y_{rc}$. To obtain its variance we note that

$E_1V_2(\hat{Y}) = pM^2 \sum \sum \sigma_{rc}^2 \qquad V_1E_2(\hat{Y}) = p \sum \sum Y_{rc}^2 - \sum G_r^2$

$V_1E_2(\hat{Y}) = p\left( \sum \sum Y_{rc}^2 - \dfrac{Y^2}{p^2} \right) - \left( \sum G_r^2 - \dfrac{Y^2}{p} \right)$

$\qquad\quad = p^3\sigma^2 - p\sigma_r^2$

Hence $\quad V(\hat{Y}) = p^3\left( \sigma^2 - \dfrac{\sigma_r^2}{p^2} \right) + pM^2 \sum \sum \sigma_{rc}^2$

A comparison of the two variances shows that the two-way stratification of the Latin square will be superior to one-way stratification if

$$\frac{p^4}{p-1}\left(\sigma^2 - \frac{\sigma_r^2 + \sigma_c^2}{p^2}\right) < p^3\left(\sigma^2 - \frac{\sigma_r^2}{p^2}\right) \text{ or } \sigma_c^2 > p\left(\sigma^2 - \frac{\sigma_r^2}{p^2}\right)$$

**Remark**   One method of getting an unbiased estimate of the variance given by (4.39) is to have $m$ independent replications of the Latin square arrangement.   Then $m$ independent estimates of $Y$ can be made and an application of Theorem 3.4 provides an estimate of variance.

### REFERENCES

Ayoma, H. (1954).   A study of the stratified random sampling.   *Ann. Inst. Stat. Math.*, 6.

Cochran, W. G. (1961).   Comparison of methods for determining stratum boundaries.   *Bull. Int. Stat. Inst.*, 38.

Dalenius, T. (1950).   The problem of optimum stratification.   *Sk. Akt.*, 3, 4.

——— and J. L. Hodges, Jr. (1959).   Minimum variance stratification.   *J. Am. Stat. Assoc.*, 54.

Ekman, G. (1959).   An approximation useful in univariate stratification.   *Ann. Math. Stat.*, 30.

Goodman, R. and L. Kish (1950).   Controlled selection—a technique in probability sampling.   *J. Am. Stat. Assoc.*, 45.

Hansen, M. H. and W. N. Hurwitz (1946).   The problem of nonresponse in sample surveys.   *J. Am. Stat. Assoc.*, 41.

———, and W. G. Madow (1953).   "Sample Survey Methods and Theory." John Wiley & Sons, Inc., New York.

Mahalanobis, P. C. (1952).   Some aspects of the design of sample surveys. *Sankhya*, 12.

Neyman, J. (1934).   On the two different aspects of the representative method: the method of stratified sampling and the method of purposive selection.   *J. Roy. Stat. Soc.*, 97.

Raj, D. (1957).   On estimating parametric functions in stratified sampling designs.   *Sankhya*, 17.

——— (1963).   A note on stratification in unequal probability sampling. *Sankhya*, B 25.

——— (1964).   On forming strata of equal aggregate size.   *J. Am. Stat. Assoc.*, 59.

Stuart, A. (1954).   A simple presentation of optimum sampling results.   *J. Roy. Stat. Soc.*, B 16.

Yates, F. (1949).   "Sampling Methods for Censuses and Surveys."   Hafner Publishing Company, Inc., New York.

# CHAPTER FIVE

# FURTHER USE OF SUPPLEMENTARY INFORMATION

### 5.1 INTRODUCTION

If there is one thing that distinguishes sampling theory from general statistical theory, it is the degree of emphasis laid on the use of auxiliary information for improving the precision of estimates. We have already had some examples of it in earlier chapters. Auxiliary information was used in Chap. 4 for purposes of stratification. In Chap. 3 the probabilities of selection of the units were based on the measures of size provided by supplementary information. We shall now present some further methods of making use of auxiliary information to achieve higher precision. Another related problem, that will be discussed in this chapter, is the estimation of a population ratio $R = Y/X$. In the previous chapters attention was focused on the estimation of totals, means, and proportions.

### 5.2 RATIO ESTIMATION

Frequently we come across situations in which the ratio of $y$ to another character $x$ is believed to be less variable than the $y$'s themselves. In that case it would be better to estimate $R$, the ratio of $y$ to $x$ in the population, from the sample and then multiply it by the known total of $x$ to estimate the total for $y$. This procedure is called ratio estimation. For example, suppose it is desired to estimate the total agricultural area in a region containing $N$ communes. There are very big communes and very small communes and this makes the character $y$ vary tremendously over the region. But the ratio of agricultural area and the population of the commune, which is the per capita agricultural area, would be less variable. If population figures $x$ are known for each commune, say, from an earlier population census, it would be preferable to estimate the ratio of agricultural area and the census population from the sample of communes and multiply this figure by the known census population total of all the communes in the region. If a random sample of $n$ communes gives $S\,y_i$ and $S\,x_i$ as the totals for $y$ and $x$, respectively, the total of $y$ for the region is estimated by $\hat{Y} = XS y_i/S x_i$ where $X$ is the known total of $x$ for the region. In case the information on $x$ is not used, $\hat{Y} = NS y_i/n$.

Now suppose that the problem is to estimate the per-capita agricultural area in the region. This quantity can be written as $R = Y/X$, where $Y$ is the total agricultural area and $X$ is the total population in the region. If we take a random sample of communes and determine the agricultural area and the population (existing number of persons, not the census population), it is natural to estimate $R$ by $\hat{R} = S\,y_i/S\,x_i$. It should be noted that the two problems are different, although they are connected. For estimating $Y$ we could have used information on any character $x$; this information need not be recent, but must be known for the entire universe. On the other hand, information on a sample basis is required for $y$ as well as for $x$ (the denominator of the ratio) if the purpose is to estimate the ratio $R = \Sigma Y_i/\Sigma X_i$ in the population. Since the theory is the same in either case, most of the subsequent results will relate to the problem of estimating a ratio.

### 5.3  BIAS OF THE RATIO ESTIMATE

The following theorem shows that $\hat{R}$ and $\hat{Y}$ are usually biased estimators of $R$ and $Y$ (Goodman and Hartley, 1958).

#### Theorem 5.1

*In simple random sampling, the bias of the ratio estimator* $\hat{R} = S y_i/S x_i = \bar{y}/\bar{x}$ *is given by*

$$B(\hat{R}) = -[E(\bar{x})]^{-1} \operatorname{Cov}(\hat{R}, \bar{x}) \tag{5.1}$$

PROOF   As Cov $(\bar{y}/\bar{x},\bar{x}) = E(\bar{y}) - E(\bar{y}/\bar{x})E(\bar{x})$ we have

$$\bar{X}E\frac{\bar{y}}{\bar{x}} = \bar{Y} - \text{Cov}\left(\frac{\bar{y}}{\bar{x}}, \bar{x}\right)$$

or $\qquad\qquad E(\hat{R}) = R - \frac{1}{\bar{X}}\,\text{Cov}\,(\hat{R},\bar{x})$

or $\qquad E(\hat{R}) - R = B(\hat{R}) = -\frac{1}{\bar{X}}\,\text{Cov}\,(\hat{R},\bar{x})$ ∎

### Corollary

Denoting the standard deviation of $\hat{R}$ by $\sigma(\hat{R})$ we have

$$B(\hat{R}) = -\sigma(\hat{R})\sigma(\bar{x})\frac{\rho(\hat{R},\bar{x})}{\bar{X}}$$

or $\qquad \dfrac{B(\hat{R})}{\sigma(\hat{R})} = -\rho(\hat{R},\bar{x})\dfrac{\sigma(\bar{x})}{\bar{X}} = -\rho(\hat{R},\bar{x})\text{CV}(\bar{x})$

Hence

$$\frac{|B(\hat{R})|}{\sigma(\hat{R})} \leq \text{CV}(\bar{x}) \tag{5.2}$$

where CV stands for the coefficient of variation, and $\rho$ is the correlation coefficient. This result is extremely useful in practice when it is considered important that the bias of the estimator be negligibly small in order that proper confidence statements (Sec. 2.11) be made. In that case the sample size $n$ is to be so chosen that $\text{CV}(\bar{x}) = (1/n - 1/N)^{\frac{1}{2}}S_x/\bar{X}$ is smaller than $\frac{1}{10}$, say.

*Remark*   The bias associated with $\hat{Y} = X\bar{y}/\bar{x}$ would be $XB(\hat{R})$.

*Remark*   $\hat{R}$ is unbiased if $\rho(\hat{R},\bar{x}) = 0$.

#### 5.4 AN APPROXIMATE EXPRESSION FOR BIAS

The exact expression for the bias of the ratio estimate derived in Sec. 5.3 is not always very useful. An approximation involving the coefficients of variation of $x$ and $y$ is obtained in Theorem 5.2.

### Theorem 5.2

*In simple random sampling an approximate value of the bias of $\hat{R} = \bar{y}/\bar{x}$ is given by*

$$B(\hat{R}) \doteq R\text{CV}(\bar{x})[\text{CV}(\bar{x}) - \rho\text{CV}(\bar{y})] \tag{5.3}$$

PROOF   We have

$$E(\hat{R}) - R = E\left(\frac{\bar{y} - R\bar{x}}{\bar{x}}\right)$$

$$= E\left(\frac{\bar{y} - R\bar{x}}{\bar{X} + \delta\bar{x}}\right) \qquad \delta\bar{x} = \bar{x} - \bar{X}$$

Hence           $B(\hat{R}) = f(\theta)$           calculated at $\theta = 1$

where $f(\theta) = E(\bar{y} - R\bar{x})/(\bar{X} + \theta\delta\bar{x})$. We shall find Taylor's expansion of $f(\theta)$ around $\theta = 0$. This expansion is

$$f(\theta) = f(0) + \theta f'(0) + \frac{\theta^2 f''(0)}{2!} + \cdots$$

Now     $f(0) = \dfrac{E(\bar{y} - R\bar{x})}{\bar{X}}$     $f'(0) = -E\dfrac{[(\bar{y} - R\bar{x})\delta\bar{x}]}{\bar{X}^2}$     $\cdots$

Hence   $B(\hat{R}) = \dfrac{E(\bar{y} - R\bar{x})}{\bar{X}} - \dfrac{E[(\bar{y} - R\bar{x})\delta\bar{x}]}{\bar{X}^2} + \dfrac{E[(\bar{y} - R\bar{x})(\delta\bar{x})^2]}{\bar{X}^3} - \cdots$

The expansion proceeds in powers of $\delta\bar{x}$, the successive terms becoming smaller and smaller. If only the first two terms in the expansion are used, an approximation for the bias is obtained as

$$B(\hat{R}) = \frac{-\operatorname{Cov}(\bar{y} - R\bar{x}, \delta\bar{x})}{\bar{X}^2} = \frac{-\operatorname{Cov}(\bar{y} - R\bar{x}, \bar{x})}{\bar{X}^2}$$

$$= -\frac{\rho\sigma(\bar{y})\sigma(\bar{x}) - R\sigma^2(\bar{x})}{\bar{X}^2}$$

$$= R\operatorname{CV}(\bar{x})[\operatorname{CV}(\bar{x}) - \rho\operatorname{CV}(\bar{y})]$$

A closer approximation can be obtained by retaining more terms. Evidently the expression will involve moments of the joint distribution of $y$ and $x$.     ∎

**Remark**   The reader may wonder why the estimator based on the simple average of the ratios has not been considered. An application of this theorem shows that under a certain sampling scheme (see Exercise 35) the bias of this estimator is larger than that of the estimator based on the ratio of the two averages.

### 5.5   MEAN SQUARE ERROR

We now come to the question of the precision of the ratio estimator. Since the estimator is generally biased, its mean square error around $R$ would be of greater interest.

## Theorem 5.3

*In* wtr *simple random sampling, an approximation to the mean square error of* $\hat{R} = \bar{y}/\bar{x}$ *around* $R = Y/X$ *is given by*

$$E(\hat{R} - R)^2 \doteq \frac{1}{n}(1 - f)\frac{S_y^2 + R^2 S_x^2 - 2\rho R S_x S_y}{X^2} \qquad (5.4)$$

PROOF   We have

$$E(\hat{R} - R)^2 = E\left(\frac{\bar{y} - R\bar{x}}{\bar{x}}\right)^2 = E\left(\frac{\bar{y} - R\bar{x}}{\bar{X} + \delta\bar{x}}\right)^2 \qquad \delta\bar{x} = \bar{x} - \bar{X}$$

Then the mean square error is the value at $\theta = 1$ of the function

$$f(\theta) = E\left(\frac{\bar{y} - R\bar{x}}{\bar{X} + \theta\delta\bar{x}}\right)^2$$

Developing Taylor's expansion of $f(\theta)$ as in Sec. 5.4, we get

$$E(\hat{R} - R)^2 = \frac{E(\bar{y} - R\bar{x})^2}{\bar{X}^2} - \frac{2E[(\bar{y} - R\bar{x})^2\delta\bar{x}]}{\bar{X}^3} + \cdots \qquad (5.5)$$

As before, the expansion proceeds in powers of $\delta\bar{x}$, the leading term being the first term which is of order $1/n$. By retaining only the leading term in the expansion, a first approximation to the mean square error, denoted by $V_1(\hat{R})$, would be

$$V_1(\hat{R}) = \frac{E[(\bar{y} - \bar{Y}) - R(\bar{x} - \bar{X})]^2}{\bar{X}^2} = \frac{V(\bar{y}) + R^2 V(\bar{x}) - 2R\rho\sigma(\bar{y})\sigma(\bar{x})}{\bar{X}^2}$$

since $\qquad\qquad \rho(\bar{x},\bar{y}) = \rho(x,y) = \rho$

Hence   $V_1(\hat{R}) = \dfrac{1 - f}{n}\dfrac{(S_y^2 + R^2 S_x^2 - 2R\rho S_y S_x)}{\bar{X}^2}$

$$= \frac{1 - f}{n} R^2[\mathrm{CV}^2(y) + \mathrm{CV}^2(x) - 2\rho\mathrm{CV}(y)\mathrm{CV}(x)] \qquad ∎$$

A second approximation to $E(\hat{R} - R)^2$ can be obtained by including the succeeding lower order term and so on. Fortunately, it is possible to find bounds for the error made if only the first approximation, given by $V_1(\hat{R})$, be used.

**Corollary**

An approximate expression for the mean square error of $\hat{Y} = X\hat{R}$ would be given by

$$V_1(\hat{Y}) = X^2 V_1(\hat{R}) = \frac{N^2(1 - f)}{n} (S_y^2 + R^2 S_x^2 - 2R\rho S_y S_x)$$

$$= \frac{Y^2(1 - f)}{n} [CV^2(y) + CV^2(x) - 2\rho CV(y)CV(x)]$$

**Remark**   $V_1(\hat{R}) = 0$ if $y$ is proportional to $x$.

**Further reading**   Refer to Exercise 32 for a sufficient condition that the first approximation to the true variance be an understatement.

## 5.6  BOUNDS ON THE MSE

In view of the fact that the method of ratio estimation is widely used in sample surveys, and only an approximate formula is available by which its precision can be measured, it is a matter of considerable importance to see how far this approximation is satisfactory.   This will be done in this section by finding bounds for the exact-remainder term in the expansion (5.5).   The first-derivative exact-remainder term would be $-2E[(\bar{y} - R\bar{x})^2 \delta\bar{x}/(\bar{X} + \theta'\delta\bar{x})^3]$, with $0 < \theta' < 1$.   Since its derivative with respect to $\theta'$ is positive, it is an increasing function of $\theta'$ and its lower and upper limits are (Raj, 1964a)

$$G_1 = \frac{-2E[(\bar{y} - R\bar{x})^2 \delta\bar{x}]}{\bar{X}^3} \quad \text{and} \quad G_2 = -2E\frac{(\bar{y} - R\bar{x})^2 \delta\bar{x}}{\bar{x}^3}$$

Hence we obtain

$$G_1 < E(\hat{R} - R)^2 - V_1(\hat{R}) < G_2 \tag{5.6}$$

Similarly, by stopping at the third-derivative exact-remainder term, we get the bounds

$$A + B + C_1 < E(\hat{R} - R)^2 - V_1(\hat{R}) < A + B + C_2 \tag{5.7}$$

where

$$A = -2E\frac{(\bar{y} - R\bar{x})^2 \delta\bar{x}}{\bar{X}^3} \qquad B = 3E\frac{(\bar{y} - R\bar{x})^2 (\delta\bar{x})^2}{\bar{X}^4}$$

$$C_1 = -4E\frac{(\bar{y} - R\bar{x})^2 (\delta\bar{x})^3}{\bar{X}^5} \qquad C_2 = -4E\frac{(\bar{y} - R\bar{x})^2 (\delta\bar{x})^3}{(\bar{x})^5}$$

We shall now assume that the relationship between $y$ and $x$ is a straight line through the origin. This is the situation in which the ratio estimate is going to prove more useful. Theorem 5.4 gives the bounds on the mean square error in this case.

### Theorem 5.4

*Under the model*

$$y = Rx + e \qquad E(e|x) = 0$$

*and assuming zero correlation between* $(\bar{e})^2$ *and each of* $\delta\bar{x}$, $(\delta\bar{x})^2$, $(\delta\bar{x})^3$, *and* $(\delta\bar{x})^3/(\bar{x})^5$, *the bounds on* MSE $(\hat{R})$ *are given by*

$$F < \frac{\mathrm{MSE}(\hat{R}) - V_1(\hat{R})}{V_1(\hat{R})} < G \qquad (5.8)$$

*where*

$$F = 3\mathrm{CV}^2(\bar{x}) - 4E\left(\frac{\delta\bar{x}}{\bar{X}}\right)^3$$

$$G = 3\mathrm{CV}^2(\bar{x}) - 4\bar{X}^2 E\frac{(\delta\bar{x})^3}{(\bar{x})^5}$$

PROOF Using the result that $E(UW) = E(U)E(W)$ if the random variables $U$ and $W$ are uncorrelated, it follows immediately from the assumptions made that

$$A = 0 \qquad B = 3V(\bar{e})V(\bar{x})/\bar{X}^4 = 3\mathrm{CV}^2(\bar{x})V_1(\hat{R})$$

$$C_1 = -4V_1(\hat{R})E(\delta\bar{x}/\bar{X})^3 \qquad C_2 = -4\bar{X}^2V_1(\hat{R})E\frac{(\delta\bar{x})^3}{(\bar{x})^5}$$

Making these substitutions in (5.7) we get (5.8). ■

*Remark* If the distribution of $x$ is symmetrical, $E(\delta\bar{x})^3 = 0$. In this situation the use of $V_1(\hat{R})$ results in understating the true mean square error. The amount of understatement, as a proportion of $V_1(\hat{R})$, is $3\mathrm{CV}^2(\bar{x})$. The understatement is higher if the third moment of $\bar{x}$ is negative.

### 5.7 COMPARISON WITH THE SIMPLE AVERAGE

The circumstances under which the ratio estimate will be superior to the simple average (the sample mean) will now be pointed out. The variance of $\hat{Y} = N\bar{y}$ in wtr simple random sampling is given by

$$V(\hat{Y}) = N^2(1 - f)\frac{S_y^2}{n}$$

In this case no use is made of the auxiliary information provided by $x$. If this information is used to form the ratio estimate $\hat{Y} = X\hat{R}$, a first approximation (which sometimes understates) to the mean square error around $Y$ has been found to be

$$V_1(\hat{Y}) = N^2(1-f)\frac{(S_y{}^2 + R^2S_x{}^2 - 2R\rho S_xS_y)}{n}$$

Judging by this approximation, the ratio method will give a more precise result whenever

$$2\rho > \frac{RS_x}{S_y} \quad \text{or} \quad \rho > \frac{CV(x)}{2CV(y)} \tag{5.9}$$

Thus the issue depends by and large on the strength of correlation between $y$ and $x$. If $x$ is the same character as $y$, but has been measured on a previous occasion, the coefficients of variation may be taken as equal. In that case it pays to use the ratio method of estimation if $\rho$ exceeds $\frac{1}{2}$. But one should not be dogmatic about inequality (5.9), since it is based on an approximation. In fact it can be proved that even in the presence of perfect correlation between $y$ and $x$, the ratio estimate may not be as good as the simple average. This is evident from the following (Raj, 1954) theorem.

### Theorem 5.5

*Let there be perfect correlation between $y$ and $x$, so that $y = a + bx$. In* wtr *simple random sampling, the estimator $N\bar{y}$ will be superior to the ratio estimator $X\hat{R}$ if*

$$\frac{\bar{X}^2V(1/\bar{x})}{S_x{}^2} > \frac{b^2}{a^2}\frac{1-f}{n} \tag{5.10}$$

The proof follows immediately from the observation that, in view of the linear relationship, $V(\bar{y}/\bar{x}) = a^2V(1/\bar{x})$.

*Remark* For very large values of $a$, inequality (5.10) may be easily satisfied. A large value of $a$ means that the regression line passes through a point far from the origin. Then near-proportionality between $y$ and $x$ does not exist. In such a case it may be futile to make the ratio estimate with $x$ in the denominator.

*Remark* It would be a sound practice to examine the relationship between $y$ and $x$ on the basis of past surveys and use this information in the future.

## 5.8 SAMPLE ESTIMATE OF MSE

Denoting the random variable $y - Rx$ by $U$, the approximation to the mean square error of $\hat{R}$ may be written as

$$V_1(\hat{R}) = \frac{V(\bar{u})}{\bar{X}^2} = \frac{(\bar{X})^{-2}(1 - f)S_u^2}{n}$$

where

$$S_u^2 = \frac{\sum_{i=1}^{N} (U_i - \bar{U})^2}{N - 1}$$

It is thus natural to estimate $V_1(\hat{R})$ from the sample by

$$V_1(\hat{R}) \cong \frac{(1 - f)s_u^2}{n\bar{x}^2} \qquad (5.11)$$

where

$$s_u^2 = \frac{S[y_i - \bar{y} - \hat{R}(x_i - \bar{x})]^2}{n - 1}$$

The estimator (5.11) is biased, since it is a ratio estimator. As $\hat{R} = \bar{y}/\bar{x}$, $s_u^2$ can also be written as

$$s_u^2 = (n - 1)^{-1}S(y_i - \hat{R}x_i)^2 = (n - 1)^{-1}(Sy_i^2 + \hat{R}^2Sx_i^2 - 2\hat{R}Sx_iy_i)$$

## 5.9 UNBIASED RATIO ESTIMATION

In view of the fact that, under simple random sampling, the ratio estimator $X\bar{y}/\bar{x}$ is biased, one line of recent research has been to modify the sampling procedure so that the same estimator becomes unbiased. This will retain the simplicity of the estimator and make it unbiased at the same time. The procedure (Lahiri, 1951; Midzuno, 1950) consists in selecting the sample with probability proportionate to its aggregate size (ppas). This is best done by selecting the first unit in the sample with pp to $x$ and the other $(n - 1)$ units with equal probabilities without replacement. The proof is given in the following Theorem 5.6.

### Theorem 5.6

*If from a finite population of size $N$, the first unit in the sample is selected with probabilities $p_i$ $(i = 1, \ldots, N)$, $\Sigma p_i = 1$, and the remaining $(n - 1)$ units with equal probabilities without replacement, the probability of selecting a particular sample s is given by*

$$Pr(s) = \frac{Sx_i}{N'X} \qquad N' = \binom{N - 1}{n - 1}$$

PROOF   The probability that the unit $U_i$ is the first one to be selected and the subsequent units form a wtr simple random sample of size $(n - 1)$ is $p_i/N'$. Similarly the probability that $U_j$ is the first selection and the other units form a simple random sample is $p_j/N'$, and so on.   Hence the probability of selecting the sample $s$ in this manner is

$$\frac{Sp_i}{N'} = \frac{Sx_i}{N'X} \qquad \blacksquare$$

### Corollary

The expected value of $\hat{Y} = XSy_i/Sx_i$ is given by

$$E(\hat{Y}) = \sum^{''} X \frac{Sy_i}{Sx_i} \frac{Sx_i}{XN'} = \sum^{''} \frac{Sy_i}{N'} = Y$$

where $\sum^{''}$ denotes summation over all possible samples $s$.   Thus the usual ratio estimator becomes unbiased in this scheme.

### 5.10   THE VARIANCE OF THE UNBIASED RATIO ESTIMATOR

A formal expression for the variance of the unbiased ratio estimator under the modified sampling scheme could be written down from first principles (Raj, 1964$b$) as

$$V(\hat{Y}) = (N')^{-1}X \sum^{''} \frac{(Sy_i)^2}{Sx_i} - Y^2 = V_{\text{ppas}} \qquad (5.12)$$

where $\sum^{''}$ denotes summation over all possible samples $s$.   It is obvious that $V(\hat{Y})$ vanishes when $y_i$ is proportionate to $x_i$.   Nothing more is revealed by this expression as such.   An unbiased estimate of $V(\hat{Y})$ from the sample will now be obtained.

### Theorem 5.7

*In sampling with* ppas, *an unbiased estimator of $Y^2$ is given by*

$$Y^2 \cong \frac{(Sy_i^2/N' + 2S'y_iy_j/N'')}{Pr(s)} = G$$

*where* $N'' = \binom{N-2}{n-2}$, $Pr(s) = Sx_i/XN'$, *and* $S'$ *denotes summation over the different pairs in the sample.*

PROOF    From first principles, we have

$$E \frac{Sy_i^2}{N'Pr(s)} = \sum^{''} \frac{Sy_i^2}{N'} = \sum_1^N Y_i^2$$

$$E \frac{S'y_iy_j}{N''Pr(s)} = \sum_i \sum_{j>i} Y_iY_j$$

and this completes the proof.                                        ∎

### Corollary

An unbiased estimator of $V(\hat{Y})$ is given by

$$V(\hat{Y}) \,\hat{=}\, \hat{Y}^2 - G \qquad \text{since} \qquad E(\hat{Y}^2 - G) = E(\hat{Y}^2) - Y^2 = V(\hat{Y})$$

*Remark*    The estimator of variance may assume negative values for some samples.

### 5.11  RELATIVE PRECISION OF THE UNBIASED RATIO ESTIMATOR

A comparison of $V_{\text{ppas}}$ with the variance of some other estimators will now be made.    The discussion will be restricted to samples of two units only.    (This is appropriate when the units are psu's of Chap. 6 and only two units are selected from a stratum.)    In this case the variance of the unbiased ratio estimator is

$$V_{\text{ppas}} = X \sum{}' (Y_i + Y_j) \frac{[(Y_i + Y_j)/(X_i + X_j) - R]}{N - 1}$$

where $\sum'$ denotes summation over all different pairs in the population. (It will be noted that the contribution of a number of pairs of units to $V_{\text{ppas}}$ would be negative.)    We shall assume that the $N$ units are divided up into a number of arrays with $x_i$ being the measure of size for all the $N_i$ units in the $i$th array.    Further, we assume the model

$$y_{im} = Rx_i + e_{im}$$

where $\sum_m e_{im} = 0$, $\sum_m e_{im}^2 = aN_ix_i^g$.    Thus for a given $x$, the residuals are assumed to have a mean value of zero and a variance proportionate to

$x^g(g > 0)$. Under this model, we have (Raj, 1964b)

$$V_{\text{ppas}} = (N - 1)^{-1}X \sum' \frac{(e_{im} + e_{jm'})^2}{x_i + x_j}$$

$$= [2(N - 1)]^{-1}aX \left[ 2 \sum_i \sum_{j>i} N_i N_j \frac{x_i^g + x_j^g}{x_i + x_j} + \sum N_i(N_i - 2)x_i^{g-1} \right]$$

If the sample is selected with replacement with pp to $x$, we have

$$V_{\text{pps}} = aX \sum \frac{N_i x_i^{g-1}}{2}$$

$$= [2(N - 1)]^{-1}aX \left[ \sum_i \sum_{j>i} N_i N_j(x_i^{g-1} + x_j^{g-1}) + \sum_i N_i(N_i - 1)x_i^{g-1} \right]$$

Thus the quantity $\Delta = V_{\text{pps}} - V_{\text{ppas}}$ is given by

$$= [2(N - 1)]^{-1}aX \left[ \sum N_i x_i^{g-1} - \sum_{j>i} \sum \frac{N_i N_j(x_i - x_j)(x_i^{g-1} - x_j^{g-1})}{x_i + x_j} \right]$$

The quantity $\Delta$ can now be examined for different values of $g$. It is obvious that $\Delta > 0$ for $g = 0$ and 1. But, for $g = 1$, the relative increase in variance (with pps as the base) can be as small as $1/(N - 1)$. For $g = 2$, pps sampling will be found to be superior whenever

$$\sum_{j>i} \sum \frac{N_i N_j(x_i - x_j)^2}{x_i + x_j} > X$$

For $g = 3$, $\Delta = (aX/2)[N/(N - 1)][\bar{X}^2 - (N - 1)V(x)]$. In this case, pps sampling will produce a lower variance if $CV^2(x) > 1/(N - 1)$.

In order to make a comparison with equal probability sampling, we have for this model

$$V_{ep} = \frac{N(N - 2)}{2} \left( R^2 S_x^2 + a \sum \frac{N_i x_i^g}{N - 1} \right)$$

Hence, for $g = 1$, ppas sampling is superior to equal probability sampling and is only slightly better than pps sampling.

## 5.12 UNBIASED RATIO-TYPE ESTIMATORS

Another line of research has been to modify the usual ratio estimator itself (and not the sampling scheme) so that a ratio-type estimator is obtained that is unbiased under simple random sampling. Actually, the estimator $\bar{r} = n^{-1}Sr_i = n^{-1}S(y_i/x_i)$ is corrected for its bias (Goodman and Hartley, 1958) to obtain an unbiased estimator. This is proved in the following theorem.

### Theorem 5.8

*In* wtr *simple random sampling, an unbiased estimator of* $R = Y/X$ *is given by*

$$\hat{R} = \bar{r} + \frac{(N-1)n}{N(n-1)} \frac{\bar{y} - \bar{r}\bar{x}}{\bar{X}} \tag{5.13}$$

*with a large sample approximation to its variance as*

$$V(\hat{R}) \doteq \frac{S_y{}^2 + \bar{R}^2 S_x{}^2 - 2\bar{R}\rho S_x S_y}{n\bar{X}^2} \tag{5.14}$$

*where* 
$$\bar{r} = n^{-1}S\left(\frac{y_i}{x_i}\right) \qquad \bar{R} = E\left(\frac{y_i}{x_i}\right)$$

PROOF   We have

$$E(\bar{r}) = E(r_i) = \frac{E(r_i)E(x_i)}{\bar{X}}$$

$$= \frac{\bar{Y} - \text{Cov }(r_i,x_i)}{\bar{X}}$$

$$= R - \frac{\text{Cov }(r_i,x_i)}{\bar{X}}$$

Using the result that the sample covariance $S(u_i - \bar{u})(v_i - \bar{v})/(n-1)$ is an unbiased estimate of $N/(N-1)$ times the population covariance, we find that Cov $(r_i,x_i)$ is estimated unbiasedly by

$$h = \frac{N-1}{(n-1)N} Sr_i(x_i - \bar{x}) = \frac{(N-1)n}{(n-1)N} (\bar{y} - \bar{r}\bar{x})$$

Hence

$$E\left(\bar{r} + \frac{h}{\bar{X}}\right) = R - \frac{\text{Cov }(r_i,x_i)}{\bar{X}} + \frac{\text{Cov }(r_i,x_i)}{\bar{X}} = R$$

In order to obtain the large sample variance of $\hat{R}$ defined by (5.13), we note that in large samples $\hat{R}$ reduces to $[\bar{y} - \bar{r}(\bar{x} - \bar{X})]/\bar{X}$ when the population is assumed to be infinite. By the law of large numbers the random variable $\bar{r}$ converges in probability to $\bar{R}$. Hence the limiting distribution of $\sqrt{n} \, [\bar{y} - \bar{r}(\bar{x} - \bar{X}) - \bar{Y}]$ is the same as the distribution of $\sqrt{n} \, [\bar{y} - \bar{R}(\bar{x} - \bar{X}) - \bar{Y}]$. Thus, for large values of $n$, the variance of $[\bar{y} - \bar{r}(\bar{x} - \bar{X})]/\bar{X}$ is approximately given by

$$\frac{S_y{}^2 + \bar{R}^2 S_x{}^2 - 2\bar{R}\rho S_x S_y}{n\bar{X}^2} \qquad \blacksquare$$

### Corollary

The large sample approximation to the mean square error of the biased ratio estimator $\bar{y}/\bar{x}$ has been obtained (Theorem 5.3) as

$$V_1(\hat{R}) = \frac{S_y{}^2 + R^2 S_x{}^2 - 2R\rho S_x S_y}{n\bar{X}^2}$$

Denoting the large sample variance of the unbiased ratio-type estimator as $V_2(\hat{R})$, we get

$$V_1(\hat{R}) - V_2(\hat{R}) = \frac{(R^2 - \bar{R}^2)S_x{}^2 - 2\rho S_x S_y(R - \bar{R})}{n\bar{X}^2}$$

$$= \frac{[(R - \beta)^2 - (\bar{R} - \beta)^2]S_x{}^2}{n\bar{X}^2}$$

where $\beta$ is the regression coefficient, $\rho S_y/S_x$, of $y$ on $x$. Hence the biased ratio estimator will give a more precise result if the regression coefficient $\beta$ is nearer to $R = Y/X$ than to $\bar{R} = E(y/x)$. The two variances are equal if $R = \bar{R}$.

**Remark**  Since the expression for the unbiased ratio-type estimator involves $\bar{r} = S(y_i/x_i)/n$, which is not simple to calculate when many items are involved, the unbiased ratio-type estimator is unlikely to be used in large-scale work. It may be appropriate in some specialized investigations.

**Remark**  An exact expression for the variance of the unbiased ratio-type estimator has been obtained by Goodman and Hartley (1958).

### Further reading

**1.**  See Exercise 42, in which another procedure of reducing the bias of a ratio estimator is presented.
**2.**  When the entire sample is built up of $m$ independent subsamples of the same size (called interpenetrating subsamples), a procedure of obtaining an unbiased ratio-type estimator is presented in Exercise 33.
**3.**  When the regression of $y$ on $x$ is linear, it is shown in Exercise 34 that the usual ratio estimator is better than the ratio-type estimator.

## 5.13 DIFFERENCE ESTIMATION

As stated before, the ratio estimator is at its best when the relation between $y$ and $x$ is a straight line through the origin, that is, $y - kx = 0$. In case the relationship is of the type $y - kx = a$ (constant), it is natural to try an estimator based on differences of the form $y_i - kx_i$. Such estimators are called difference estimators. Instead of estimating the ratio of $Y$ to $X$ and multiplying it by the known mean of $x$ to estimate the population mean $\bar{Y}$, we estimate the difference between $\bar{Y}$ and $k\bar{X}$ and add to this the known quantity $k\bar{X}$ to estimate $\bar{Y}$. In simple random sampling the difference estimator and its variance are presented in the following theorem.

### Theorem 5.9

*In wtr simple random sampling, an unbiased estimator of the population mean is given by*

$$\hat{\mu} = (\bar{y} - k\bar{x}) + k\bar{X} \tag{5.15}$$

*with a variance of*

$$V(\hat{\mu}) = (1 - f)\frac{S_y{}^2 + k^2 S_x{}^2 - 2k\rho S_x S_y}{n} \tag{5.16}$$

*where $k$ is a constant.*

PROOF Since $E(\bar{y} - k\bar{x}) = \bar{Y} - k\bar{X}$, the unbiasedness of $\hat{\mu}$ follows. Denoting $y_i - kx_i$ by $u_i$, we have

$$V(\hat{\mu}) = V(\bar{u}) = (1 - f)\frac{S_u{}^2}{n}$$

where $S_u{}^2 = (N - 1)^{-1}\Sigma(u_i - \bar{u})^2 = (N - 1)^{-1}\Sigma[y_i - \bar{Y} - k(x_i - \bar{X})]^2$
$= S_y{}^2 + k^2 S_x{}^2 - 2k\rho S_x S_y$

This proves the theorem. ∎

### Corollary

In order to find the best value of $k$ to use, we differentiate $V(\hat{\mu})$ with respect to $k$ and equate it with zero. This gives $k = B = \rho S_y/S_x$, the population regression coefficient. Since the second derivative is positive, the variance would be a minimum for $k = B$ and the minimum variance is $(1 - f)S_y{}^2(1 - \rho^2)/n$.

*Remark* For $k = R = Y/X$, the variance of the difference estimator is exactly the same as the approximation, $V_1(\bar{X}\hat{R})$, to the mean square error of the biased ratio estimator $\bar{X}\bar{y}/\bar{x}$.

*Remark*   The difference estimator is superior to the simple average $\bar{y}$ if $kS_x{}^2(k - 2\rho S_y/S_x) < 0$ or $k(k - 2B) < 0$, that is, if $k$ lies between 0 and $2B$. For values of $k$ outside this range, the simple average $\bar{y}$ would be better.

*Remark*   In order to estimate the variance of the difference estimator from the sample, we note that $s_u{}^2 = S(u_i - \bar{u})^2/(n - 1)$ is an unbiased estimator of $S_u{}^2$.

*Remark*   The foregoing analysis shows that the method of difference estimation gives exact results which are simple to apply. Its relative precision depends on whether a good guess can be made of the regression coefficient $B$. In one practical situation it is not difficult to guess $B$. This is the case in which the auxiliary variate $x$ is the character $y$ enumerated on a previous occasion, in which case $k$ could be set at unity.

## 5.14  REGRESSION ESTIMATION

Instead of making a guess of the value of $B$, the population regression coefficient, to form the more precise difference estimate, we could as well estimate $B$ from the sample and use this value in place of $k$. Since the sample estimate of $B$ is $b = S(x_i - \bar{x})(y_i - \bar{y})/S(x_i - \bar{x})^2$, the estimator obtained thereby is

$$\hat{\mu} = \bar{y} - b(\bar{x} - \bar{X}) \tag{5.17}$$

which is called the regression estimator. Since $b$ is a random variable, exact expressions for the expected value and the variance of the regression estimator are hard to obtain. At the same time the calculation of $b$ is laborious, especially when many items are to be estimated from the same survey. The result is that the regression estimator (5.17) has not been used as extensively as have the ratio estimator or the difference estimator in large-scale work. In this section only a large sample approximation to its variance will be given.

### Theorem 5.10

*In simple random sampling, the large sample variance of the regression estimator*

$$\hat{\mu} = \bar{y} - b(\bar{x} - \bar{X})$$

*is given by*

$$V(\hat{\mu}) = \frac{S_y{}^2(1 - \rho^2)}{n} \tag{5.18}$$

PROOF    Since the sample regression coefficient $b$ converges in probability to a finite value, namely $B$, the random variable $\sqrt{n}\,(b - B)(\bar{x} - \bar{X})$ converges to zero.   Hence the limiting distribution of

$$\sqrt{n}\,[\bar{y} - b(\bar{x} - \bar{X}) - \bar{Y}] = \sqrt{n}\,[\bar{y} - B(\bar{x} - \bar{X}) \\ - \bar{Y} - (b - B)(\bar{x} - \bar{X})]$$

will be the same as that of $\sqrt{n}\,[\bar{y} - B(\bar{x} - \bar{X}) - \bar{Y}]$.   Thus, for large $n$, the variance of the regression estimator is

$$V(\hat{\mu}) = \frac{S_y^2 + B^2 S_x^2 - 2B\rho S_x S_y}{n}$$

$$= \frac{S_y^2(1 - \rho^2)}{n}$$

since $B = \rho S_y / S_x$.                                   ∎

**Remark**    This analysis suggests that we could use any random variable $h$, in place of $b$, where $h$ converges to a finite value.   But, it can be easily shown that the limiting variance is a minimum when $h = b$.

**Remark**    The simple average $\bar{y}$, the ratio estimator $\bar{X}\bar{y}/\bar{x}$, the difference estimator $\bar{y} - k(\bar{x} - \bar{X})$, and the regression estimator $\bar{y} - b(\bar{x} - \bar{X})$ all belong to the class of estimators

$$\bar{y} - h(\bar{x} - \bar{X})$$

where $h$ is a random variable converging to some finite value.   The variable $h$ is zero for the simple average, $\bar{y}/\bar{x}$ for the ratio estimator, $k =$ a constant for the difference estimator, and the sample regression coefficient $b$ for the regression estimator.   In large samples the regression estimator is the most precise for estimating the population mean or total. But its use will be justified only in those cases where the gain in precision offsets the additional costs involved in computations.   If a good guess of $B$ can be made on the basis of previous information, the difference estimator will be as good as the regression estimator from the point of view of precision.   It is the best choice in this situation.

**Remark**    It follows from the proof of the theorem that the contribution to the variance arising from the estimation of the population regression coefficient $B$ through $b$ is small relative to the total variance when the sample size is fairly large.

## Further reading

**1.** Refer to Exercise 36 for an alternative derivation of the variance of the regression estimator.

**2.** For general methods of generating unbiased ratio and regression estimators, see Exercises 37 and 38.

### 5.15 USE OF MULTIAUXILIARY INFORMATION

The discussion so far has been restricted to the situation in which auxiliary information on just one $x$-variate is to be used for improving the precision of estimates. Frequently we possess information about several $x$-variates, and it may be considered important to make use of all the available material to our advantage. We shall therefore, present some methods of using information on several variates $x_1$, $x_2$, . . . , $x_p$. One method consists in forming a difference estimator of the mean of $y$'s based on each $x$-variate and then combining them, using appropriate weights (Raj, 1965). Let

$$t_i = \bar{y} - k_i(\bar{x}_i - \bar{X}_i) \qquad (5.19)$$

where $k_i$ is any constant. Let $w_i(i = 1, 2, . . . , p)$ be weights adding up to unity. Then

$$\hat{\mu} = \sum_1^p w_i t_i \qquad (5.20)$$

is an unbiased estimator of $\bar{Y}$. Its variance is given by (Theorem 1.5)

$$V(\hat{\mu}) = \sum_i \sum_j w_i w_j \, \text{Cov} \, (t_i, t_j).$$

Defining $S_{uv}$ as the covariance between $u$ and $v$ and letting 0, 1, . . . , $p$ stand for the variates $y$, $x_1$, . . . , $x_p$, respectively, we have

$$\text{Cov} \, (t_i, t_j) = \frac{1 - f}{n} (S_{00} - k_i S_{0i} - k_j S_{0j} + k_i k_j S_{ij})$$

$$= \frac{1 - f}{n} a_{ij}$$

Thus

$$V(\hat{\mu}) = \frac{1 - f}{n} \sum \sum w_i w_j a_{ij}$$

$$= \frac{1 - f}{n} \mathbf{w} A \mathbf{w}' \qquad (5.21)$$

where the matrix $A = (a_{ij})$, and $\mathbf{w} = (w_1, w_2, \ldots, w_p)$, $\mathbf{w}'$ being the transpose of $\mathbf{w}$. Using the procedure (Sec. 1.10) of combining a number of estimators, we establish that the optimum $w_i$ is given by

$$w_i = \frac{\text{sum of the elements in the } i\text{th column of } A^{-1}}{\text{sum of all the } p^2 \text{ elements in } A^{-1}}$$

where $A^{-1}$ is the matrix inverse to $A$. Using the optimum weights, the minimum variance is found to be

$$V(\hat{\mu}) = \frac{1}{n} \frac{1 - f}{\text{sum of the } p^2 \text{ elements in } A^{-1}}$$

In order to estimate the variance of $\hat{\mu}$, we note that

$$\hat{\mu} = \bar{y} - \sum_i w_i k_i (\bar{x}_i - \bar{X}_i)$$

$$V(\hat{\mu}) = V\left(\bar{y} - \sum w_i k_i \bar{x}_i\right) = V\left[\frac{1}{n} S_j \left(y_j - \sum_i w_i k_i x_{ij}\right)\right]$$

and hence an unbiased estimator of the variance is given by

$$V(\hat{\mu}) \cong \frac{1}{n}(1 - f)\frac{1}{n-1} \mathop{S}_{j=1}^{n} \left[y_j - \sum w_i k_i (x_{ij} - \bar{x}_i)\right]^2 \qquad (5.22)$$

### 5.16  THE CASE OF TWO $x$-VARIATES

The most frequent application will be the use of two $x$-variates. In this case the formulas assume the following form:

$$\hat{\mu} = \bar{y} - w_1 k_1 (\bar{x}_1 - \bar{X}_1) - w_2 k_2 (\bar{x}_2 - \bar{X}_2)$$

$$V(\hat{\mu}) = \frac{1}{n}(1 - f)(S_{00} + w_1^2 k_1^2 S_{11} + w_2^2 k_2^2 S_{22}$$

$$- 2w_1 k_1 S_{01} - 2w_2 k_2 S_{02} + 2w_1 w_2 k_1 k_2 S_{12})$$

The best weights are

$$w_1 = \frac{a_{22} - a_{12}}{a_{11} + a_{22} - 2a_{12}} \qquad w_2 = \frac{a_{11} - a_{12}}{a_{11} + a_{22} - 2a_{12}}$$

The minimum variance is

$$V(\hat{\mu}) = \frac{1}{n}(1 - f)\frac{a_{11}a_{12} - (a_{12})^2}{a_{11} + a_{22} - 2a_{12}}$$

We shall consider the particular case in which the coefficients of variation of $x_1$ and $x_2$ are equal to $c$, there is the same correlation $\rho_0$

between $y$ and the $x_i$ $(i = 1, 2)$, and the $k_i$ are the population ratios $R_i = Y/X_i$. Further, let $\rho$ denote the correlation coefficient between $x_1$ and $x_2$ and let $c_0$ be the coefficient of variation of $y$. Then, it is easy to check that the best weights are $w_1 = w_2 = \frac{1}{2}$ and

$$V(\hat{\mu}) = \frac{1}{n}(1 - f)\bar{Y}^2\left[\frac{1}{2}c^2(1 + \rho) + (c_0{}^2 - 2\rho_0 cc_0)\right]$$

If only one $x$-variate is used, the variance is

$$V(\hat{\mu}) = \frac{1}{n}(1 - f)\bar{Y}^2(c^2 + c_0{}^2 - 2\rho_0 cc_0)$$

Thus it is always better to use the second variate provided $\rho$ differs from unity. A comparison can also be made with the case in which no $x$-variate is employed. It will be found that the use of a one-variate is justified if $\rho_0 > 2^{-1}c/c_0$. In the case of two $x$-variates the criterion is $\rho_0 > 4^{-1}(1 + \rho)c/c_0$.

## 5.17 MULTIVARIATE RATIO ESTIMATION

Another method of using information on several variates is to form ratio estimates instead of difference estimates and weight them suitably. Olkin (1958) has considered this technique. It is clear that the estimators will be biased and only approximate expressions for the variances can be obtained. Denoting by $u_i$ the ratio estimator $\bar{X}_i\bar{y}/\bar{x}_i$ based on the variate $x_i$, the weighted estimator of $\bar{Y}$ is $\hat{\mu} = \Sigma w_i\bar{X}_i\bar{y}/\bar{x}_i = \Sigma w_i\bar{X}_i\hat{R}_i$, where $\Sigma w_i = 1$. The expected value and the variance are given by

$$E(\hat{\mu}) = \Sigma w_i\bar{X}_iE(\hat{R}_i),$$
$$V(\hat{\mu}) = \Sigma\Sigma w_iw_j\bar{X}_i\bar{X}_j \operatorname{Cov}(\hat{R}_i,\hat{R}_j)$$

The analysis proceeds on the same lines as discussed before for the case of the difference estimator. The large sample variance of the ratio estimator is found to be the same as the exact variance of the difference estimator when $k_i = R_i$.

*Remark* A question may be asked whether to base the ratio estimator on $p$ variates or on $p + q$. Exercise 39 shows that it is always better to include an additional variate.

## 5.18 RATIO ESTIMATION IN STRATIFIED SAMPLING

We shall now discuss the situation in which the population has been divided up into a number of strata and the population total is estimated by the ratio method. Two different estimators are given. They are

$$\hat{Y}_s = \sum_h X_h \frac{\bar{y}_h}{\bar{x}_h} \qquad \hat{Y}_c = X \frac{\Sigma N_h \bar{y}_h}{\Sigma N_h \bar{x}_h} = X\hat{R} \qquad (5.23)$$

In the first case a separate estimate is made for each stratum total and in the latter a combined estimate is made for the population total. Using the methods of Sec. 5.3, the bias in $\hat{Y}_c$ relative to the standard error is given by

$$\frac{|B(\hat{Y}_c)|}{\sigma(\hat{Y}_c)} = \frac{|B(\hat{R})|}{\sigma(\hat{R})} \leq \text{CV}\left(\sum N_h \bar{x}_h\right)$$

Hence the bias in the combined-ratio estimate will not be important if the coefficient of variation of $\hat{X}$ is small. In the second case $B(\hat{Y}_s)/\sigma(\hat{Y}_s) = \Sigma B(\hat{Y}_h)/[\Sigma V(\hat{Y}_h)]^{1/2}$. If the bias and the variance of $\hat{Y}_h$ do not vary from stratum to stratum, the numerator is $L$ times $B(\hat{Y}_h)$, and the denominator is $\sqrt{L}$ times $\sigma(\hat{Y}_h)$, which shows that the ratio of the bias to the standard error will increase as the number of strata increases. This analysis shows that the bias in the separate-ratio estimate may not be negligible if the number of strata is large. With regard to the variances of the two estimators, it may be noted that a first approximation to the variance of $\hat{Y}_s$ is easy to write down by adding $V(\hat{Y}_h)$ over strata. For the combined-ratio estimator the quantities $\Sigma N_h \bar{y}_h/N$ and $\Sigma N_h \bar{x}_h/N$ take the role of $\bar{y}$ and $\bar{x}$ of Sec. 5.5. Hence a first approximation to the mean square error of $\hat{Y}_c$ is given by

$$\text{MSE } (\hat{Y}_c) \doteq E\left[\sum N_h(\bar{y}_h - R\bar{x}_h)\right]^2$$

$$= \sum \frac{N_h{}^2}{n_h}(1 - f_h)(S_{yh}{}^2 + R^2 S_{xh}{}^2 - 2R\rho_h S_{yh}S_{xh}) \qquad (5.24)$$

As stated before,

$$\text{MSE } (\hat{Y}_s) \doteq \sum \frac{N_h{}^2}{n_h}(1 - f_h)(S_{yh}{}^2 + R_h{}^2 S_{xh}{}^2 - 2R_h\rho_h S_{yh}S_{xh}) \qquad (5.25)$$

The two expressions for the mean square error have the same form. If the strata ratios $R_h$ differ considerably from each other and the sample size within each stratum is reasonably large, the separate-ratio estimate will be better. Otherwise, the combined-ratio estimate should be used.

### Further reading

**1.** When it is considered important to form a type of combined unbiased ratio estimator, the procedure of Exercise 40 may be used.

**2.** When two units are selected from each stratum and the combined-ratio estimator is formed, Exercise 41 presents a short cut to the computation of the variance.

**3.** Exercises 26 and 28 present two methods of forming unbiased ratio estimators in stratified sampling.

**4.** When the strata frames are not available but the strata sizes are known, it is possible to achieve higher precision by making an adjustment to the sample average based on a random sample from the entire population. This is shown in Exercises 22 and 31.

**5.** In case the correlation between $y$ and $x$ is negative, it is advisable to use the product estimator rather than the ratio estimator. The product estimator is considered in Exercise 105.

## REFERENCES

Goodman, L. A. and H. O. Hartley (1958). The precision of unbiased ratio-type estimators. *J. Am. Stat. Assoc.*, 53.

Lahiri, D. B. (1951). A method of sample selection providing unbiased ratio estimates. *Intern. Stat. Inst. Bull.*, 33.

Midzuno, H. (1950). An outline of the theory of sampling systems. *Ann. Inst. Stat. Math.*, 1.

Olkin, I. (1958). Multivariate ratio estimation for finite populations. *Biometrika*, 45.

Raj, D. (1954). Ratio estimation in sampling with equal and unequal probabilities. *J. Ind. Soc. Agr. Stat.*, 6.

—— (1964a). A note on the variance of the ratio estimate. *J. Amer. Stat. Assoc.*, 59.

—— (1964b). On sampling with probability proportionate to aggregate size. *J. Ind. Soc. Agr. Stat.*, 16.

—— (1965). On a method of using multiauxiliary information in sample surveys. *J. Am. Stat. Assoc.*, 60.

# CHAPTER SIX

# SAMPLING AND SUBSAMPLING OF CLUSTERS

## 6.1 INTRODUCTION

We have assumed so far that it is convenient to take a sample of units to be investigated directly from the entire population or from within strata. While this may be true in some kind of surveys, it is generally not so when we are concerned with countrywide investigations. The principal reason is that no usable list (called a frame) of units to be enumerated generally exists from which to select the sample. As an example, suppose it is desired to conduct a sample survey in Greece in which individuals would be asked at the time of interview whether they worked for a living last week. It is not possible to take a simple random or systematic sample of persons from the entire country or from within strata, since there is no such list (verified to be correct) in which the Greek people are numbered from 1 to $N$. And it would be impossible to make such a list. Even if such a list existed, it would not be economical to base the enquiry on a simple random sample of persons because this would require interviewers to visit almost every commune in the country and resources do not permit it. All these considerations point to the need of selecting larger units or clusters, rather than elements (individuals in this case) directly from the population. One way of selecting the sample would be to secure a list of communes (which is readily available), take a probability sample of communes, and enumerate every one in the sample communes. This is called single-stage cluster sampling. (The clusters are communes and the selection is made in one stage only.) Or, instead of interviewing every individual in the commune, we interview only a sample of them. This is called two-stage sampling, since now the sample is selected in two stages—first the communes (called first-stage or primary sampling units), and then the persons within communes. This is also called subsampling, since a further sample (of persons) has been taken from a sample (of communes). A more convenient way of subsampling the commune would be to take a sample of census enumeration districts (ED's) and select a sample of households from each selected ED. This will be three-stage sampling—first the commune, then the ED (second-stage unit), and then the household (third-stage unit). The interviewer visits the households in the sample and collects the information required. The advantages of this procedure are: lists have to be prepared for the selected primary (psu) and subsequent-stage units only; it is easy to check the correctness of the lists; the sample gets concentrated in the selected psu's and this reduces costs of travel, etc.

## 6.2 SINGLE-STAGE CLUSTER SAMPLING

No new principles are involved in making estimates when a probability sample of clusters has been taken and each sample cluster is enumerated completely (i.e., there is no subsampling). A problem to be considered is the optimum size of the cluster. This will naturally depend upon the cost of collecting information from clusters of different size and the resulting variance. We shall begin by proving the following theorem.

### Theorem 6.1

*In simple random sampling of n clusters, each containing M elements, from a population of N clusters, an estimate of the population total Y is given by*

$$\hat{Y} = \frac{N}{n} S y_i = \frac{N}{n} S \sum_i \sum_j y_{ij} \tag{6.1}$$

$$\text{and} \qquad V(\hat{Y}) = \frac{N^2}{n}\left(1 - \frac{n}{N}\right)\frac{1}{N-1}\sum (Y_i - \bar{Y})^2 \tag{6.2}$$

$$= \frac{N^2}{n}\left(1 - \frac{n}{N}\right)\frac{NM - 1}{N - 1} S_y{}^2[1 + (M - 1)\rho] \tag{6.3}$$

*where*
$$\bar{Y} = \frac{1}{N} \sum Y_i = \frac{\Sigma\Sigma Y_{ij}}{N}$$

$$S_y{}^2 = \frac{\Sigma\Sigma(y_{ij} - \bar{Y}_e)^2}{NM - 1} \qquad \bar{Y}_e = \frac{\bar{Y}}{M}$$

*and $\rho$ is the intracluster correlation coefficient (Sec. 1.9) and $y_i = \Sigma y_{ij}$ is the total of $y$ for the $i$th cluster in the sample.*

PROOF  The relations (6.1) and (6.2) are obvious.  To prove (6.3), we have

$$\sum (Y_i - \bar{Y})^2 = \sum \left( \sum y_{ij} - M\bar{Y}_e \right)^2 = \sum \left[ \sum (y_{ij} - \bar{Y}_e) \right]^2$$
$$= \sum \sum (y_{ij} - \bar{Y}_e)^2 + 2 \sum_i \sum_{j<k} (y_{ij} - \bar{Y}_e)(y_{ik} - \bar{Y}_e)$$
$$= (NM - 1)S_y{}^2 + (M - 1)(NM - 1)\rho S_y{}^2$$
$$= (NM - 1)S_y{}^2[1 + (M - 1)\rho]$$

Hence

$$V(\hat{Y}) = \frac{N^2}{n}\left(1 - \frac{n}{N}\right)\frac{NM - 1}{N - 1} S_y{}^2[1 + (M - 1)\rho]$$

$$\doteq \frac{N^2}{n}\left(1 - \frac{n}{N}\right) M S_y{}^2[1 + (M - 1)\rho] \qquad (6.4)$$

■

*Remark*  The variance in cluster sampling depends on the number of clusters in the sample, the variance $S_y{}^2$, the size of the cluster $M$, and the intracluster correlation coefficient $\rho$.

*Remark*  If, instead of sampling in clusters, a simple random sample of $nM$ elements be taken directly from the population,

$$V(\hat{Y}) = \frac{(NM)^2}{nM}\left(1 - \frac{nM}{NM}\right) S_y{}^2$$

$$= \frac{N^2}{n}\left(1 - \frac{n}{N}\right) M S_y{}^2$$

Thus, for the same number of elements in the sample, the relationship between $V_c$ (variance when clusters of size $M$ are taken) and $V_e$ (variance when elements are taken directly) is

$$V_c \doteq [1 + (M - 1)\rho]V_e \qquad (6.5)$$

Generally $\rho$ is positive, since clusters are usually formed by putting together geographically contiguous farms, stores, establishments, families, etc.  Thus for the same number of elements in the sample, cluster sampling will give a higher variance than sampling elements directly. But the real point is that it is far cheaper to collect information on a per-element basis if sampling is done in clusters. If $\rho$ is negative, both cost and the variance point to the use of clusters.

**Remark**   An expression for the intracluster correlation coefficient $\rho$ can be given in terms of

$$NM\sigma^2 = \sum \sum (y_{ij} - \bar{Y}_e)^2$$

$$\sigma_b^2 = \frac{\Sigma(\bar{Y}_i - \bar{Y}_e)^2}{N}$$

and

$$\sigma_w^2 = \frac{\Sigma\Sigma(y_{ij} - \bar{Y}_i)^2}{NM}$$

in which case

$$\sigma^2 = \sigma_b^2 + \sigma_w^2$$

By definition

$$NM(M-1)\rho\sigma^2 = \sum_i \left[ \sum_j (y_{ij} - \bar{Y}_e) \right]^2 - \sum \sum (y_{ij} - \bar{Y}_e)^2$$

$$= NM^2\sigma_b^2 - NM\sigma^2$$

or

$$(M-1)\rho = \frac{M\sigma_b^2 - \sigma^2}{\sigma^2}$$

which means that

$$\rho = \frac{\sigma_b^2 - \sigma^2/M}{(M-1)\sigma^2/M} = \frac{\sigma_b^2 - \sigma_w^2/(M-1)}{\sigma^2} \tag{6.6}$$

**Further reading**

*1.*   See Exercise 43 in which the optimum size of the cluster is found for specified cost and variance functions.
*2.*   When some information on each element is available, Exercise 53 suggests a useful way of forming clusters of two elements each.

### 6.2.1   ESTIMATION OF PROPORTIONS

Suppose it is desired to estimate the proportion of elements belonging to a given class when the population consists of $N$ clusters each of size $M$ and a random sample of $n$ clusters is selected.   Defining $y_{ij}$ as 1 if the $j$th element of the $i$th cluster belongs to the class and 0 otherwise, it is easy to note that $Y_i$ gives the total number of elements in the $i$th cluster belonging to the class.   Hence, the proportion $P$ will be

$$P = \frac{1}{NM} \sum' Y_i = \frac{Y}{NM} \tag{6.7}$$

Applying Theorem 6.1, an unbiased estimate of $P$ is

$$\hat{P} = \frac{1}{NM} \frac{N}{n} Sy_i = \frac{1}{nM} Sy_i = \frac{1}{n} Sp_i$$

$$V(\hat{P}) = \frac{1}{n} \left(1 - \frac{n}{N}\right) \frac{\Sigma(P_i - P)^2}{N - 1} \tag{6.8}$$

since                    $y_i = Mp_i \qquad \bar{Y} = MP$

If, however, a simple random sample of $nM$ elements could be taken, the variance of the sample proportion $p$ would be

$$\frac{1}{nM} \left(1 - \frac{nM}{NM}\right) \frac{NPQ}{N - 1} = \frac{1}{n} \left(1 - \frac{n}{N}\right) \frac{1}{M} \frac{NPQ}{N - 1}$$

In case the cluster size is variable, let $M_i$ be the number of elements in the $i$th cluster.   Then

$$P = \frac{\Sigma Y_i}{\Sigma M_i} \qquad \hat{P} = \frac{Sy_i}{SM_i} \tag{6.9}$$

and a first approximation to the mean square error of $\hat{P}$ is obtained as

$$\text{MSE}(\hat{P}) = \frac{1}{\bar{M}^2} \frac{1}{n} \left(1 - \frac{n}{N}\right) \frac{\Sigma M_i^2 (P_i - P)^2}{N - 1} \tag{6.10}$$

where                    $\bar{M} = \frac{\Sigma M_i}{N} \qquad$ (Sec. 5.5)

### 6.2.2   ESTIMATION OF EFFICIENCY OF CLUSTER SAMPLING

If the sample is selected in clusters, it is possible to estimate from the sample itself the variance that would have been obtained if elementary units had been selected directly from the population without using clusters.   Suppose the cluster size is $M$ and a wtr random sample of $n$ clusters has been selected.   The total of the $i$th cluster is $Y_i = M\bar{Y}_i$. By Theorem 3.2, an unbiased estimate of $V(\hat{Y})$ from cluster sampling is given by

$$N^2 \left(\frac{1}{n} - \frac{1}{N}\right) \frac{S(y_i - \bar{y})^2}{n - 1}$$

where $y_i = M\bar{y}_i$ is the total of the $i$th cluster in the sample and $\bar{y} = (1/n)Sy_i$.   The variance of the population-total estimate based on a simple random sample of $nM$ elements would be

$$V_1(\hat{Y}) = \left(\frac{1}{nM} - \frac{1}{NM}\right) N^2 M^2 \frac{\Sigma\Sigma(y_{ij} - \bar{Y}_e)^2}{NM - 1}$$

$$= M^2 N^2 \left(\frac{1}{nM} - \frac{1}{NM}\right) \frac{\sum\sum (y_{ij} - \bar{Y}_i)^2 + M \sum \left(\bar{Y}_i - \frac{1}{N}\sum \bar{Y}_i\right)^2}{NM - 1}$$

The purpose is to estimate $V_1(\hat{Y})$ from the cluster sample. By Theorem 3.1 the sample mean is an unbiased estimate of the population mean, which gives

$$E\underset{i}{S} \frac{\sum_j (y_{ij} - \bar{y}_i)^2}{n} = \frac{\sum_i \sum_j (y_{ij} - \bar{Y}_i)^2}{N}$$

Similarly, by Theorem 3.2,

$$E\underset{i}{S} \frac{(\bar{y}_i - S\bar{y}_i/n)^2}{n - 1} = \frac{\Sigma(\bar{Y}_i - \Sigma\bar{Y}_i/N)^2}{N - 1}$$

Thus both terms comprising $V_1(\hat{Y})$ can be estimated from the cluster sample if a record is made of observations on all elements included in the sample clusters.


### 6.2.3  OTHER ESTIMATORS IN CLUSTER SAMPLING

The unbiased estimator (6.1) will not be found to be very precise when the cluster sizes vary. This is clear from the expression for its variance, namely

$$V(\hat{Y}) = N^2 \left(\frac{1}{n} - \frac{1}{N}\right) \frac{\Sigma[M_i\bar{Y}_i - (1/N)\Sigma M_i\bar{Y}_i]^2}{N - 1}$$

If the average per element $\bar{Y}_i$ does not differ much from cluster to cluster but the cluster sizes $M_i$ vary considerably, the quantity $M_i\bar{Y}_i$ will be very variable, and thus $V(\hat{Y})$ will be large. In this situation one may use the mean of the means, namely

$$\hat{Y}_1 = \frac{M_0}{n} S\bar{y}_i$$

where $M_0 = \Sigma M_i$ is the total number of elements in the population. This estimator is biased with a bias of $E(\hat{Y}_1) - \Sigma M_i\bar{Y}_i = \Sigma(\bar{M} - M_i)\bar{Y}_i$, where $\bar{M} = M_0/N$ is the average number of elements per cluster. By Theorem 3.1,

$$V(\hat{Y}_1) = M_0^2 \left(\frac{1}{n} - \frac{1}{N}\right) \frac{\Sigma[\bar{Y}_i - (1/N)\Sigma\bar{Y}_i]^2}{N - 1}$$

which would be small if the $\bar{Y}_i$ do not differ much. If the bias in $\hat{Y}_1$ is important, the sampling scheme can be modified so that $\hat{Y}_1$ becomes unbiased. This will happen when the clusters are selected with replacement with probability proportionate to $M_i$. In this situation the variance of $\hat{Y}_1$ would be given by Sec. 3.14. That is, $V(\hat{Y}_1) = M_0 \Sigma M_i (\bar{Y}_i - \bar{Y}_e)^2 / n$, where $\bar{Y}_e$ is the average per element in the population. A comparable estimate would be the ratio estimate $\hat{Y}_2 = (M_0 N S y_i / n) / (N S M_i / n)$. A first approximation to its variance would be (Sec. 5.5)

$$N^2 \left( \frac{1}{n} - \frac{1}{N} \right) \frac{\Sigma M_i^2 (\bar{Y}_i - \bar{Y}_e)^2}{N - 1}$$

the quantity $R = Y/X$ occurring in the variance of the ratio estimate being $\Sigma Y_i / M_0 = \bar{Y}_e$, the population mean per element.

*Further reading* Another method of selecting two different clusters with varying probabilities consists in making two independent selections with pp to $x$ and accepting the sample when both units are different. If the simple average of the means is used as the estimator, its status is studied in Exercise 11.

### 6.3 MULTISTAGE SAMPLING

We now turn to the situation in which the sample clusters are subsampled. The first thing to be understood is the formation of estimates of population totals, means, ratios, and proportions from a given subsampling (or multistage) design. The basic principle is that of building up estimates from the bottom (last stage units) to the top. For example, suppose a commune contains $N$ ED's from which one ED is selected at random. Let the selected ED contain $M$ households from which $m$ are selected at random. Every household in the sample provides information on $y$ (which is, say, expenditure on bread last week). The sample mean $\bar{y} = (1/m) S y_i$ estimates the average expenditure per household in the ED and $M\bar{y}$ estimates the total expenditure on bread in the ED. But since this ED was selected at random from the $N$ in the commune, the estimate of the total in the commune is $N M \bar{y}$. Now suppose that not 1 but $n$ ED's were selected without replacement with equal probabilities and the selected ED's contained $M_1$, $M_2$, . . . , $M_n$ households, respectively, from which random samples of $m_1$, $m_2$, . . . , $m_n$ households were taken. Then, $M_i (1/m_i) S y = M_i \bar{y}_i$ $(i = 1, \ldots , n)$ will estimate the totals of the sample ED's, and therefore $(1/n) S M_i \bar{y}_i$ will estimate the average per ED, and hence $\hat{Y} = (N/n) S M_i \bar{y}_i$ will estimate the total expenditure on bread for the whole commune. We can also estimate the total number of households in the commune. The quantity $(1/n)SM_i$ estimates the average number of households per ED, and hence $\hat{X} = N(1/n)SM_i$ estimates the total number of households. Dividing the estimated expenditure $\hat{Y}$ by $\hat{X}$, we get an estimate of the average expenditure per household. Algebraically, we can find the expectation of $\hat{Y}$ as

$$E(\hat{Y}) = E_1 E_2(\hat{Y}) = E_1 \left[ N \frac{1}{n} SM_i E_2(\bar{y}_i) \right] = E_1 \left( N \frac{1}{n} SM_i \bar{Y}_i \right)$$

$$= E_1 \left( N \frac{1}{n} SY_i \right) = NE_1 \left( \frac{1}{n} SY_i \right) = N\bar{Y} = Y$$

### 6.3.1 CALCULATION OF VARIANCE

The variance of $\hat{Y}$ will be obtained by using the conditional argument. By Theorem 1.8,

$$V(\hat{Y}) = E_1 V_2(\hat{Y}) + V_1 E_2(\hat{Y})$$

Here $E_2$ and $V_2$ represent the conditional expectation and variance over all selections of $m_1, m_2, \ldots, m_n$ households from the ED's which are kept fixed (like strata); $E_1$ and $V_1$ denote similar operations over all possible samples of $n$ ED's from the $N$ in the commune.

Thus

$$E_2(\hat{Y}) = N \frac{1}{n} SY_i$$

$$V_1 E_2(\hat{Y}) = N^2 \left( \frac{1}{n} - \frac{1}{N} \right) S_b^2$$

$$S_b^2 = \frac{\Sigma(Y_i - \bar{Y})^2}{N - 1}$$

$$\bar{Y} = \frac{\Sigma Y_i}{N}$$

$$V_2(\hat{Y}) = \frac{N^2}{n^2} SM_i^2 \left( \frac{1}{m_i} - \frac{1}{M_i} \right) S_{wi}^2$$

$$S_{wi}^2 = \frac{\Sigma(y_{ij} - \bar{Y}_i)^2}{M_i - 1}$$

and

$$E_1 V_2(\hat{Y}) = \frac{N^2}{n} \frac{1}{N} \sum_{i=1}^{N} M_i^2 \left( \frac{1}{m_i} - \frac{1}{M_i} \right) S_{wi}^2$$

This gives

$$V(\hat{Y}) = \frac{N}{n} \sum M_i^2 \left( \frac{1}{m_i} - \frac{1}{M_i} \right) S_{wi}^2 + N^2 \left( \frac{1}{n} - \frac{1}{N} \right) S_b^2$$

We note that $V(\hat{Y})$ in two-stage sampling is the sum of two components. One component comes from the variability of second-stage units within psu's and the other arises from the variance of psu totals. If a direct sample of second-stage units can be taken, the variance of psu totals will not come into the picture.

### 6.3.2 ESTIMATION OF VARIANCE

To continue with the previous illustration, we shall now estimate $V(\hat{Y})$ from the sample. It is natural to try the variance between the estimates of the ED totals. We have

$$ES\left(M_i\bar{y}_i - \frac{1}{n}SM_i\bar{y}_i\right)^2 = E\left[SM_i^2\bar{y}_i^2 - \frac{1}{n}(SM_i\bar{y}_i)^2\right]$$

Using the formula $E(x^2) = E^2(x) + V(x)$, we get

$$ESM_i^2\bar{y}_i^2 = E_1SM_i^2\left[\bar{Y}_i^2 + \left(\frac{1}{m_i} - \frac{1}{M_i}\right)S_{wi}^2\right]$$

$$= \frac{n}{N}\sum Y_i^2 + \frac{n}{N}\sum M_i^2\left(\frac{1}{m_i} - \frac{1}{M_i}\right)S_{wi}^2$$

and $\quad E\frac{1}{n}(SM_i\bar{y}_i)^2 = \frac{1}{n}E_1\left[(SY_i)^2 + SM_i^2\left(\frac{1}{m_i} - \frac{1}{M_i}\right)S_{wi}^2\right]$

$$= n\bar{Y}^2 + n\left(\frac{1}{n} - \frac{1}{N}\right)\frac{\Sigma(Y_i - \bar{Y})^2}{N - 1}$$

$$+ \frac{1}{N}\sum M_i^2\left(\frac{1}{m_i} - \frac{1}{M_i}\right)S_{wi}^2$$

Hence

$$ES\left(M_i\bar{y}_i - \frac{1}{n}SM_i\bar{y}_i\right)^2 = (n - 1)\left[\frac{\Sigma(Y_i - \bar{Y})^2}{N - 1}\right.$$

$$\left. + \frac{1}{N}\sum M_i^2\left(\frac{1}{m_i} - \frac{1}{M_i}\right)S_{wi}^2\right]$$

$$\therefore EN^2\left(\frac{1}{n} - \frac{1}{N}\right)\frac{1}{n - 1}S\left(M_i\bar{y}_i - \frac{1}{n}SM_i\bar{y}_i\right)^2$$

$$= V(\hat{Y}) - \sum M_i^2\left(\frac{1}{m_i} - \frac{1}{M_i}\right)S_{wi}^2$$

But $\quad \sum M_i^2\left(\frac{1}{m_i} - \frac{1}{m_i}\right)S_{wi}^2 \cong \frac{N}{n}SM_i^2\left(\frac{1}{m_i} - \frac{1}{M_i}\right)s_{wi}^2$

Hence $\quad V(\hat{Y}) \cong N^2\left(\frac{1}{n} - \frac{1}{N}\right)\frac{1}{N - 1}S\left(M_i\bar{y}_i - \frac{1}{n}SM_i\bar{y}_i\right)^2$

$$+ \frac{N}{n}SM_i^2\left(\frac{1}{m_i} - \frac{1}{M_i}\right)s_{wi}^2$$

We have therefore proved the following theorem.

### Theorem 6.2

*Let $n$ psu's be selected at random from a population of $N$ psu's. Let random samples of $m_i$ $(i = 1, \ldots, n)$ second-stage units be taken from the $M_i$ $(i = 1, \ldots, n)$ second-stage units in the selected psu's. Then*

$$\hat{Y} = \frac{N}{n} SM_i \bar{y}_i \tag{6.11}$$

$$V(\hat{Y}) = N^2 \left( \frac{1}{n} - \frac{1}{N} \right) S_b{}^2 + \frac{N}{n} \sum M_i{}^2 \left( \frac{1}{m_i} - \frac{1}{M_i} \right) S_{wi}{}^2 \tag{6.12}$$

*and*

$$\hat{V}(\hat{Y}) = N^2 \left( \frac{1}{n} - \frac{1}{N} \right) s_b{}^2 + \frac{N}{n} SM_i{}^2 \left( \frac{1}{m_i} - \frac{1}{M_i} \right) s_{wi}{}^2 \tag{6.13}$$

*where*   $\bar{y}_i = \dfrac{1}{m_i} Sy_{ij}$    $S_b{}^2 = \dfrac{1}{N-1} \sum (Y_i - \bar{Y})^2$    $\bar{Y} = \dfrac{1}{N} \sum Y_i$

$$S_{wi}{}^2 = \frac{1}{M_i - 1} \sum (y_{ij} - \bar{Y}_i)^2 \qquad s_b{}^2 = \frac{1}{n-1} S \left( M_i \bar{y}_i - \frac{1}{n} SM_i \bar{y}_i \right)^2$$

$$s_{wi}{}^2 = \frac{1}{m_i - 1} S(y_{ij} - \bar{y}_i)^2$$

***Remark***   In case the same number of second-stage units is taken in the sample from every psu, $m_i = m$. However, in many practical applications the $m_i$ are determined such that

$$\hat{Y} = \frac{N}{n} S \frac{M_i}{m_i} Sy_{ij} = \frac{1}{k} S S y_{ij}$$

which means that the estimate is made by simply adding the observations from all the psu's. In this case

$$\frac{m_i}{M_i} = \frac{kN}{n}$$

which gives a constant sampling fraction from each psu.

***Remark***   If all psu's have the same number of second-stage units $M$ and a constant number $m$ of them sampled from every sample psu, we have

$$\hat{Y} = \frac{N}{n} \frac{M}{m} SSy_{ij} = \frac{SSy_{ij}}{f_1 f_2} \qquad \text{where} \qquad f_1 = \frac{n}{N}, f_2 = \frac{m}{M}$$

and        $V(\hat{Y}) = N^2 S_b{}^2 \dfrac{1 - f_1}{n} + N^2 M^2 \dfrac{(1 - f_2) S_w{}^2}{mn}$

where $S_w{}^2 = \Sigma S_{wi}{}^2 / N$.

Assume the simple cost function $C = c_1 n + c_2 nm$, in which the two components are proportional to the number of psu's and the number of second-stage units. It is then possible to find the best values of $n$ and $m$ for which $V(\hat{Y})$ is a minimum for a given cost $C$. Using Lagrange's method of undetermined multipliers, we construct the function $G(n,m,\lambda) = V(\hat{Y}) + \lambda(c_1 n + c_2 nm - C)$. Differentiating $G$ with respect to $n$ and $m$, equating the resulting expressions to zero, and eliminating $\lambda$, we have

$$m = MS_w \frac{\sqrt{c_1/c_2}}{(S_b{}^2 - MS_w{}^2)^{1/2}} \qquad (6.14)$$

The best value of $n$ is obtained from the relation $C = c_1 n + c_2 nm$ by the substitution of $m$ from (6.14). Equation (6.14) shows that $m$, the number of second-stage units to be taken from a psu, should be larger if $S_w$, the variability of $y$ within psu's is larger, or the cost per primary unit ($c_1$) is larger, or the cost per secondary unit ($c_2$) is smaller, and if $S_b{}^2$, the variability of psu totals, is smaller.

**Remark**   It must be pointed out that the above analysis holds only when the cost function employed is appropriate.   If travel between psu's is a major component of field costs, a more relevant cost function appears to be (see Exercise 100)

$$C = c_0 \sqrt{n} + c_1 n + c_2 nm$$

since travel between $n$ points (Mahalanobis, 1940; Hansen, et al., 1953) is represented more appropriately by a quantity proportional to $\sqrt{n}$. The simplest cost function, which is not realistic in large scale surveys, would be $C = cnm$.   In this case the cost is simply proportional to the number of second-stage units.   It is obvious from the expression for $V(\hat{Y})$ that, in this situation, $n$ should be as large as possible so that $m = 1$.

### 6.4 SELECTION OF PSU'S WITH UNEQUAL PROBABILITIES

We shall now prove a very general result applicable whenever the psu's are selected without replacement.   Let $\pi_i$ be the probability that psu $U_i$ is in the sample of $n$ out of $N$.   Further, let $\pi_{ij}$ be the probability that both $U_i$ and $U_j$ are in the sample.   Each selected psu is subsampled in a known manner, whatever the number of stages of subsampling be. Let $T_i$ be an unbiased estimator of the $i$th psu total ($Y_i$) based on subsampling at the second and subsequent stages with $V_2(T_i) = \sigma_i{}^2$ and let $E_2(\hat{\sigma}_i{}^2) = \sigma_i{}^2$.   Calling this sampling method scheme $A$, we prove the following theorem.

### Theorem 6.3

*Under scheme A, an unbiased estimator of the population total Y is given by*

$$\hat{Y} = S \frac{T_i}{\pi_i} \tag{6.15}$$

*with*

$$V(\hat{Y}) = \sum' (\pi_i \pi_j - \pi_{ij}) \left( \frac{Y_i}{\pi_i} - \frac{Y_j}{\pi_j} \right)^2 + \sum \frac{\sigma_i^2}{\pi_i} \tag{6.16}$$

*and*

$$V(\hat{Y}) \,\hat{=}\, S' \left( \frac{\pi_i \pi_j - \pi_{ij}}{\pi_{ij}} \right) \left( \frac{T_i}{\pi_i} - \frac{T_j}{\pi_j} \right)^2 + S \frac{\acute{\sigma}_i^2}{\pi_i} \tag{6.17}$$

PROOF

$$E(\hat{Y}) = E_1 S \frac{1}{\pi_i} E_2(T_i) = E_1 S \frac{Y_i}{\pi_i} = Y \qquad \text{by (3.32)}$$

Since $E_2(\hat{Y}) = S Y_i / \pi_i$, $V_1 E_2(\hat{Y}) = \sum' (\pi_i \pi_j - \pi_{ij})(y_i / \pi_i - y_j / \pi_j)^2$. Again

$$V_2(\hat{Y}) = S \frac{\sigma_i^2}{\pi_i^2} \qquad E_1 V_2(\hat{Y}) = \sum \frac{\sigma_i^2}{\pi_i}$$

Hence $V(\hat{Y})$ is obtained as given in (6.16). Again

$$ES' \left( \frac{\pi_i \pi_j - \pi_{ij}}{\pi_{ij}} \right) \left( \frac{T_i}{\pi_i} - \frac{T_j}{\pi_j} \right)^2 = E_1 S' \frac{\pi_i \pi_j - \pi_{ij}}{\pi_{ij}} E_2 \left( \frac{T_i}{\pi_i} - \frac{T_j}{\pi_j} \right)^2$$

But

$$E_2 \left( \frac{T_i}{\pi_i} - \frac{T_j}{\pi_j} \right)^2 = \left( \frac{Y_i}{\pi_i} - \frac{Y_j}{\pi_j} \right)^2 + V_2 \left( \frac{T_i}{\pi_i} - \frac{T_j}{\pi_j} \right)$$

$$= \left( \frac{Y_i}{\pi_i} - \frac{Y_j}{\pi_j} \right)^2 + \left( \frac{\sigma_i^2}{\pi_i^2} + \frac{\sigma_j^2}{\pi_j^2} \right) \tag{6.18}$$

Hence $\quad ES' \left( \frac{\pi_i \pi_j - \pi_{ij}}{\pi_{ij}} \right) \left( \frac{T_i}{\pi_i} - \frac{T_j}{\pi_j} \right)^2 = \sum' (\pi_i \pi_j - \pi_{ij}) \left[ \left( \frac{Y_i}{\pi_i} - \frac{Y_j}{\pi_j} \right)^2 \right.$

$$\left. + \left( \frac{\sigma_i^2}{\pi_i^2} + \frac{\sigma_j^2}{\pi_j^2} \right) \right]$$

Now $\quad \displaystyle\sum_i \sum_{j>i} (\pi_i \pi_j - \pi_{ij}) \left( \frac{\sigma_i^2}{\pi_i^2} + \frac{\sigma_j^2}{\pi_j^2} \right) = \sum_i \sum_{j \neq i} (\pi_i \pi_j - \pi_{ij}) \frac{\sigma_i^2}{\pi_i^2}$

$$= \sum_i \frac{\sigma_i^2}{\pi_i^2} \sum_{j \neq i} \pi_j - \sum \frac{\sigma_i^2}{\pi_i^2} \sum_{j \neq i} \pi_{ij} = \sum (n - \pi_i) \frac{\sigma_i^2}{\pi_i} - (n - 1) \sum \frac{\sigma_i^2}{\pi_i}$$

$$= \sum (1 - \pi_i) \frac{\sigma_i^2}{\pi_i}$$

Hence
$$ES'\left(\frac{\pi_i\pi_j - \pi_{ij}}{\pi_{ij}}\right)\left(\frac{T_i}{\pi_i} - \frac{T_j}{\pi_j}\right)^2 = V(\hat{Y}) - \sum \sigma_i^2$$

But
$$\sum \sigma_i^2 \cong S\frac{\hat{\sigma}_i^2}{\pi_i}$$

Hence $V(\hat{Y})$ is estimated by the expression given in (6.17).    ■

### Corollary

In case of two-stage sampling when selection is simple random at both stages, we have

$$\pi_i = \frac{n}{N}$$

$$\pi_{ij} = \frac{n(n-1)}{N(N-1)}$$

$$T_i = M_i\bar{y}_i$$

$$\sigma_i^2 = V_2(T_i) = M_i^2\left(\frac{1}{m_i} - \frac{1}{M_i}\right)S_{wi}^2$$

$$\hat{\sigma}_i^2 = M_i^2\left(\frac{1}{m_i} - \frac{1}{M_i}\right)s_{wi}^2$$

Substituting these values in formulas (6.15) to (6.17), we prove Theorem 6.2.

**Remark**   Note that the first term in $V(\hat{Y})$ represents the variance in unistage sampling (as if the psu's are measured without error), and the second term gives the contribution to variance from subsampling of the psu's.   The same remarks apply to the estimate of variance.

**Remark**   One of the requirements of this scheme is the existence of unbiased estimators of $\sigma_i^2$.   Hence systematic sampling cannot be used at the second stage if an unbiased estimate of the variance is desired.

**Remark**   A comparison of Eqs. (6.16) and (6.17) suggests a useful method of estimating the variance in multistage designs.   This is proved in Sec. 9.9 and Exercise 56.

### 6.5   SELECTION OF PSU'S WITH REPLACEMENT

Another sampling scheme, which we shall call scheme $B$, consists in selecting a sample of $n$ psu's with replacement with probabilities $p_j$ $(j = 1, 2, \ldots, N)$, $\Sigma p_j = 1$.   An independent subsample is taken from every selection $i$ (whether a repetition or not).   The quantities $T_i$ and

$\sigma_i^2 = V_2(T_i)$ are defined as in scheme $A$ of Sec. 6.4.   We then prove the following theorem.

### Theorem 6.4

*Under scheme B, an unbiased estimator of the population total is given by*

$$\hat{Y} = \frac{1}{n} S \frac{T_i}{p_i} \tag{6.19}$$

$$V(\hat{Y}) = \frac{1}{n} \sum p_i \left( \frac{Y_i}{p_i} - Y \right)^2 + \frac{1}{n} \sum \frac{\sigma_i^2}{p_i} = \frac{1}{n} V \frac{T_i}{p_i} \tag{6.20}$$

*and*

$$V(\hat{Y}) \cong \frac{1}{n(n-1)} S \left( \frac{T_i}{p_i} - \frac{1}{n} S \frac{T_i}{p_i} \right)^2 \tag{6.21}$$

PROOF

$$E(\hat{Y}) = E_1 \frac{1}{n} S \frac{Y_i}{p_i} = Y$$

$V(\hat{Y}) = (1/n)V(T_i/p_i)$ because of independence of random variables $T_i/p_i$ $(i = 1, \ldots, n)$.   But

$$V \frac{T_i}{p_i} = V_1 \left( \frac{Y_i}{p_i} \right) + E_1 \left( \frac{\sigma_i^2}{p_i^2} \right)$$

$$= \frac{1}{n} \sum p_i \left( \frac{Y_i}{p_i} - Y \right)^2 + \sum \frac{\sigma_i^2}{p_i}$$

Hence $V(\hat{Y})$ is given by (6.20).   Again, since the random variables $T_i/p_i$ are independent, we establish from Theorem 3.4 that $V(\hat{Y})$ has an unbiased estimator given by (6.21).                                            ∎

### Corollary

Let the psu's be villages selected with probabilities $p_i$ based on measures of size $x_i$, $\Sigma x_i = X$.   Within a selected psu a simple random sample of $m_i$ households is taken from the $M_i$.   Then

$$T_i = M_i \bar{y}_i \qquad \hat{Y} = \frac{1}{n} S \frac{M_i \bar{y}_i}{p_i}$$

$$V(\hat{Y}) = \frac{1}{n} \sum p_i \left( \frac{Y_i}{p_i} - Y \right)^2 + \frac{1}{n} \sum \frac{M_i^2}{p_i} \left( \frac{1}{m_i} - \frac{1}{M_i} \right) S_{wi}^2$$

The estimator becomes self-weighting if $m_i$ is chosen such that it is proportional to $M_i/p_i$.   If the measure of size $x_i$ is the number of households or the number of persons enumerated at a previous census, the quantity $M_i/p_i$ may be nearly constant. In that case a constant number of households will be taken in the sample from each psu. This is an important requirement in some surveys.

**Remark** An unbiased estimator of the variance is calculable simply from the quantities $T_i/p_i$, and within-psu variances $\sigma_i^2$ need not be estimated. Thus, if desired, systematic sampling could be used at the beginning of the second stage of sampling. For example, in a two-stage design, villages could be selected with pps and households within villages could be selected using systematic sampling.

**Further reading**

**1.** See Exercise 55 for a better estimator based on distinct subunits.
**2.** Instead of subsampling a psu independently $\lambda$ times (the frequency of its occurrence in the sample), it may be better to take a wtr random sample of $m\lambda$ subunits from it. This is done in Exercise 46.
**3.** See Exercise 14, in which it is shown that it may be better to select the random starts in complementary pairs rather than take them independently when sample selection within psu's is systematic.

### 6.5.1 SELECTION WITH REPLACEMENT (SCHEME C)

Instead of subsampling a psu independently every time it enters the sample, it would be cheaper to subsample it only once (like scheme $A$) and weight it by the frequency with which it occurs in the sample (Raj, 1954). If $\lambda_i$ is the number of times $U_i$ appears in the sample, we use the estimator

$$\hat{Y} = \frac{1}{n} \sum_{i=1}^{N} \lambda_i \frac{T_i}{p_i} \tag{6.22}$$

where

$$E(\lambda_i) = np_i \qquad E(\lambda_i^2) = np_i(1 - p_i) + n^2p_i^2 \qquad \text{Cov } (\lambda_i,\lambda_j) = -np_ip_j$$

We have
$$E(\hat{Y}) = E_1 \frac{1}{n} \sum \lambda_i \frac{Y_i}{p_i} = Y$$

And

$$V(\hat{Y}) = E_1 \left( \frac{1}{n^2} \sum \lambda_i^2 \frac{\sigma_i^2}{p_i^2} \right) + V_1 \left( \frac{1}{n} \sum \lambda_i \frac{Y_i}{p_i} \right)$$

$$= \frac{1}{n} \sum \frac{\sigma_i^2}{p_i} + \frac{n-1}{n} \sum \sigma_i^2 + \frac{1}{n} \sum p_i \left( \frac{Y_i}{p_i} - Y \right)^2 \tag{6.23}$$

which is larger than $V(\hat{Y})$ of scheme $B$ (Eq. 6.20).

## 6.6 COMPARISON OF SCHEMES $A$ AND $B$

Let the without-replacement sampling scheme of psu's be such that $\pi_i = np_i$. (An illustration of this is given in Sec. 3.18 where the psu's may be randomized before selection to ensure that no $\pi_{ij}$ is zero.) Then the two unbiased estimators have the same form. The component of variance arising from subsampling of the psu's is also the same in each case. Thus a comparison of the two schemes in multistage sampling reduces to a comparison in unistage sampling, which has been discussed in Sec. 3.23.

### 6.6.1 COMPARISON BASED ON THE SAMPLE

Given the results of a multistage survey in which the psu's have been selected with unequal probabilities without replacement, it is possible to estimate the variance that would have been obtained if the psu's had been selected with replacement (Raj, 1964).

This is done by estimating

$$V_{\mathrm{wr}} = \sum' \frac{\pi_i \pi_j}{n} \left( \frac{Y_i}{\pi_i} - \frac{Y_j}{\pi_j} \right)^2 + \sum \frac{\sigma_i^2}{\pi_i} \tag{6.24}$$

from the sample, where "wr" stands for with-replacement sampling and the $np_i$ of the wr scheme equal $\pi_i$ of the wtr (without-replacement) scheme.

We have

$$ES' \frac{\pi_i \pi_j}{\pi_{ij}} \left( \frac{T_i}{\pi_i} - \frac{T_j}{\pi_j} \right)^2 = E_1 S' \frac{\pi_i \pi_j}{\pi_{ij}} E_2 \left( \frac{T_i}{\pi_i} - \frac{T_j}{\pi_j} \right)^2$$

$$= E_1 S' \frac{\pi_i \pi_j}{\pi_{ij}} \left[ \left( \frac{Y_i}{\pi_i} - \frac{Y_j}{\pi_j} \right)^2 \right.$$

$$\left. + \left( \frac{\sigma_i^2}{\pi_i^2} + \frac{\sigma_j^2}{\pi_j^2} \right) \right] \quad \text{by (6.18)}$$

$$= \sum' \pi_i \pi_j \left( \frac{Y_i}{\pi_i} - \frac{Y_j}{\pi_j} \right)^2 + \sum' \pi_i \pi_j \left( \frac{\sigma_i^2}{\pi_i^2} + \frac{\sigma_j^2}{\pi_j^2} \right)$$

But

$$\sum' \pi_i \pi_j \left( \frac{\sigma_i^2}{\pi_i^2} + \frac{\sigma_j^2}{\pi_j^2} \right) = \sum_i \sum_{j \neq i} \pi_i \pi_j \frac{\sigma_i^2}{\pi_i^2} = \sum \frac{\sigma_i^2}{\pi_i} \sum_{j \neq i} \pi_j$$

$$= \sum \frac{n - \pi_i}{\pi_i} \sigma_i^2$$

Hence

$$\sum' \pi_i \pi_j \left( \frac{Y_i}{\pi_i} - \frac{Y_j}{\pi_j} \right)^2 \cong S' \frac{\pi_i \pi_j}{\pi_{ij}} \left( \frac{T_i}{\pi_i} - \frac{T_j}{\pi_j} \right)^2 - S \frac{n - \pi_i}{\pi_i{}^2} \hat{\sigma}_i{}^2 \quad (6.25)$$

Thus

$$V_{\mathrm{wr}} \cong \frac{1}{n} \left[ S' \frac{\pi_i \pi_j}{\pi_{ij}} \left( \frac{T_i}{\pi_i} - \frac{T_j}{\pi_j} \right)^2 - S \frac{(n - \pi_i)\hat{\sigma}_i{}^2}{\pi_i{}^2} + S \frac{n}{\pi_i{}^2} \hat{\sigma}_i{}^2 \right]$$

$$= \frac{1}{n} \left[ S' \frac{\pi_i \pi_j}{\pi_{ij}} \left( \frac{T_i}{\pi_i} - \frac{T_j}{\pi_j} \right)^2 + S \frac{\hat{\sigma}_i{}^2}{\pi_i} \right]$$

or

$$\hat{V}_{\mathrm{wr}} = \frac{1}{n} \left[ \hat{V}_{\mathrm{wtr}} + S' \left( \frac{T_i}{\pi_i} - \frac{T_j}{\pi_j} \right)^2 \right] \quad (6.26)$$

By comparing $\hat{V}_{\mathrm{wr}}$ with $\hat{V}_{\mathrm{wtr}}$, we can make an estimate of the gain due to the use of without-replacement sampling.

### 6.7 STRATIFIED MULTISTAGE SAMPLING

The theory discussed in the earlier sections is applicable when psu's are selected from a stratum. No new principles are involved when the object is to estimate the total of a population divided up into $L$ strata, and sampling within one stratum is independent of sampling within another. The estimates, as well as the variance, are simply added, and the same holds for variance estimation. For example, suppose $n_h$ psu's are selected without replacement from the $h$th stratum, and a simple random sample of $m_{hi}$ subunits is taken from the $M_{hi}$ contained in the $i$th psu there. Then the population total $Y$ may be estimated by

$$\hat{Y} = \sum_h \left[ S \frac{M_i}{\pi_i} \frac{S y_{ij}}{m_i} \right]_h \quad (6.27)$$

and

$$V(\hat{Y}) = \sum_h \left[ \sum' (\pi_i \pi_j - \pi_{ij}) \left( \frac{Y_i}{\pi_i} - \frac{Y_j}{\pi_j} \right)^2 + \sum \frac{1}{\pi_i} M_i{}^2 \left( \frac{1}{m_i} - \frac{1}{M_i} \right) S_{wi}{}^2 \right]_h$$

$$(6.28)$$

Formulas (6.27) and (6.28) are obtained by setting

$$T_i = M_i \bar{y}_i = \frac{M_i}{m_i} S y_{ij}$$

in Theorem 6.3. An unbiased estimator of $V(\hat{Y})$ is obtained by adding the expression in (6.17) over strata.

It is of great interest to note that a particular choice of the $m_i$ from the $M_i$ subunits makes the estimate $\hat{Y}$ very convenient to calculate. In fact, for

$$\left(\frac{M_i}{\pi_i m_i}\right)_h = \frac{1}{k} \tag{6.29}$$

the estimator becomes

$$\hat{Y} = \frac{1}{k} \sum_h S\,S\, y_{ij} \tag{6.30}$$

which means that observations over the subunits are simply added up without regard to the psu or the stratum to which these belong. As stated before, such an estimator is called "self-weighting." The quantity $k$ admits of a simple interpretation. The number of subunits in the sample form a particular stratum in $Sm_i$. Its expected value is $ESm_i = \Sigma\pi_i m_i = k\Sigma M_i$, from (6.29).

Hence $k = ESm_i/\Sigma M_i =$ expected sampling fraction for subunits. Thus, if it is desired to take into the sample 1 percent of the subunits (on the average) from each stratum, we shall set $k = 1/100$ in (6.29) and ask the field investigator to take a sampling fraction of $1/(100\,\pi_i)$ from the $i$th psu, where $\pi_i$ is known. If different $k$'s are used in different strata, strata estimates would have to be properly weighted.

*Further reading*   See Exercise 47 in which the gain due to stratification is evaluated.

## 6.8 ESTIMATION OF RATIOS

In unistage sampling where the number of units $N$ is known, the mean per unit is simply estimated by dividing the estimate of the population total by $N$. This is different from estimating, say, the average income per household from a two-stage design in which villages are the psu's and households are the second-stage units. The reason is that the total number of households in the population will not be known ordinarily, but will have to be estimated from the sample. Thus the estimator of the mean will assume the form of a ratio of two random variables. If the object is to estimate the ratio of $y$, expenditure on foods, to $x$, expenditure on furniture, the estimator again will be a ratio estimator in which an unbiased estimate is made of $Y$ as well as of $X$. Again, we may wish to use information on $x$ as auxiliary information to improve the estimate of the population total when the sample is selected through several stages. In all these situations ratio estimators will be involved. We now develop theory appropriate to these situations. Two-stage sampling will be considered in which a random sample of $m_i$ subunits is taken from the $M_i$ contained in the $i$th psu which has been selected with probability $\pi_i$ in case of wtr sampling and with probability $p_i$ in a sample of size 1 in case of wr sampling.

### 6.8.1 SAMPLING WITHOUT REPLACEMENT

If the psu's are selected following scheme $A$ of Sec. 6.4, an estimator of $R = Y/X$ will be given by

$$\hat{R} = \frac{S(M_i \bar{y}_i / \pi_i)}{S(M_i \bar{x}_i / \pi_i)} = \frac{\hat{Y}}{\hat{X}} \qquad (6.31)$$

where $\hat{Y}$, $\hat{X}$ are unbiased estimates of $Y$ and $X$, respectively. By using[1] the corollary to Theorem 5.1 (Sec. 5.3), we find that $|B(\hat{R})|/\sigma(\hat{R}) < \mathrm{CV}(\hat{X})$. Hence the bias in $\hat{R}$ will not be important if $\mathrm{CV}(\hat{X})$ is small. The mean square error of $\hat{R}$ about $R$ is $E(\hat{R} - R)^2 = E[(\hat{Y} - R\hat{X})/(X + \theta\, \delta\hat{X})]^2$ evaluated at $\theta = 1$. By setting $\bar{y} = \hat{Y}$ and $\bar{x} = \hat{X}$ in Theorem 5.3, a first approximation to $\mathrm{MSE}(\hat{R})$ is given by

$$\mathrm{MSE}(\hat{R}) \doteq \frac{1}{X^2} E(\hat{Y} - R\hat{X})^2 = \frac{1}{X^2} V(\hat{Y} - R\hat{X})$$

$$= \frac{1}{X^2} V\left[ S\frac{1}{\pi_i} M_i(\bar{y}_i - R\bar{x}_i) \right]$$

Now setting $T_i = M_i(\bar{y}_i - R\bar{x}_i)$ in Theorem 6.3, the variance involved can be calculated and we get

$$X^2 \mathrm{MSE}(\hat{R}) \doteq \sum' (\pi_i \pi_j - \pi_{ij}) \left[ \left( \frac{Y_i}{\pi_i} - \frac{Y_j}{\pi_j} \right) - R\left( \frac{X_i}{\pi_i} - \frac{X_j}{\pi_j} \right) \right]^2$$

$$+ \sum \frac{1}{\pi_i} M_i^2 \left( \frac{1}{m_i} - \frac{1}{M_i} \right) \frac{1}{M_i - 1} \sum_j [y_{ij} - \bar{Y}_i - R(x_{ij} - \bar{X}_i)]^2 \quad (6.32)$$

As an estimate of $\mathrm{MSE}(\hat{R})$ from the sample, we may calculate, on using (6.17), the quantity

$$\frac{1}{\hat{X}^2} \left\{ S' \left( \frac{\pi_i \pi_j - \pi_{ij}}{\pi_{ij}} \right) \left[ \frac{M_i \bar{y}_i}{\pi_i} - \frac{M_j \bar{y}_j}{\pi_j} - \hat{R} \left( \frac{M_i \bar{x}_i}{\pi_i} - \frac{M_j \bar{x}_j}{\pi_j} \right) \right]^2 \right.$$

$$\left. + S\frac{1}{\pi_i} M_i^2 \left( \frac{1}{m_i} - \frac{1}{M_i} \right) \frac{1}{m_i - 1} S[y_{ij} - \bar{y}_i - \hat{R}(x_{ij} - \bar{x}_i)]^2 \right\} \quad (6.33)$$

[1] It may be noted that Theorems 5.1 and 5.3 are quite general, as is shown in Exercise 107.

### Corollary

If the psu's are selected with equal probabilities without replacement, we have $\pi_i\pi_j - \pi_{ij} = (n/N)(1 - n/N)[1/(N - 1)]$

$$\hat{R} = \frac{SM_i\bar{y}_i}{SM_i\bar{x}_i} \tag{6.34}$$

Hence
$$\sum' [Y_i - RX_i - (Y_j - RX_j)]^2 = N \sum (Y_i - RX_i)^2$$

$$\text{MSE}(\hat{R}) \doteq \left(1 - \frac{n}{N}\right) \frac{1}{n\bar{X}^2} \frac{1}{N - 1} \sum (Y_i - RX_i)^2$$

$$+ \frac{1}{nN\bar{X}^2} \sum \frac{M_i^2}{m_i} \left(1 - \frac{m_i}{M_i}\right) S_{ui}^2 \tag{6.35}$$

where $\qquad S_{ui}^2 = \frac{1}{M_i - 1} \sum [y_{ij} - \bar{Y}_i - R(x_{ij} - \bar{X}_i)]^2 \tag{6.36}$

And an estimate of $\text{MSE}(\hat{R})$ from the sample is given by

$$\left(1 - \frac{n}{N}\right) \frac{N^2}{n\hat{X}^2} \frac{1}{n - 1} S(M_i\bar{y}_i - \hat{R}M_i\bar{x}_i)^2$$

$$+ \frac{N}{n\hat{X}^2} S \frac{M_i^2}{m_i} \left(1 - \frac{m_i}{M_i}\right) \frac{1}{m_i - 1} S[y_{ij} - \bar{y}_i - \hat{R}(x_{ij} - \bar{x}_i)]^2 \tag{6.37}$$

In case $m_i/M_i = $ constant, the estimator $\hat{R}$ reduces to the self-weighting form $\hat{R} = SSy_{ij}/SSx_{ij}$.

### Corollary

If the psu's are selected at random to estimate the mean per subunit, the estimator is

$$\hat{R} = \frac{S(M_i\bar{y}_i)}{SM_i} \tag{6.38}$$

This is obtained from (6.34) by substituting $x_{ij} = 1$ in the equation. Then $\bar{x}_i = 1$, $X_i = M_i$ and $R = $ population mean per subunit.

And a first approximation to $\text{MSE}(\hat{R})$ is obtained as

$$\text{MSE}(\hat{R}) = \frac{1 - \dfrac{n}{N}}{n\bar{X}^2} \frac{1}{N - 1} \sum (Y_i - RM_i)^2$$

$$+ \frac{1}{nN\bar{X}^2} \sum \frac{M_i^2}{m_i} \left(1 - \frac{m_i}{M_i}\right) S_{wi}^2 \tag{6.39}$$

where $\qquad S_{wi}^2 = \frac{1}{M_i - 1} \sum (y_{ij} - \bar{Y}_i)^2 \tag{6.40}$

As a sample estimate of the mean square error, we take

$$\left(1 - \frac{n}{N}\right)\frac{N^2}{n\hat{X}^2}\frac{1}{n-1}SM_i^2(\bar{y}_i - \hat{R})^2$$

$$+ \frac{N}{n\hat{X}^2}S\frac{M_i^2}{m_i}\left(1 - \frac{m_i}{M_i}\right)\frac{1}{m_i - 1}S(y_{ij} - \bar{y}_i)^2 \quad (6.41)$$

**Further reading**  See Exercise 49, in which an unbiased estimator of the ratio is obtained from a different design.

### 6.8.2 SAMPLING WITH REPLACEMENT

If the $n$ psu's are selected following scheme $B$ of Sec. 6.5, the estimate of $R$ is

$$\hat{R} = \frac{(1/n)S(M_i/p_i)\bar{y}_i}{(1/n)S(M_i/p_i)\bar{x}_i} = \frac{\hat{Y}}{\hat{X}} \quad (6.42)$$

The bias of $\hat{R}$ will be unimportant relative to its standard error if $CV(\hat{X})$ is small.  As shown in the previous section, a first approximation to $MSE(\hat{R})$ would be given by

$$MSE(\hat{R}) \doteq \frac{1}{X^2}E(\hat{Y} - R\hat{X})^2 = \frac{1}{X^2}V\left[\frac{1}{n}S\frac{1}{p_i}M_i(\bar{y}_i - R\bar{x}_i)\right]$$

Now, setting $T_i = M_i(\bar{y}_i - R\bar{x}_i)$ in Theorem 6.4, we have

$$X^2MSE(\hat{R}) \doteq \frac{1}{n}\sum\frac{1}{p_i}(Y_i - RX_i)^2 + \frac{1}{n}\sum\frac{1}{p_i}\frac{M_i^2}{m_i}\left(1 - \frac{m_i}{M_i}\right)S_{ui}^2 \quad (6.43)$$

where $S_{ui}^2$ is defined by (6.36).  By (6.21) of Theorem 6.4, an estimator of $MSE(\hat{R})$ is

$$\frac{1}{\hat{X}^2}\frac{1}{n(n-1)}S\left(\frac{M_i\bar{y}_i}{p_i} - \hat{R}\frac{M_i\bar{x}_i}{p_i}\right)^2 \quad (6.44)$$

### Corollary

If the object is to estimate the mean per subunit, an unbiased estimate of the total number of subunits is provided by $(1/n)SM_i/p_i$, and hence the mean per subunit is estimated by

$$\hat{R} = \frac{(1/n)S(M_i/p_i)\bar{y}_i}{(1/n)S(M_i/p_i)} \quad (6.45)$$

This can be obtained from (6.42) by setting $x_{ij} = 1$, which gives $\bar{x}_i = 1$, $X_i = M_i$, $X = \Sigma M_i$, and $R$ = population mean per subunit.

Thus a first approximation to the mean square error from (6.43) is

$$\text{MSE}(\hat{R}) \doteq \frac{1}{n(\Sigma M_i)^2} \sum \frac{1}{p_i} (Y_i - RM_i)^2$$

$$+ \frac{1}{n(\Sigma M_i)^2} \sum \frac{M_i^2}{p_i m_i} \left(1 - \frac{m_i}{M_i}\right) S_{wi}^2 \quad (6.46)$$

where $S_{wi}^2$ is given by (6.40). An estimate of $\text{MSE}(\hat{R})$ is provided by

$$\frac{1}{\hat{X}^2} \frac{1}{n(n-1)} S \left[\frac{M_i}{p_i} (\bar{y}_i - \hat{R})\right]^2 \quad (6.47)$$

### 6.8.3 EXTENSION TO STRATIFIED SAMPLING

If a separate ratio estimate is made for each stratum to build up the final population estimate, no new principles are involved, since the variance will be obtained by simple addition over the strata. This will be adequate if sample sizes within strata are large enough for the bias to be negligible and the strata ratios vary considerably from each other. Otherwise, a combined-ratio estimate will be preferred. This procedure will be carried through for scheme $B$, in which the psu's are selected with pps with replacement. An estimate of the population ratio $R$ will be

$$\hat{R} = \frac{\hat{Y}}{\hat{X}} = \frac{\sum \hat{Y}_h}{\sum \hat{X}_h} = \frac{\sum\limits_h \frac{1}{n_h} S \frac{M_{hi}}{p_{hi}} \bar{y}_{hi}}{\sum\limits_h \frac{1}{n_h} S \frac{M_{hi}}{p_{hi}} \bar{x}_{hi}} \quad (6.48)$$

By Theorem 5.1 the bias of $\hat{R}$ will be negligible relative to its standard error when $\text{CV}(\Sigma \hat{X}_h)$ is small. A first approximation to the mean square error of $\hat{R}$ (by Sec. 5.5) will be given by

$$\left(\frac{1}{X^2}\right) E(\hat{Y} - R\hat{X})^2 = \left(\frac{1}{X^2}\right) V \left[\sum_h (\hat{Y}_h - R\hat{X}_h)\right]$$

This shows that the results of Sec. 6.8.2 apply with the difference that addition over strata will be made. Thus we have

$$X^2 \text{MSE}(\hat{R}) \doteq \sum_h \frac{1}{n_h} \sum_i p_{hi} \left(\frac{Y_{hi} - RX_{hi}}{p_{hi}} - Y_h + RX_h\right)^2$$

$$+ \sum_h \frac{1}{n_h} \sum_i \frac{1}{p_{hi}} \frac{M_{hi}^2}{m_{hi}} \left(1 - \frac{m_{hi}}{M_{hi}}\right) S_{hui}^2 \quad (6.49)$$

where

$$S_{hui}^2 = \frac{1}{M_{hi} - 1} \sum [y_{hij} - \bar{Y}_{hi} - R(x_{hij} - \bar{X}_{hi})]^2 \quad (6.50)$$

Further, the mean square error of $\hat{R}$ is estimated by

$$\frac{1}{\hat{X}^2} \sum_h \frac{1}{n_h(n_h - 1)} S \left[ \frac{M_{hi}(\bar{y}_{hi} - \hat{R}\bar{x}_{hi})}{p_{hi}} - \frac{1}{n_h} S \frac{M_{hi}(\bar{y}_{hi} - \hat{R}\bar{x}_{hi})}{p_{hi}} \right]^2 \quad (6.51)$$

*Note* The reader is advised to work out Exercise 45 in which wtr simple random sampling is used at both stages.

### 6.9  CHOICE OF SAMPLING AND SUBSAMPLING FRACTIONS

The question of the number of psu's to select in the sample and the number of subunits to subsample will now be discussed for the two-stage scheme of Sec. 6.5, in which $n$ psu's are selected with replacement with given probabilities $p_i$ and a simple random sample of $m_i$ subunits is taken from the $M_i$ if psu $U_i$ is in the sample. By Theorem 6.4, we have

$$\hat{Y} = \frac{1}{n} S \frac{M_i}{p_i m_i} S y_{ij}$$

$$V(\hat{Y}) = \frac{1}{n} \left[ V_p + \sum \frac{1}{p_i} M_i^2 \left( \frac{1}{m_i} - \frac{1}{M_i} \right) S_{wi}^2 \right] \qquad V_p = \sum p_i \left( \frac{Y_i}{p_i} - Y \right)^2$$

Let $c_1$ be the fixed cost per psu on travel, setting up an office, etc.; $c_2$ be the cost of listing a second-stage unit in a selected psu; and $c_3$ be the cost per second-stage unit of collecting information. Then the cost of the survey would be $nc_1 + c_2 S M_i + c_3 S m_i$, its expected value being

$$C = nc_1 + nc_2 \Sigma p_i M_i + nc_3 \Sigma p_i m_i \qquad (6.52)$$

In order to minimize the variance for a fixed expected budget, we construct the function

$$G = V(\hat{Y}) + \lambda(nc_1 + nc_2 \Sigma p_i M_i + nc_3 \Sigma p_i m_i)$$

The equations based on differentiation with respect to $m_i$ $(i = 1, 2, \ldots, N)$ immediately give

$$m_i \propto \frac{M_i S_{wi}}{p_i} \qquad \text{or} \qquad m_i = \frac{a M_i S_{wi}}{p_i}$$

Since the $p_i$ are known, the only quantities to be determined are $n$ and $na = a'$. Differentiating with respect to $n$ and $a'$, respectively, and equating to zero, we have

$$\frac{a'^2}{n^2} = \frac{c_1 + c_2 \Sigma p_i M_i}{c_3(V_p - \Sigma M_i^2 S_{wi}^2 / p_i)}$$

This gives the value of $a$, from which we get

$$m_i = \left(\frac{c_1 + c_2 \Sigma p_i M_i}{c_3}\right)^{1/2} \frac{M_i S_{wi}}{p_i} \left(V_p - \sum \frac{M_i S_{wi}^2}{p_i}\right)^{-1/2} \quad (6.53)$$

Substituting in the cost function (6.52), the value of $n$ can be obtained. Equation (6.53) leads to a very useful result. Provided $S_{wi}^2$ are not very different, the optimum choice of $m_i$ consists in making it proportional to $M_i/p_i$, in which case the estimator $\hat{Y}$ becomes self-weighting. Thus the self-weighting system is not only very convenient for making computations but is also efficient if the variances $S_{wi}^2$ within psu's are not very different. In case $S_{wi}$ depends directly on $M_i$, stratification by size ($M_i$) would help in making $S_{wi}$ nearly constant within strata.

**Remark**   Another advantage of the self-weighting estimator is that it may give a constant sample size from each sample psu. Thus, the investigators will not be responsible for differing work loads in the different psu's.

**Further reading**   When sampling is simple random at both stages, Exercise 48 suggests that it is better to make the total sample size a random variable.

### 6.9.1  CHOICE OF OPTIMUM PROBABILITIES

In the previous section the probabilities $p_i$ were supposed to be given. We shall now discuss the question of the determination of the best values of $p_i$ as well as the sampling and subsampling fractions. The analysis will be presented for the sampling scheme of Sec. 6.9 when a self-weighting estimator is used for estimating the population ratio $R$ (Hansen and Hurwitz, 1949). By Sec. 6.8.2,

$$\hat{R} = \frac{\dfrac{1}{n} S \dfrac{M_i}{p_i} S \dfrac{y_{ij}}{m_i}}{\dfrac{1}{n} S \dfrac{M_i}{p_i} S \dfrac{x_{ij}}{m_i}}$$

This will become self-weighting if $m_i = kM_i/p_i$. The expected cost will be given by $C = nc_1 + nc_2 \Sigma p_i M_i + nk c_3 \Sigma M_i$. From (6.43),

$$X^2 V(\hat{R}) \doteq \frac{1}{n} \sum \left[\frac{1}{p_i}(Y_i - RX_i)^2 + \frac{1}{p_i} M_i^2 \left(\frac{1}{m_i} - \frac{1}{M_i}\right) S_{ui}^2\right]$$

$$= \frac{1}{n} \sum \left[\frac{M_i^2}{p_i}\left(\bar{U}_i^2 - \frac{S_{ui}^2}{M_i}\right) + \frac{M_i}{k} S_{ui}^2\right]$$

where $u_{ij} = y_{ij} - Rx_{ij}$, $\bar{U}_i = \bar{Y}_i - R\bar{X}_i$ and $S_{ui}{}^2$ is defined by (6.36). Letting $np_i = p_i'$ and $nk = k'$, we have

$$X^2 V(\hat{R}) = \sum \frac{1}{p_i'} M_i{}^2 \left( \bar{U}_i{}^2 - \frac{S_{ui}{}^2}{M_i} \right) + \frac{1}{k'} \sum M_i S_{ui}{}^2$$

and
$$C = nc_1 + c_2 \sum p_i' M_i + k' c_3 \sum M_i$$

Thus the problem is to find $n$, $k'$, and $p_i'$ such that $X^2 V(\hat{R})$ is a minimum for a given value of the expected budget and subject to the condition that $\Sigma p_i' - n = 0$ (or $\Sigma p_i = 1$). For this purpose we construct

$$G = X^2 V(\hat{R}) + \lambda(nc_i + c_2 \Sigma p_i' M_i + c_3 k' \Sigma M_i - C) + \mu(\Sigma p_i' - n)$$

Equating $\partial G/\partial n$ and $\partial G/\partial p_i'$ to zero, we have

$$\lambda c_1 - \mu = 0$$

$$- \frac{M_i{}^2}{p_i'^2} D_{ui}{}^2 + \lambda c_2 M_i + \mu = 0 \qquad D_{ui}{}^2 = \bar{U}_i{}^2 - \frac{S_{ui}{}^2}{M_i}$$

From these equations we get

$$\lambda p_i'^2 = \frac{M_i{}^2 D_{ui}{}^2}{c_1 + c_2 M_i}$$

or
$$p_i = \frac{M_i D_{ui}/\sqrt{c_1 + c_2 M_i}}{\Sigma M_i D_{ui}/\sqrt{c_1 + c_2 M_i}} \qquad (6.54)$$

Now
$$\sum_i D_{ui}{}^2 = \sum (\bar{Y}_i - R\bar{X}_i)^2$$

$$- \sum \frac{1}{M_i} \frac{1}{M_i - 1} \sum [y_{ij} - \bar{Y}_i - R(x_{ij} - \bar{X}_i)]^2$$

If the psu sizes $M_i$ are all equal to $M$, we find from (6.6) that $\Sigma D_{ui}{}^2$ is proportional to the intra-psu correlation coefficient $\rho_M$ applied to the variate $y_{ij} - Rx_{ij}$. We are going to assume that $\rho_M$ is positive. It is generally found that $\rho_M$ tends to decrease with increasing $M$, since an increase in the size of the cluster brings about greater heterogeneity. Substituting for $D_{ui}{}^2$ its average value, we have from (6.54)

$$p_i \propto \frac{M_i \sqrt{E(D_{ui}{}^2)}}{(c_1 + c_2 M_i)^{1/2}}$$

If $E(D_{ui}{}^2)$ is assumed to be constant, we find that $p_i \propto M_i$ if $c_2 M_i$, the cost of listing the psu, is negligibly small as compared with $c_1$, the fixed cost per psu. If, however, $c_1$ is negligibly small as compared with $c_2 M_i$, $p_i$ would be proportional to the square root of $M_i$. If we assume that

$E(D_{ui}{}^2) \propto 1/M_i$, the corresponding results in the two situations are $p_i \propto \sqrt{M_i}$, and $p_i =$ a constant. Having determined the $p_i$, it is a simple matter to put down expressions for the optimum values of $n$ and $k$.

## 6.10  SOME USEFUL MULTISTAGE DESIGNS

A number of multistage designs which have become popular or are likely to be increasingly used will now be described. In a number of national surveys the population is stratified thoroughly to the point that only one or two psu's are selected from each stratum. Each sample psu is sub-sampled in a manner depending on the type of material available (like maps, airphotographs, lists, etc.) for subdividing it. Thus the discussion will be restricted to the selection of psu's from within strata. The quantity $T_i$ will denote an unbiased estimator of the $i$th psu total based on subsampling.

### 6.10.1  RANDOMIZED SYSTEMATIC SAMPLING OF PSU'S

In this procedure (Sec. 3.18) the psu's are listed at random and their measures of size (like population, area, number of stores at the last census) are cumulated. If $n$ psu's are to be selected from a stratum with total measure of size $X$, a random number is taken between 1 and $k = X/n$. The psu's in the sample are those in whose range lie the random number $i$ and all other numbers $i + k$, $i + 2k$, . . . obtained by adding $k$ successively to $i$. It is obvious that with this procedure $\pi_i = nX_i/X$, which is exactly proportional to $X_i$. The estimate of the population total, its variance, and an estimate of variance can be obtained with the help of Theorem 6.3. The one point to be mentioned here is the calculation of $\pi_{ij}$ in order to make an unbiased estimate of the variance. If the number of psu's in the stratum is small, such as 4 or 5, $\pi_{ij}$ for the two units in the stratum can be calculated by listing all possible arrangements of the psu's and calculating $\pi_{ij}$ for each arrangement (by finding out which random numbers out of the $k$ would pick up both $U_i$ and $U_j$). If $N$, the number of psu's in a stratum, is large, Hartley and Rao (1962) give approximate expressions for $\pi_{ij}$ which are based on expansions in inverse powers of $N$. This design was used by Raj (1964) in Greece for collecting employment/unemployment statistics.

### 6.10.2  ONE PSU PER STRATUM

If a large number of strata must be used, only one psu per stratum can be taken. The selection will be made with probability proportional to some measure of size. The estimate and the variance will be given by formulas

(6.19) and (6.20) with $n = 1$. A conservative estimate of the variance can be made by grouping the strata in pairs and calculating

$$A_j = \left(\frac{T_{j1}}{p_{j1}} - \frac{T_{j2}}{p_{j2}}\right)^2 = (\bar{Y}_{j1} - \bar{Y}_{j2})^2$$

from the $j$th pair. The expected value of $A_j$ would be

$$E(A_j) = V\frac{T_{j1}}{p_{j1}} + V\frac{T_{j2}}{p_{j2}} + (Y_{j1} - Y_{j2})^2$$

so that $\Sigma A_j$ will overstate the true variance $\Sigma V(T_i/p_i)$. The overstatement could be controlled by pairing those strata (in advance of the survey) which have approximately the same total for the character under study. This design is being used by the United States Bureau of the Census for collecting data on employment and unemployment.

### 6.10.3 ONE PSU PER RANDOMIZED SUBSTRATUM

In this method the stratum is divided up into $n$ substrata by allocation of the psu's at random to them. (As will be seen, the number of psu's per substratum should be about the same.) One psu is selected with pps from each substratum. This gives a sample of $n$ psu's selected without replacement with pps. This procedure is due to Rao, Hartley, and Cochran (1962). Suppose the stratum is divided up into $n$ substrata containing $N_i$ $(i = 1, \ldots, n)$ psu's. Let $X_i$ be the measure of size of the $i$th substratum ($X_i$ is a random variable). Then the estimator of the stratum total $Y$, in single-stage sampling is

$$\hat{Y} = \sum_{i=1}^{n} X_i \frac{y_{ij}}{x_{ij}}$$

For a given subdivision of the stratum into substrata, we have

$$E\left(X_i \frac{y_{ij}}{x_{ij}}\right) = E\frac{y_{ij}}{p'_{ij}} = Y_i$$

so that $E(\hat{Y}) = \sum_i Y_i = Y$. Also $V_1 E_2(\hat{Y}) = 0$.

And

$$V_2(\hat{Y}) = \sum_i^n \sum_j \frac{x_{ij}}{X_i}\left(\frac{y_{ij}}{x_{ij}/X_i} - Y_i\right)^2$$

$$= \sum_1^n \sum_{j<k}^{N_i} \frac{x_{ij}}{X_i}\frac{x_{ik}}{X_i}\left(\frac{y_{ij}}{x_{ij}/X_i} - \frac{y_{ik}}{x_{ik}/X_i}\right)^2 \qquad \text{by (3.23)}$$

$$= \sum_1^n \sum_{j<k} x_{ij}x_{ik}\left(\frac{y_{ij}}{x_{ij}} - \frac{y_{ik}}{x_{ik}}\right)^2$$

Now the probability that two specified units belong to the $i$th substratum is $(N_i/N)[(N_i - 1)/(N - 1)]$.  Hence

$$E_1 V_2(\hat{Y}) = \sum_{i=1}^{n} \frac{N_i}{N} \frac{N_i - 1}{N - 1} \sum_{\mu > \lambda}^{N} x_\lambda x_\mu \left( \frac{y_\lambda}{x_\lambda} - \frac{y_\mu}{x_\mu} \right)^2$$

or $$V(\hat{Y}) = \frac{\Sigma N_i^2 - N}{N(N - 1)} \sum_{1}^{N} p_i \left( \frac{y_i}{p_i} - Y \right)^2$$

This shows that for best results the $N_i$ should be equal.  In that case

$$V(\hat{Y}) = \left( 1 - \frac{n - 1}{N - 1} \right) \frac{1}{n} \sum p_i \left( \frac{y_i}{p_i} - Y \right)^2 = \left( 1 - \frac{n - 1}{N - 1} \right) V_{\text{pps}}$$

where $V_{\text{pps}}$ stands for the variance when sampling is with pps with replacement.

In the multistage case, let $T_{ij}$ be an unbiased estimator of the $j$th psu total in the $i$th substratum with $V(T_{ij}) = \sigma_{ij}^2$.  Then an unbiased estimator of the population total will be (Raj, 1966a)

$$\hat{Y} = \sum_{1}^{n} X_i \frac{T_{ij}}{x_{ij}}$$

and its variance will be given by

$$V(\hat{Y}) = \frac{\Sigma N_i^2 - N}{N(N - 1)} \sum p_i \left( \frac{Y_i}{p_i} - Y \right)^2 + E \sum_{1}^{n} X_i^2 \frac{\sigma_{ij}^2}{x_{ij}^2}$$

Now $$E \sum X_i^2 \frac{\sigma_{ij}^2}{x_{ij}^2} = E_1 \sum_{1}^{n} X_i \sum_{j} \frac{\sigma_{ij}^2}{x_{ij}} = \sum \frac{N_i(N - N_i)}{N(N - 1)} \sum \sum \sigma_{ij}^2$$

$$+ \sum \frac{N_i(N_i - 1)}{N(N - 1)} \sum \sum \frac{\sigma_{ij}^2}{x_{ij}/X_i}$$

since in random samples of size $N_i$ from a population of size $N$, the expected value of $Sx_i S(y_i/x_i)$ is, from first principles, given by $[1/N(N - 1)][N_i(N - N_i)\Sigma y_i + N_i(N_i - 1)X\Sigma(y_i/x_i)]$.

Hence $$V(\hat{Y}) = \frac{\Sigma N_i^2 - N}{N(N - 1)} \sum p_i \left( \frac{Y_i}{p_i} - Y \right)^2 + \frac{N^2 - \Sigma N_i^2}{N(N - 1)} \sum \sigma_i^2$$

$$+ \frac{\Sigma N_i^2 - N}{N(N - 1)} \sum \frac{\sigma_i^2}{p_i}$$

***Further reading***   For a method of estimating the variance, refer to Exercise 16(a) and Exercise 54.   A general method of estimating the variance is presented in Sec. 9.9.

### 6.10.4  PSU'S SELECTED WITH PPS OF REMAINDER

In this method the first psu in the sample is selected with pps and the second with pps of the remaining psu's, and so on (Sec. 3.24).   Considering the practical situation of $n = 2$ psu's per stratum, the following are unbiased estimators of the stratum total (Raj, 1956, 1966b)

$$Z_1 = \frac{T_1}{p_1} \qquad Z_2 = T_1 + \frac{T_2}{p_2}(1 - p_1) \qquad Z = \frac{1}{2}(Z_1 + Z_2)$$

To find the variance of $Z_i$, we have

$$V_1 E_2 \frac{T_1}{p_1} = V(t_1)$$

where the $t_i$'s are defined in Sec. 3.24.

$$E_1 V_2 \left( \frac{T_1}{p_1} \right) = E_1 \frac{\sigma_1{}^2}{p_1{}^2} = \sum \frac{\sigma_i{}^2}{p_i}$$

Hence
$$V(Z_1) = V(t_1) + \sum \frac{\sigma_i{}^2}{p_i}$$

Similarly,
$$V(Z_2) = V(t_2) + E\left[ \sigma_1{}^2 + \frac{\sigma_2{}^2}{p_2{}^2}(1 - p_1)^2 \right]$$

But

$$E\left[ \sigma_1{}^2 + \frac{\sigma_2{}^2}{p_2{}^2}(1 - p_1)^2 \right] = E_1\left[ \sigma_1{}^2 + \sum \frac{\sigma_j{}^2}{p_j}(1 - p_1) \right]$$

$$= p_1\left[ \sigma_1{}^2 + (1 - p_1)\sum \frac{\sigma_j{}^2}{p_j} \right]$$

$$+ p_2\left[ \sigma_2{}^2 + (1 - p_2)\sum \frac{\sigma_j{}^2}{p_j} \right] + \cdots$$

$$= \sum \left( 2p_i - 1 + \frac{1 - A}{p_i} \right)\sigma_i{}^2 \qquad A = \sum p_i{}^2$$

Hence
$$V(Z_2) = V(t_2) + \sum \left( 2p_i - 1 + \frac{1 - A}{p_i} \right)\sigma_i{}^2$$

Also
$$\text{Cov}(Z_1, Z_2) = \Sigma\sigma_i{}^2$$

Hence

$$V(Z) = \frac{1}{4}\left[ V(t_1) + V(t_2) + \sum \frac{\sigma_i^2}{p_i} + \sum \left( 2p_i - 1 + \frac{1 - A}{p_i} \right) \sigma_i^2 \right.$$

$$\left. + 2 \sum' \sigma_i^2 \right] = \sum \left( 1 - \frac{p_i + p_j}{2} \right) \frac{p_i p_j}{2} \left( \frac{Y_i}{p_i} - \frac{Y_j}{p_j} \right)^2$$

$$+ \frac{1}{4} \sum \left( 1 + 2p_i - \frac{A - 2}{p_i} \right) \sigma_i^2$$

Note the correction factor $1 - (p_i + p_j)/2$, which brings down the between-psu contribution to the variance. An unbiased estimator of $V(Z)$ is
found to be

$$\frac{1}{4}(1 - p_1)^2 \left( \frac{T_1}{p_1} - \frac{T_2}{p_2} \right)^2 + \frac{1 + p_1}{p_1} \hat{\sigma}_1^2 + \frac{1 - p_1}{p_2} \hat{\sigma}_2^2$$

It may also be noted that the estimator $Z$ becomes self-weighting of the
form $(1/k)SSy_{ij}$ if

$$\frac{M_1}{m_1} = \frac{2p_1}{k(1 + p_1)} \qquad \frac{M_2}{m_2} = \frac{2p_2}{k(1 - p_1)}$$

when $m_i$ second-stage units are selected at random from the $M_i$ second-
stage units in the $i$th psu in a two-stage sample.

**Remark**  It can be proved (Exercise 51) that $V(Z_2)$ is smaller than
$V(Z_1)$.

**Further reading**

**1.**  See Exercise 50 for an alternative estimator.
**2.**  For an alternative but equivalent sampling scheme, refer to Exercise
44 and Exercises 18 and 19.
**3.**  For another sampling scheme see Exercise 52 where the sample of
psu's is selected with probability proportionate to its aggregate measure
of size.

REFERENCES

Hansen, M. H. and W. N. Hurwitz (1949).  On the determination of the optimum probabilities in sampling.  *Ann. Math. Stat.*, 20.

——— W. N. Hurwitz, and W. G. Madow (1953).  "Sample Survey Methods
and Theory."  John Wiley & Sons, Inc., New York.

Hartley, H. O. and J. N. K. Rao (1962).  Sampling with unequal probabilities
without replacement.  *Ann. Math. Stat.*, 33.

Mahalanobis, P. C. (1940). A sample survey of the acreage under jute in Bengal. *Sankhya*, 4.

Raj, D. (1954). On sampling with varying probabilities in multistage designs. *Ganita*, 5.

——— (1956). Some estimators in sampling with varying probabilities without replacement. *J. Am. Stat. Assoc.*, 51.

——— (1964). The use of systematic sampling with probability proportionate to size in a large scale survey. *J. Am. Stat. Assoc.*, 59.

——— (1966a). Some remarks on a simple procedure of sampling without replacement. *J. Am. Stat. Assoc.*, 61.

——— (1966b). On a method of sampling with unequal probabilities. *Ganita*, 17.

Rao, J. N. K., H. O. Hartley, and W. G. Cochran (1962). A simple procedure of unequal probability sampling without replacement. *J. Roy. Stat. Soc.*, B 24.

# CHAPTER SEVEN

# DOUBLE-SAMPLING PROCEDURES AND REPETITIVE SURVEYS

## 7.1 INTRODUCTION

Numerous examples have been given in the previous chapters to show how the available auxiliary information could be used to achieve greater precision. However if auxiliary information is not available but can be collected rather inexpensively on a somewhat large scale, it may pay to collect such information in the first instance and then take a sample for the measurement of $y$, the character under study. As an example, suppose it is considered desirable to select a sample of agricultural holdings with probability proportionate to area, but information on area is not available. We may then decide to take an initial random sample of holdings and collect information on their areas (say, by asking the holders) and then take a subsample of holdings with probability proportionate to area and collect information on the characters under study from this subsample. No doubt, within the allowable budget, the size of the second sample will be reduced from that originally planned, but the use of areas in selecting the second sample may more than compensate for the reduction in sample size. There are several ways of using the initial sample. It may be employed for introducing a desirable stratification or for making a good estimate of $X$ for purposes of ratio, regression, or difference estimation. The main point of departure from previous theory is that the sample is now taken in two phases—first an initial sample and then a second sample. That is why this procedure is called double sampling or two-phase sampling. Several examples of the application of this technique in sampling work will now be presented.

## 7.2 DOUBLE SAMPLING FOR DIFFERENCE ESTIMATION

In order to estimate the population mean for $y$, it may be considered important to use the method of differences although information on $x$ is not available. Then an initial random sample of size $n'$ is selected without replacement and information on $x$ is collected. The second sample is a subsample of size $n$ taken without replacement from the first sample and $y$ is measured on it. Let $k$ denote a good guess of the ratio of $y$ to $x$ in the population. Then the following estimator is used for estimating $\bar{Y}$ (Raj, 1965a):

$$\hat{\mu} = \bar{y} - k\bar{x} + k\bar{x}' \tag{7.1}$$

where $\bar{y}$, $\bar{x}$ are the sample means for the subsample and $\bar{x}'$ is the mean of $x$ in the initial sample. Given the initial sample,

$$E_2(\bar{y} - k\bar{x} + k\bar{x}') = \bar{y}'$$

and $E_1(\bar{y}') = \bar{Y}$. Hence the estimator used is unbiased for $\bar{Y}$. For the variance of $\hat{\mu}$, we have

$$V_1 E_2(\hat{\mu}) = V_1(\bar{y}') = \frac{1}{n'}\left(1 - \frac{n'}{N}\right)S_y{}^2 \tag{7.2}$$

$$E_1 V_2(\hat{\mu}) = E_1 \frac{1}{n}\left(1 - \frac{n}{n'}\right)\sum_1^{n'} \frac{(y_i - kx_i - \bar{y}' + k\bar{x}')^2}{n' - 1}$$

$$= \frac{1}{n}\left(1 - \frac{n}{n'}\right)\sum_1^N \frac{(y_i - kx_i - \bar{Y} + k\bar{X})^2}{N - 1} \tag{7.3}$$

$$= \frac{1}{n}\left(1 - \frac{n}{n'}\right)(S_y{}^2 + k^2 S_x{}^2 - 2k\rho S_x S_y)$$

Hence

$$V(\hat{\mu}) = \left(\frac{1}{n} - \frac{1}{N}\right)S_y{}^2 - \left(\frac{1}{n} - \frac{1}{n'}\right)kS_x(2\rho S_y - kS_x) \tag{7.4}$$

If $c'$ and $c$ denote the unit costs of collecting information on $x$ and $y$, respectively ($c'$ will usually be much smaller than $c$), the total cost of the double-sampling procedure would be

$$C = c'n' + cn \qquad (7.5)$$

If a straight random sample is taken (without using the double-sampling procedure) for $y$, the sample size for the same cost will be

$$n_0 = \frac{c'n' + cn}{c} = n + \frac{c'n'}{c}$$

and the variance of the sample mean will be

$$\left(\frac{1}{n_0} - \frac{1}{N}\right)S_y^2$$

Denoting $kS_x/S_y$ by $h$, the condition that the double-sampling technique is the more precise of the two will be found to be

$$2\rho - h > 1 \bigg/ \left[h\left(1 - \frac{n}{n'}\right)\left(1 + \frac{nc}{n'c'}\right)\right] \qquad (7.6)$$

As an example, let $k$ be the regression coefficient $\rho S_y/S_x$, $h = \rho$. Further, let $n/n' = \frac{1}{10}$ and $nc/n'c' = 4$. Then the condition is that the correlation between $y$ and $x$ be higher than 0.47.

**Remark** By finding unbiased estimates of the expressions in (7.2) and (7.3), we can easily find an unbiased estimator of the variance [given by Eq. (7.4)] to be

$$\hat{V}(\hat{\mu}) = \left(\frac{1}{n'} - \frac{1}{N}\right)s_y^2 + \left(\frac{1}{n} - \frac{1}{n'}\right)s_d^2 \qquad (7.7)$$

where $\quad s_y^2 = \frac{1}{n-1}\overset{n}{\underset{1}{S}}(y_i - \bar{y})^2 \qquad s_d^2 = \frac{1}{n-1}\overset{n}{\underset{1}{S}}[y_i - \bar{y} - k(x_i - \bar{x})]^2$

**Further reading** Say that information is collected on not just one but several $x$-variates in the initial sample. Then Exercise 58 shows how this information may be used for achieving higher precision.

## 7.2.1 INDEPENDENT SAMPLES

The case in which the second sample is taken independently of the initial large sample will now be considered. This is done when, for instance, information on $x$ is available with one agency and information on both $y$ and $x$ on a small independent sample has been collected by another agency. It is possible to make use of the information collected by both agencies for improving the estimate of the mean of $y$. The estimator given in (7.1) will again be unbiased. This is so because

$$E(\bar{y} - k\bar{x}) = \bar{Y} - k\bar{X} \quad \text{and} \quad E(k\bar{x}') = k\bar{X}$$

Since the two samples are taken independently, the variance of $\hat{\mu}$ is given by the sum of the variances of $\bar{y} - k\bar{x}$ and $k\bar{x}'$. Thus

$$V(\hat{\mu}) = \left(\frac{1}{n} - \frac{1}{N}\right)(S_y^2 + k^2 S_x^2 - 2k\rho S_x S_y) + k^2\left(\frac{1}{n'} - \frac{1}{N}\right)S_x^2 \quad (7.8)$$

By the same argument, an unbiased estimator of the variance would be

$$\left(\frac{1}{n} - \frac{1}{N}\right)s_d^2 + k^2\left(\frac{1}{n'} - \frac{1}{N}\right)s_x^2$$

where $s_x^2 = \sum_1^{n'} (x_i - \bar{x}')^2/(n' - 1)$.

### 7.3　DOUBLE SAMPLING FOR PPS ESTIMATION

We now come to the case mentioned in Sec. 7.1 in which it is considered desirable to select the sample with pp to $x$ but information on $x$ is not available. This information is then collected from an initial sample (simple random) of size $n'$ from which a subsample of size $n$ is selected with replacement with pp to $x$. Then we prove the following theorem (Raj, 1964).

#### Theorem 7.1

*When the initial sample of size $n'$ is simple random and the subsample of size $n$ is selected with pp to $x$, the population total is estimated by*

$$\hat{Y} = \frac{N}{n'}\frac{x'}{n}\, \mathop{S}_1^n \frac{y_i}{x_i} \qquad x' = \mathop{S}_1^{n'} x_i \qquad (7.9)$$

*with*

$$V(\hat{Y}) = \frac{N}{N-1}\frac{n'-1}{nn'}V_p(y) + N\frac{N-n'}{n'}S_y^2 \qquad (7.10)$$

$$\widehat{=} \frac{N^2}{n'^2}\frac{x'^2}{n(n-1)}\left[S\frac{y_i^2}{x_i^2} - \frac{1}{n}\left(S\frac{y_i}{x_i}\right)^2\right]$$

$$+ \frac{N(N-n')}{nn'(n'-1)}\left\{x'S\frac{y_i^2}{x_i} - \frac{x'^2}{n'}\frac{1}{(n-1)}\left[\left(S\frac{y_i}{x_i}\right)^2 - S\frac{y_i^2}{x_i^2}\right]\right\} \qquad (7.11)$$

*where*

$$V_p(y) = \sum \frac{x_i}{X}\left(\frac{y_i}{x_i/X} - Y\right)^2$$

PROOF  Given the initial sample, $E[(x'/n)S(y_i/x_i)] = y'$ so that $E(\hat{Y}) = E(N\bar{y}') = Y$. Regarding the variance of $\hat{Y}$,

$$E_2(\hat{Y}) = N\bar{y}' \qquad V_1E_2(\hat{Y}) = N^2\left(\frac{1}{n'} - \frac{1}{N}\right)S_y^2$$

$$V_2(\hat{Y}) = \frac{N^2}{n'^2}\frac{1}{n}\sum_1^{n'}\frac{x_i}{x'}\left(\frac{y_i}{x_i/x'} - y'\right)^2 = \frac{N^2}{n'^2}\frac{1}{n}\sum_{i=1}^{n'}\sum_{i<j}x_ix_j\left(\frac{y_i}{x_i} - \frac{y_j}{x_j}\right)^2$$

$$E_1V_2(\hat{Y}) = \frac{N^2}{n'^2}\frac{1}{n}\frac{n'(n'-1)}{N(N-1)}\sum_{i=1}^{N}\sum_{j>i}x_ix_j\left(\frac{y_i}{x_i} - \frac{y_j}{x_j}\right)^2$$

since the probability of a specified pair of units being selected in the sample is $n'(n'-1)/N(N-1)$.

Hence
$$E_1V_2(\hat{Y}) = \frac{N}{N-1}\frac{n'-1}{nn'}V_p(y)$$

This proves (7.10).  In order to get an unbiased estimator of the variance, we note that given the first sample, $(1/n)\overset{n}{\underset{1}{S}}(y_i^2/p_i)$ estimates $\overset{n'}{\underset{1}{S}}y_i^2$,

and $S'(y_i/p_i)(y_j/p_j)\big/\binom{n}{2}$ estimates $\left(\overset{n'}{\underset{1}{S}}y_i\right)^2$, from which we get that $\overset{n'}{\underset{1}{S}}(y_i - \bar{y})^2/(n'-1)$ is estimated by

$$\frac{\dfrac{1}{n}S\dfrac{y_i^2}{p_i} - \dfrac{2}{n'n(n-1)}S'\dfrac{y_i\,y_j}{p_i\,p_j}}{n'-1}$$

But $E_1\overset{n'}{\underset{1}{S}}(y_i - \bar{y})^2/(n'-1) = S_y^2$.  Hence $V_1E_2(\hat{Y})$ can be estimated from the sample.  Noting that

$$E_1V_2(\hat{Y}) \cong \frac{N^2}{n'^2}\frac{1}{n(n-1)}S\left(x'\frac{y_i}{x_i} - \frac{x'}{n}S\frac{y_i}{x_i}\right)^2$$

the proof of (7.11) is complete.                                    ∎

### Corollary

For the cost function considered in Sec. 7.2, double sampling for pps estimation will be superior to one-sample simple random sampling if

$$V_p(y) < \frac{n'-n_0}{n'-1}\frac{n}{n_0}N(N-1)S_y^2 \tag{7.12}$$

It may be noted that $V_p(y)$ is the variance of $\hat{Y}$ based on a pps sample of size unity, while $N(N-1)S_y^2$ is a similar quantity based on a simple random sample. And $(n'-n_0)/(n'-1) < 1$, $n/n_0 < 1$. Thus inequality (7.12) will be satisfied when a pps sample is far better than a simple random sample.

**Further reading**   See Exercise 59 for a generalization to multistage sampling.

### 7.3.1 THE CASE OF INDEPENDENT SAMPLES

In this case the first sample is used solely for estimating $X$. An independent sample of size $n$ is selected with pps using the procedure described in Sec. 3.8 [due to Lahiri (1951)], in which it is not necessary to know $X$.

**Theorem 7.2**

*When the first sample is simple random and the second sample is independently selected with* pp *to* $x$,

$$\hat{Y} = \hat{X}\hat{R} = \left(\frac{N}{n'}x'\right)\left(\frac{1}{n}S\frac{y_i}{x_i}\right) \tag{7.13}$$

$$V(\hat{Y}) = \left(\frac{1}{n'} - \frac{1}{N}\right)N^2R^2S_x^2 + \frac{1}{n}V_p(y)\left[1 + \left(\frac{1}{n'} - \frac{1}{N}\right)\frac{S_x^2}{\bar{X}^2}\right] \tag{7.14}$$

*and an unbiased estimator of* $V(\hat{Y})$ *is given by*

$$V(\hat{Y}) \cong \frac{N^2}{n(n-1)n'}S\left(\frac{y_i}{x_i} - \hat{R}\right)^2\left[\frac{x'^2}{n'} - \left(1 - \frac{n'}{N}\right)s_x^2\right]$$

$$+ \left(\frac{1}{n}S\frac{y_i}{x_i}\right)^2 N^2\left(\frac{1}{n'} - \frac{1}{N}\right)s_x^2 \tag{7.15}$$

PROOF   Since $E(\hat{X}) = X$ and $E(\hat{R}) = Y/X = R$, we have $E(\hat{Y}) = Y$. In order to find the variance of $\hat{Y}$ we make use of the result (Sec. 1.5) relating to the variance of the product of two random variables.

We have   $V(\hat{X}) = N^2\left(\frac{1}{n'} - \frac{1}{N}\right)S_x^2$    $V(\hat{R}) = \frac{1}{X^2}\frac{1}{n}V_p(y)$

Hence   $V(\hat{Y}) = X^2\frac{1}{nX^2}V_p(y) + R^2N^2\left(\frac{1}{n'} - \frac{1}{N}\right)S_x^2$

$$+ N^2\left(\frac{1}{n'} - \frac{1}{N}\right)\frac{1}{nX^2}S_x^2V_p(y) = \left(\frac{1}{n'} - \frac{1}{N}\right)N^2R^2S_x^2$$

$$+ \frac{1}{n}V_p(y)\left[1 + \left(\frac{1}{n'} - \frac{1}{N}\right)\frac{S_x^2}{\bar{X}^2}\right]$$

Again, an unbiased estimator of $V(\hat{X})$ is

$$\hat{V}(\hat{X}) = N^2 \left(\frac{1}{n'} - \frac{1}{N}\right) s_x^2 \qquad s_x^2 = \frac{1}{n' - 1} S(x_i - \bar{x}')^2$$

and an unbiased estimator of $V(\hat{R})$ is

$$\hat{V}(\hat{R}) = \frac{1}{n(n - 1)} S\left(\frac{y_i}{x_i} - \hat{R}\right)^2$$

Hence, by the same result (Sec. 1.5), we have

$$V(\hat{Y}) \cong \hat{X}^2 \hat{V}(\hat{R}) + \hat{R}^2 \hat{V}(\hat{X}) - \hat{V}(\hat{R})\hat{V}(\hat{X})$$

which is the same as the expression given in (7.15). ■

## 7.4 DOUBLE SAMPLING WITH PPS SELECTION

In the situations considered so far the initial sample was always taken with equal probabilities in the absence of any auxiliary information. In case information on a character $z$ is available, we may select the initial sample $A_1$ with probabilities $p_i$ ($i = 1, \ldots, N$) proportionate to $z$ and collect information on $x$. The second sample is a subsample of $A_1$, selected with equal probabilities without replacement in which information on $y$ is collected. We then prove (Raj, 1965b) the following theorem.

### Theorem 7.3

*When the initial sample is selected with pp to $z$ and the second sample is a simple random subsample,*

$$\hat{Y} = \frac{1}{n} S_1^n \frac{y_i}{p_i} - \frac{k}{n} S_1^n \frac{x_i}{p_i} + \frac{k}{n'} S_1^{n'} \frac{x_i}{p_i} \tag{7.16}$$

$$V(\hat{Y}) = \frac{1}{n} V_p(y) + \left(\frac{1}{n} - \frac{1}{n'}\right) [k^2 V_p(x) - 2k\delta\sigma_p(y)\sigma_p(x)] \tag{7.17}$$

$$\hat{V}(\hat{Y}) = \frac{1}{n'(n' - 1)} S_1^n \left(\frac{y_i}{p_i} - \frac{1}{n} S \frac{y_i}{p_i}\right)^2$$

$$+ \left(\frac{1}{n} - \frac{1}{n'}\right) \frac{1}{n - 1} S_1^n \left(\frac{d_i}{p_i} - \frac{1}{n} S \frac{d_i}{p_i}\right)^2 \tag{7.18}$$

*where* $d_i = y_i - kx_i$

$$V_p(x) = \sum p_i \left( \frac{x_i}{p_i} - X \right)^2$$

$$\delta = \frac{\sum p_i \left( \frac{y_i}{p_i} - Y \right) \left( \frac{x_i}{p_i} - X \right)}{\left[ \sum p_i \left( \frac{y_i}{p_i} - Y \right)^2 \sum p_i \left( \frac{x_i}{p_i} - X \right)^2 \right]^{\frac{1}{2}}} = \rho \left( \frac{y}{p}, \frac{x}{p} \right) \qquad (7.19)$$

PROOF   Given $A_1$, $E_2(\hat{Y}) = (1/n') \overset{n'}{\underset{1}{S}} (y_i/p_i)$ so that $E(\hat{Y}) = Y$, and

$$V_1 E_2(\hat{Y}) = \frac{1}{n'} V_p(y)$$

where $V_p(y) = \sum p_i \left( \frac{y_i}{p_i} - Y \right)^2$. Now

$$V_2(\hat{Y}) = \left( \frac{1}{n} - \frac{1}{n'} \right) \frac{1}{n'-1} \sum_{1}^{n'} \left( \frac{y_i - kx_i}{p_i} - \frac{1}{n'} \sum_{1}^{n'} \frac{y_i - kx_i}{p_i} \right)^2$$

since we take a random sample of $n$ from $n'$. And

$$E_1 V_2(\hat{Y}) = \left( \frac{1}{n} - \frac{1}{n'} \right) \sum p_i \left[ \frac{y_i - kx_i}{p_i} - (Y - kX) \right]^2$$

$$= \left( \frac{1}{n} - \frac{1}{n'} \right) [V_p(y) + k^2 V_p(x) - 2k\delta\sigma_p(y)\sigma_p(x)]$$

This proves the expression for the variance of $\hat{Y}$. Regarding the question of making an unbiased estimate of variance, we note that

$$E \frac{1}{n-1} \overset{n}{\underset{1}{S}} \left( \frac{y_i}{p_i} - \frac{1}{n} S \frac{y_i}{p_i} \right)^2 = V_p(y)$$

and      $E \frac{1}{n-1} \overset{n}{\underset{1}{S}} \left( \frac{d_i}{p_i} - \frac{1}{n} S \frac{d_i}{p_i} \right)^2 = \sum p_i \left[ \frac{d_i}{p_i} - (Y - kX) \right]^2$

Hence the estimator given in (7.18) is unbiased for $V(\hat{Y})$.   ∎

## Corollary

Under the cost function (7.5) it is possible to find the condition in which the double-sampling procedure would be preferable to taking a single sample of size $n_0$ with pp to $z$.   Denoting $k\sigma_p(x)/\sigma_p(y)$ by $h$, the condition is

$$2\delta - h > \left[ h\left(1 - \frac{n}{n'}\right)\left(1 + \frac{nc}{n'c'}\right)\right]^{-1} \tag{7.20}$$

### 7.4.1  INDEPENDENT SAMPLES

If the two samples are selected independently, both with pp to $z$, it is fairly simple to see that an unbiased estimator of the population total $Y$ is given by

$$\hat{Y} = \left(\frac{1}{n}\overset{n}{\underset{1}{S}}\frac{y_i}{p_i} - \frac{k}{n}\overset{n}{\underset{1}{S}}\frac{x_i}{p_i}\right) + \frac{k}{n'}\overset{n'}{\underset{1}{S}}\frac{x_i}{p_i} \tag{7.21}$$

where the terms in the bracket come from the second sample.   The variance of $\hat{Y}$ now is

$$V(\hat{Y}) = \frac{1}{n}\left[V_p(y) + k^2 V_p(x) - 2k\delta\sigma_p(y)\sigma_p(x)\right] + \frac{k^2}{n'}V_p(x) \tag{7.22}$$

and an unbiased estimator will be found to be

$$\hat{V}(\hat{Y}) = \frac{k^2}{n'}\frac{1}{n'-1}\overset{n'}{\underset{1}{S}}\left(\frac{x_i}{p_i} - \frac{1}{n}S\frac{x_i}{p_i}\right)^2$$

$$+ \frac{1}{n(n-1)}\overset{n}{\underset{1}{S}}\left(\frac{d_i}{p_i} - \frac{1}{n}S\frac{d_i}{p_i}\right)^2 \tag{7.23}$$

### 7.5  DOUBLE SAMPLING FOR UNBIASED RATIO ESTIMATION

In most of the applications of the double-sampling technique presented so far, the method of difference estimation has been used and pps sampling carried out with replacement.   We will now illustrate the use of the ratio method.   In order to get unbiased estimates the technique of sampling with pp to aggregate size will be used.   The initial sample is simple random and the second sample is taken from it with pp to aggregate $x$, a variate measured in the first sample.   The proposed estimator for $Y$ is

$$\hat{Y} = N\frac{\bar{y}}{\bar{x}}\bar{x}' \tag{7.24}$$

where $\bar{y}$, $\bar{x}$, and $\bar{x}'$ are defined in Sec. 7.2.   Given the initial sample,

$$E_2\frac{\bar{y}}{\bar{x}} = \frac{\bar{y}'}{\bar{x}'} \quad \text{so that} \quad E(\hat{Y}) = Y$$

The expectation of $(\bar{y}\bar{x}'/\bar{x})^2$ can be calculated from first principles as (Raj, 1954b)

$$\left[ n\binom{n'}{n}\binom{N}{n'} \right]^{-1} \sum^{'''} \bar{x}' \sum^{''} \frac{(Sy_i)^2}{Sx_i}$$

where $\sum^{''}$ denotes summation over all possible samples of size $n$ from an initial sample of size $n'$ and $\sum^{'''}$ denotes summation over all possible samples of size $n'$ from the population of size $N$. Hence

$$V(\hat{Y}) = N^2 \left[ n\binom{n'}{n}\binom{N}{n'} \right]^{-1} \sum^{'''} \bar{x}' \sum^{''} \frac{(Sy_i)^2}{Sx_i} - Y^2 \qquad (7.25)$$

To get an unbiased estimator of the variance we note that

$$E\left( \frac{Sy_i^2}{Sx_i} \bar{x}' \right) = \frac{1}{N} \sum_1^N Y_i^2$$

$$E\left( \frac{S'y_iy_j}{Sx_i} \bar{x}' \right) = \frac{n-1}{N(N-1)} \left( \sum{}' Y_iY_j \right)$$

from which we estimate $Y^2 = \sum Y_i^2 + 2\sum{}' Y_iY_j$ as

$$G = N\bar{x}' \left( \frac{Sy_i^2}{Sx_i} + 2\frac{N-1}{n-1}\frac{S'y_iy_j}{Sx_i} \right) \qquad (7.26)$$

Hence an unbiased estimator of $V(\hat{Y})$ is given by

$$V(\hat{Y}) \cong (\hat{Y})^2 - G \qquad (7.27)$$

**Further reading**  See Exercise 60 for an unbiased ratio-type estimator.

## 7.6 DOUBLE SAMPLING FOR BIASED RATIO ESTIMATION

Instead of selecting a subsample with pp to aggregate $x$, one could take a simple random sample (as in Sec. 7.2) and use the familiar biased ratio estimator

$$\hat{M} = \frac{\bar{y}}{\bar{x}} \bar{x}' \qquad (7.28)$$

appropriate to this scheme. By applying Theorem 5.1, we have

$$E\left( \frac{\bar{y}}{\bar{x}} \bar{x}' \right) = \bar{Y} - E_1 \operatorname{Cov}\left( \frac{\bar{y}}{\bar{x}}, \bar{x}|\bar{x}' \right) \qquad (7.29)$$

which gives a formal expression for the bias of $\hat{M}$. In case the two samples are independent, the bias in $\hat{M}$ is the same as that in the usual ratio estimator applicable to single-phase sampling. With the help of Theorem 5.3, a first approximation to the mean square error of $\hat{M}$ will be obtained as

$$\text{MSE}(\hat{M}) = \frac{1}{\bar{X}^2} E(\bar{y}\bar{x}' - \bar{Y}\bar{x})^2 = \frac{N^2}{X^2} V(\bar{y}\bar{x}' - \bar{Y}\bar{x})$$

Now, applying the result (Sec. 1.5), which gives the variance of the product of two independent random variables, we have

$$V(\bar{y}\bar{x}') = \bar{X}^2 \left(\frac{1}{n} - \frac{1}{N}\right) S_y^2 + \bar{Y}^2 \left(\frac{1}{n'} - \frac{1}{N}\right) S_x^2$$

$$+ \left(\frac{1}{n} - \frac{1}{N}\right)\left(\frac{1}{n'} - \frac{1}{N}\right) S_x^2 S_y^2$$

And $V(\bar{Y}\bar{x}) = \bar{Y}^2 \left(\frac{1}{n} - \frac{1}{N}\right) S_x^2$    $\text{Cov}(\bar{y}\bar{x}',\bar{x}) = \bar{X}\left(\frac{1}{n} - \frac{1}{N}\right)\rho S_x S_y$

Thus

$$\text{MSE}(\hat{M}) \doteq \left(\frac{1}{n} - \frac{1}{N}\right)(S_y^2 - 2R\rho S_x S_y + R^2 S_x^2) + \left(\frac{1}{n'} - \frac{1}{N}\right) R^2 S_x^2$$

$$+ \left(\frac{1}{n} - \frac{1}{N}\right)\left(\frac{1}{n'} - \frac{1}{N}\right) S_y^2 \frac{S_x^2}{\bar{X}^2} \quad (7.30)$$

Neglecting the last term on the right-hand side of (7.30), which would be quite small, we obtain an approximate expression for $\text{MSE}(\hat{M})$, which agrees with Cochran (1963). An exact expression for the variance of the estimator can be obtained by treating $\bar{y}/\bar{x}$ and $\bar{x}'$ as two independent random variables and using Eq. (1.18). When the second sample is a subsample of the first, the random variables $\bar{y}/\bar{x}$ and $\bar{x}'$ are dependent. In this case the result given in Exercise 84 applies. It will be found that an approximate expression for the mean square error is

$$\text{MSE}(\hat{M}) \doteq \left(\frac{1}{n} - \frac{1}{N}\right)(S_y^2 - 2R\rho S_y S_x + R^2 S_x^2)$$

$$+ \left(\frac{1}{n'} - \frac{1}{N}\right)(2R\rho S_y S_x - R^2 S_x^2) \quad (7.31)$$

## 7.6.1 COMPARISON WITH THE DIFFERENCE ESTIMATOR

A comparison can now be made between double sampling for difference estimation and double sampling for ratio estimation when both samples are simple random. It will be found from (7.4), (7.8), (7.30), and (7.31) that the exact variance of the difference estimator is the same as the first (large-sample) approximation to the variance of the ratio estimator provided that $k$ of the difference estimator equals $R = Y/X$.

In case the initial sample is selected with replacement with pps and the subsample is selected with equal probabilities without replacement, the variance of the difference estimator is given by (7.17). On the other hand, the variance of the biased ratio estimator when both samples are simple random is given approximately by $N^2$ times the expression in (7.31). The two variances can be compared on the assumption that $k = R$ and that the sampling fractions are small. It will be found that the superiority of double sampling with pps selection to double sampling for biased ratio estimation lies in the selection of the first sample with unequal probabilities. The same remarks apply whether or not the two samples are independent.

### 7.7 DOUBLE SAMPLING FOR REGRESSION ESTIMATION

With the selection procedure of Sec. 7.6 we may use the regression estimator in place of the ratio estimator. The first sample is a random sample of size $n'$ from which a subsample of size $n = n'\lambda$ is taken for measuring $y$. Based on this subsample the regression coefficient $b$ is calculated, as well as $\bar{y}$ and $\bar{x}$. The double-sampling regression estimator of $\bar{Y}$ is then

$$\hat{M} = \bar{y} - b(\bar{x} - \bar{x}') \tag{7.32}$$

where $\bar{x}'$ is the mean of the initial sample. We shall obtain a large-sample approximation for the variance of this estimator. It would be convenient to write $\bar{x}'$ as $\lambda\bar{x} + \mu\bar{x}''$, where $\mu = 1 - \lambda$ and $\bar{x}''$ is the mean of the $n'\mu$ units in the first sample not common with the second sample. Then $\hat{M} = \bar{y} - \mu b(\bar{x} - \bar{x}'')$. If $n$ is large, the distribution of $\hat{M}$ will be the same as that of (Sec. 5.14)

$$\bar{y} - \mu B(\bar{x} - \bar{x}'') \qquad B = \rho S_y/S_x$$

Hence the large-sample variance of $\hat{M}$ is given by

$$V(\hat{M}) = \frac{S_y{}^2}{n'\lambda} + \mu^2 B^2 \left(\frac{1}{n'\lambda} + \frac{1}{n'\mu}\right) S_x{}^2 - 2\mu B \frac{\rho S_y S_x}{n'\lambda}$$

$$= \frac{S_y{}^2}{n'\lambda}[(1 - \rho^2) + \lambda\rho^2] = \frac{S_y{}^2(1 - \rho^2)}{n} + \frac{\rho^2 S_y{}^2}{n'}$$

$$= \frac{S_y{}^2}{n} - \frac{\rho^2 S_y{}^2 \left(1 - \dfrac{n}{n'}\right)}{n} \tag{7.33}$$

This expression for the variance shows that the double-sampling method would be better than taking a direct sample of $n$ for $y$. Using the simple cost function given by (7.5), it is possible to find the best value of $n/n'$ by calculus methods. It will be found that $n/n' = [(1 - \rho^2)/\rho^2(c'/c)]^{\frac{1}{2}}$, and for this subsampling rate the minimum variance is

$$V_{\min} = \frac{S_y{}^2[\rho \sqrt{c'} + \sqrt{(1 - \rho^2)}c]^2}{C}$$

Thus the condition under which the double-sampling method is better than taking a direct sample for $y$, for the same cost, is

$$\rho^2 > \frac{4cc'}{(c + c')^2} \tag{7.34}$$

## 7.8  DOUBLE SAMPLING FOR STRATIFICATION

If it is considered desirable to introduce a stratification with respect to $x$, an initial sample is taken to collect information on $x$. On the basis of this the sample units are allocated to the $L$ strata desired to be made. If the initial sample is simple random, the number of units $n'_h$ falling in the $h$th stratum would be a random variable. From $n'_h$ a simple random subsample of size $n_h$ is taken to collect information on $y$. It is obvious that the $n_h$ units in the $h$th stratum form a simple random sample of the $N_h$ (unknown) in the stratum. Denoting by $\bar{y}_h$ the sample mean for $y$, we have

$$E(\bar{y}_h) = \bar{Y}_h \qquad V(\bar{y}_h) = \left(\frac{1}{n_h} - \frac{1}{N_h}\right)S_h{}^2$$

Denoting $n'_h/n'$ by $a_h$ and using the method developed in Sec. 1.8, it is easy to establish that

$$E(a_h) = \frac{N_h}{N} = W_h \qquad V(a_h) = bW_h(1 - W_h)$$

$$b = \frac{N}{N - 1}\left(\frac{1}{n'} - \frac{1}{N}\right) \qquad \text{Cov}(a_h, a_k) = -bW_hW_k$$

As an estimator of the population mean we take

$$\hat{M} = \Sigma a_h\bar{y}_h \tag{7.35}$$

Since $E\Sigma a_h\bar{y}_h = E_1\Sigma a_h\bar{Y}_h = \Sigma W_h\bar{Y}_h$, the estimator is unbiased. To find its variance, we have

$$V_2(\hat{M}) = \Sigma a_h{}^2 V(\bar{y}_h)$$
$$E_1 V_2(\hat{M}) = \Sigma V(\bar{y}_h)[bW_h(1 - W_h) + W_h{}^2]$$
$$E_2(\hat{M}) = \Sigma a_h \bar{Y}_h$$
$$V_1 E_2(\hat{M}) = b\Sigma \bar{Y}_h{}^2 W_h(1 - W_h) - b\sum_h \sum_{k \neq h} \bar{Y}_h \bar{Y}_k W_h W_k$$
$$= b\Sigma W_h \bar{Y}_h{}^2 - b(\Sigma W_h{}^2 \bar{Y}_h{}^2 + \Sigma\Sigma W_h \bar{Y}_h W_k \bar{Y}_k)$$
$$= b\Sigma W_h \bar{Y}_h{}^2 - b(\Sigma W_h \bar{Y}_h)^2 = b\Sigma W_h(\bar{Y}_h - \bar{Y})^2$$

Hence

$$V(\hat{M}) = \sum \left(\frac{1}{n_h} - \frac{1}{N_h}\right) W_h{}^2 S_h{}^2 + b \sum W_h(1 - W_h) \left(\frac{1}{n_h} - \frac{1}{N_h}\right) S_h{}^2$$
$$+ b \sum W_h(\bar{Y}_h - \bar{Y})^2 \quad (7.36)$$

**Remark**  If information on $x$ is already available for the entire population, the variance obtained from a stratified random sample would be the
first term in (7.36).   The other terms in $V(\hat{M})$ represent the price to be
paid when stratification has to be introduced on the basis of a preliminary
sample.   In the latter case the strata weights will have to be estimated
from the sample.

**Remark**  For large $N$, $b$ is approximately $1/n'$.   For $n_h \propto W_h$, the variance of the double-sampling procedure is approximately given by

$$\frac{1}{n} \sum W_h S_h{}^2 + \frac{1}{n'} \sum W_h(\bar{Y}_h - \bar{Y})^2$$

For the cost function of Sec. 7.2, the variance from the single-sampling
procedure would be approximately given by

$$\frac{1}{n_0} \sum W_h S_h{}^2 + \frac{1}{n_0} \sum W_h(\bar{Y}_h - \bar{Y})^2$$

Thus the between-strata contribution to the variance would be considerably smaller with the double-sampling procedure.

**Remark**  The estimator of the variance is obtained in Exercise 57.


## 7.9 REPETITIVE SURVEYS

The discussion presented so far in this book relates to what may be called
one-time surveys.   When data on some items have been collected on a

population of $N$ units, the matter ends there. But many surveys these days are repetitive in character. Most governments collect information regularly on the same population to find out, say, the number unemployed, their characteristics, and so on. Such surveys present certain novel features; these features will form the subject matter of the remainder of this chapter. The reason for discussing repetitive surveys is that they have certain similarities to double-sampling procedures. Say that a first sample has been taken (on one occasion) and a second sample is to be taken (on another occasion). There is thus an opportunity of making use of the information contained in the first sample. The problem is how best to learn from past experience and use it for improving the precision of future estimates. Actually earlier estimates too can be revised in the light of new experience. Estimates can be made not only for the existing time period (*current estimates*) but also of the change that has taken place since the previous occasion (*estimates of change*) and of the average over a given period (*estimates of sum*). An interesting question to consider is: Should the same sample be used every time, or a completely new sample, or a mixture of the old and the new? Although the answer does not depend solely on the variances involved, we shall make a beginning by illustrating how the sample on the first occasion could possibly be used to form estimates on the second occasion.

### 7.9.1 SAMPLING OVER TWO OCCASIONS

A population is sampled over two occasions for making current estimates of a character, say, unemployment. On the first occasion a simple random sample of $n$ units is taken. A random subsample of $m = n\lambda$ units is retained (matched) for use on a second occasion, on which another independent random sample of $u = n - m = n\mu$ units is selected (unmatched with the first occasion). For simplicity we shall denote by $y$ and $x$ the measurements on the second and first occasions, respectively. The finite population corrections will be neglected, and the variate will be assumed to have the same variance $S^2$ on each occasion. The mean on occasion $h$ will be denoted by $M_h$. The mean on the first occasion will be estimated by $(1/n) \overset{n}{\underset{1}{S}} x_i$. For estimating $M_2$, two independent estimates can be made. One is $\hat{M}_{2u} = (1/u) \overset{u}{\underset{1}{S}} y_i$, which is based on the unmatched part, and the other is the difference estimator

$$\hat{M}_{2m} = \left( \frac{1}{m} \overset{m}{\underset{1}{S}} y_i - \frac{1}{m} \overset{m}{\underset{1}{S}} x_i \right) + \frac{1}{n} \overset{n}{\underset{1}{S}} x_i \qquad (7.37)$$

which is based on the matched part. Given the sample selected on the first occasion

$$E_2(\hat{M}_{2m}) = \frac{1}{n} Sy_i - \frac{1}{n} Sx_i + \frac{1}{n} Sx_i = \frac{1}{n} Sy_i$$

Hence

$$E(\hat{M}_{2m}) = E_1 \left( \frac{1}{n} Sy_i \right) = M_2$$

which shows that $\hat{M}_{2m}$ is an unbiased estimator of $M_2$. The two estimators $\hat{M}_{2u}$ and $\hat{M}_{2m}$ could be weighted inversely to their variances if we wished to find an improved estimator of $M_2$. We have

$$V(\hat{M}_1) = \frac{S^2}{n} \qquad\qquad V(\hat{M}_{2u}) = \frac{S^2}{u} = \frac{S^2}{n\mu}$$

$$E_2(\hat{M}_{2m}) = \frac{1}{n} Sy_i \qquad V_1 E_2(\hat{M}_{2m}) = \frac{S^2}{n}$$

$$V_2(\hat{M}_{2m}) = \left( \frac{1}{m} - \frac{1}{n} \right) \frac{1}{n-1} \overset{n}{\underset{1}{S}} \left[ y_i - x_i - \frac{1}{n} S(y_i - x_i) \right]^2$$

$$E_1 V_2(\hat{M}_{2m}) = \left( \frac{1}{m} - \frac{1}{n} \right) \frac{1}{N-1} \sum [(y_i - M_2) - (x_i - M_1)]^2$$

$$= \left( \frac{1}{m} - \frac{1}{n} \right) (S^2 + S^2 - 2\rho S^2) = \frac{2(1-\lambda)}{n\lambda} S^2(1-\rho)$$

Hence

$$V(\hat{M}_{2m}) = \frac{S^2}{n\lambda} [1 + (1-\lambda)(1-2\rho)] \qquad (7.38)$$

The estimates and their variances on the second occasion may thus be exhibited as below:

|  | Estimate | Variance |  |
|---|---|---|---|
| Unmatched part | $\hat{M}_{2u}$ | $\dfrac{S^2}{n\mu}$ | $= 1/W_{2u}$ |
| Matched part | $\hat{M}_{2m}$ | $\dfrac{S^2}{n\lambda} [1 + (1-\lambda)(1-2\rho)]$ | $= 1/W_{2m}$ |

By weighting the two estimates inversely to their variances, we have

$$\hat{M}_2 = \frac{W_{2u}\hat{M}_{2u} + W_{2m}\hat{M}_{2m}}{W_{2u} + W_{2m}} \qquad (7.39)$$

$$V(\hat{M}_2) = (W_{2u} + W_{2m})^{-1} = \frac{S^2}{n} [1 + (1-2\rho)\mu][1 + (1-2\rho)\mu^2]^{-1} \qquad (7.40)$$

In order to determine the best value of $\mu$ [which minimizes $V(\hat{M}_2)$], we differentiate $V(\hat{M}_2)$ with respect to $\mu$ and equate it to zero. This gives

$$\mu = \frac{1}{1 + \sqrt{2}\sqrt{1 - \rho}} \qquad \lambda = \frac{\sqrt{2}\sqrt{1 - \rho}}{1 + \sqrt{2}\sqrt{1 - \rho}} \qquad (7.41)$$

The minimum variance is found to be

$$V_{\min}(\hat{M}_2) = \frac{S^2}{2n}(1 + \sqrt{2}\sqrt{1 - \rho}) = \frac{S^2}{n}\left(\frac{1}{2} + \sqrt{\frac{1 - \rho}{2}}\right) \qquad (7.42)$$

If a completely independent sample is taken on the second occasion, the estimate will be $\hat{M}_2 = (1/n)Sy_i$, with a variance of $S^2/n$, which is greater than $V_{\min}$ for $\rho > \frac{1}{2}$. If the same sample is taken on the second occasion, the variance will again be $S^2/n$. Thus, for making current estimates (using the difference estimator) the best policy is to replace the sample partially.

The optimum percent to match and the relative gain in precision compared with no matching are given in Table 7.1 for different values of $\rho$. It is found that with this estimator no more than 50 percent should be matched and that this percentage decreases as $\rho$ increases. For low values of $\rho$ the gain in precision is quite small.

**Table 7.1  Comparison of matched and unmatched samples**

| $\rho$ | Optimum % to match | % gain in precision relative to no matching |
|---|---|---|
| 0.5 | 50 | 0 |
| 0.6 | 47 | 6 |
| 0.7 | 44 | 13 |
| 0.8 | 39 | 23 |
| 0.9 | 31 | 38 |
| 0.95 | 24 | 52 |
| 1.00 | 0 | 100 |

*Further reading*  Suppose a sample $A_1$ of $n$ clusters is selected on the first occasion with probabilities proportionate to size. On the second occasion a simple random sample of $m$ clusters is selected without replacement from $A_1$ and an independent sample of $n - m$ clusters is selected in the same manner as $A_1$. Following the procedure of Sec. 7.9.1 it is possible to make use of both samples (Raj, 1965b) for obtaining an estimate of $Y$ on the second occasion.

### 7.9.2 MINIMUM-VARIANCE CURRENT ESTIMATES

Suppose it is desired to know what is the minimum-variance unbiased linear estimator of $M_2$ and the associated optimum fraction to be replaced on the second occasion. This question can be answered if the population is assumed infinite, and if minimum-variance estimators are understood in the sense of general estimation theory. The following notation is due to Yates (1949) and Patterson (1950).

$$\text{2d occasion} \quad / \quad \bar{y}' \quad / \quad \bar{y}'' \quad / \quad$$
$$/ \quad \bar{x}'' \quad / \quad \bar{x}' \quad / \quad \text{1st occasion}$$

A single prime indicates the units common to the two occasions and double prime indicates the units selected independently. The best linear estimator sought will be of the form

$$\hat{M}_2 = a(\bar{x}'' - \bar{x}') + c\bar{y}' + (1 - c)\bar{y}'' \tag{7.43}$$

in order that this be unbiased. If it is a minimum-variance (MV) unbiased estimator, it must be uncorrelated with every zero function [Theorem 1.10 due to Rao (1952)]. Hence it is uncorrelated with $\bar{y}' - \bar{y}''$ as well as with $\bar{x}' - \bar{x}''$. Thus

(1) $\qquad\qquad \text{Cov}\,(\bar{y}',\hat{M}_2) = \text{Cov}\,(\bar{y}'',\hat{M}_2)$

(2) $\qquad\qquad \text{Cov}\,(\bar{x}',\hat{M}_2) = \text{Cov}\,(\bar{x}'',\hat{M}_2)$

Noting that $\text{Cov}\,(\bar{y}',\bar{x}'') = \text{Cov}\,(\bar{y}',\bar{y}'') = 0$, $\text{Cov}\,(\bar{y}',\bar{x}') = \rho\sigma^2/n\lambda$,

$$\text{Cov}\,(\bar{y}',\bar{y}') = \frac{\sigma^2}{n\lambda} \quad \text{Cov}\,(\bar{y}'',\bar{x}'') = \text{Cov}\,(\bar{y}'',\bar{x}') = 0 \quad \text{Cov}\,(\bar{y}'',\bar{y}'') = \frac{\sigma^2}{n\mu}$$

we have from (1)

$$-a\rho\,\frac{\sigma^2}{n\lambda} + c\,\frac{\sigma^2}{n\lambda} = (1 - c)\,\frac{\sigma^2}{n\mu}$$

Similarly (2) gives

$$-a\,\frac{\sigma^2}{n\lambda} + c\rho\,\frac{\sigma^2}{n\lambda} = a\,\frac{\sigma^2}{n\mu}$$

Solving the two equations for $a$ and $c$ we get

$$a = \frac{\lambda\mu\rho}{1 - \rho^2\mu^2} \qquad c = \frac{\lambda}{1 - \rho^2\mu^2} \tag{7.44}$$

Hence the best linear estimator of $M_2$ is given by

$$\hat{M}_2 = \frac{1}{1 - \rho^2\mu^2}\,[\lambda\mu\rho(\bar{x}'' - \bar{x}') + \lambda\bar{y}' + \mu(1 - \rho^2\mu)\bar{y}''] \tag{7.45}$$

In order to find the variance of $\hat{M}_2$ we use the Corollary to Theorem

1.10, by which the variance of $\hat{M}_2$ equals the covariance between $\hat{M}_2$ and any unbiased estimator of $M_2$. Thus

$$V(\hat{M}_2) = \mathrm{Cov}\,(\bar{y}'',\hat{M}_2) = \frac{1 - \rho^2\mu}{1 - \rho^2\mu^2}\frac{\sigma^2}{n} \tag{7.46}$$

By differentiating $V(\hat{M}_2)$ with respect to $\mu$ and equating to zero, the best values of $\mu$ and $\lambda$ are found to be

$$\mu = \frac{1}{1 + (1 - \rho^2)^{1/2}} \qquad \lambda = \frac{\sqrt{1 - \rho^2}}{1 + (1 - \rho^2)^{1/2}} \tag{7.47}$$

and

$$V_{\min}(\hat{M}_2) = \frac{\sigma^2}{n}\frac{1 + \sqrt{1 - \rho^2}}{2} = \frac{\sigma^2}{n}\frac{1}{2\mu} \tag{7.48}$$

**Remark** It can be verified that the use of the difference estimator

$$\hat{M}_{2m} = (\bar{y}' - \rho\bar{x}') + \rho(\lambda\bar{x}' + \mu\bar{x}'') \tag{7.49}$$

in place of (7.37) in Sec. 7.9.1 will lead to the minimum-variance estimator $\hat{M}_2$ given by (7.45). A value for $\rho$ will have to be substituted on the basis of past experience. This will retain the unbiased character of the estimator although the variance will increase.

### 7.9.3 ESTIMATION OF CHANGE

As in the case of $\hat{M}_2$, the best linear unbiased estimate of $M_1$ will be of the form

$$b(\bar{y}'' - \bar{y}') + d\bar{x}' + (1 - d)\bar{x}'' \tag{7.50}$$

In order to be a MV estimate, it should have zero correlation with $\bar{x}' - \bar{x}''$ as well as with $\bar{y}' - \bar{y}''$. By following the steps indicated in Sec. 7.9.2, $\hat{M}_1$ will be found as

$$\hat{M}_1 = \frac{1}{1 - \rho^2\mu^2}[\rho\lambda\mu(\bar{y}'' - \bar{y}') + \lambda\bar{x}' + \mu(1 - \rho^2\mu)\bar{x}''] \tag{7.51}$$

It follows that the best estimate of $\Delta = M_2 - M_1$ is given by

$$\hat{\Delta} = \hat{M}_2 - \hat{M}_1 = \frac{1}{1 - \mu\rho}[\mu(1 - \rho)(\bar{y}'' - \bar{x}'') + \lambda(\bar{y}' - \bar{x}')] \tag{7.52}$$

Since $\bar{y}'' - \bar{x}''$ is an unbiased estimate of $\Delta$, it follows from the Corollary to Theorem 1.10 that

$$V(\hat{\Delta}) = \mathrm{Cov}\,(\bar{y}'' - \bar{x}'',\hat{\Delta}) = \frac{1}{1 - \mu\rho}\mu(1 - \rho)\frac{2\sigma^2}{n\mu} = \frac{2(1 - \rho)\sigma^2}{n(1 - \mu\rho)} \tag{7.53}$$

If $\rho$ is positive, the best value of $\mu$ which makes $V(\hat{\Delta})$ a minimum is obviously zero. This points to complete matching of the samples on the two occasions for making estimates of change.

It is of interest to examine how good an estimate of change can be made by using simple averages on both occasions. In that case the estimate is simply

$$\hat{\Delta}' = \lambda \bar{y}' + \mu \bar{y}'' - (\lambda \bar{x}' + \mu \bar{x}'') = \lambda(\bar{y}' - \bar{x}') + \mu(\bar{y}'' - \bar{x}'')$$

and its variance is given by

$$\lambda^2 \left( \frac{\sigma^2}{n\lambda} + \frac{\sigma^2}{n\lambda} - 2 \frac{\rho\sigma^2}{n\lambda} \right) + \mu^2 \left( \frac{\sigma^2}{n\mu} + \frac{\sigma^2}{n\mu} \right) = \frac{2\sigma^2}{n} [\lambda(1 - \rho) + \mu] = 2(1 - \lambda\rho) \frac{\sigma^2}{n}$$

and the ratio of $V(\hat{\Delta})$ to $V(\hat{\Delta}')$ is given by

$$\frac{1 - \rho}{(1 - \rho) + \lambda\mu\rho^2}$$

Table 7.2 gives the relative gain in precision, namely $\lambda\mu\rho^2/(1 - \rho)$, in percentage terms for some combinations of $\lambda$ and $\rho$. It will be found from the table that substantial gains in precision can be achieved by using the better estimator when $\rho$ is high.

**Table 7.2  Percent gain in precision of $\hat{\Delta}$ over $\hat{\Delta}'$ as estimators of change**

| $\rho$ | $\lambda$ | | |
|---|---|---|---|
| | $\frac{1}{2}$ | $\frac{1}{3}$ | $\frac{2}{5}$ |
| 0.5 | 12 | 11 | 8 |
| 0.6 | 22 | 20 | 14 |
| 0.7 | 41 | 36 | 26 |
| 0.8 | 80 | 71 | 51 |
| 0.9 | 202 | 180 | 130 |

*Further reading*  See Exercise 61 for making the best estimates of the current mean and the change when the estimate for the first occasion cannot be revised (as when it has already been published).

### 7.9.4  ESTIMATION OF SUM ON TWO OCCASIONS

Since the MV estimate of $\Sigma = M_2 + M_1$ is the sum of the MV estimates of $M_2$ and $M_1$, we have from (6.45) and (6.51),

$$\hat{\Sigma} = \hat{M}_2 + \hat{M}_1 = \frac{1}{1 + \rho\mu} [\mu(1 + \rho)(\bar{y}'' + \bar{x}'') + \lambda(\bar{y}' + \bar{x}')] \quad (7.54)$$

And
$$V(\hat{\Sigma}) = \text{Cov} (\bar{y}'' + \bar{x}'', \hat{\Sigma}) = \frac{2(1 + \rho)\sigma^2}{n(1 + \mu\rho)} \tag{7.55}$$

If $\rho$ is positive (which will ordinarily hold) the best replacement policy for estimating the sum on two occasions is to have $\mu = 1$ or $\lambda = 0$, which means taking an independent sample at the second occasion. In case the sum is estimated by taking the simple average on each occasion, the estimator would be

$$\hat{\Sigma}' = \lambda(\bar{y}' + \bar{x}') + \mu(\bar{y}'' + \bar{x}'')$$

with a variance of $2(1 + \lambda\rho)(\sigma^2/n)$, and the relative gain in precision achieved by using $\hat{\Sigma}$ in place of $\hat{\Sigma}'$ would be given by

$$\frac{\lambda\mu\rho^2}{1 + \rho}$$

Table 7.3 gives the % relative gain in precision for different combinations of $\rho$ and $\lambda$. It will be found that the gain is not substantial even for high values of $\rho$.

Table 7.3 Percent gain in precision of $\hat{\Sigma}$ over $\hat{\Sigma}'$ as estimators of sum

| $\rho$ | $\lambda$ | | |
|---|---|---|---|
| | $\frac{1}{2}$ | $\frac{1}{3}$ | $\frac{1}{4}$ |
| 0.5 | 4.2 | 3.7 | 3.1 |
| 0.6 | 5.6 | 5.0 | 4.2 |
| 0.7 | 7.2 | 6.4 | 5.3 |
| 0.8 | 8.8 | 7.8 | 6.6 |
| 0.9 | 10.6 | 9.5 | 7.8 |

*Further reading* For estimating the best values of the sample size on the first occasion and the subsampling fraction at the second occasion, see Exercise 62.

## 7.10 REGRESSION ESTIMATION IN REPETITIVE SURVEYS

In Sec. 7.9.1 use was made of the difference estimator $\hat{M}_{2m}$ for forming an estimate of $M_2$ based on the matched part of the sample. Cochran (1963) and Jessen (1942) have used the regression estimator

$$\hat{M}_{2m} = \bar{y}' + b(\bar{x} - \bar{x}')$$
$$= \bar{y}' + \mu b(\bar{x}'' - \bar{x}') \qquad \bar{x} = \lambda\bar{x}' + \mu\bar{x}'' \tag{7.56}$$

in place of the difference estimator.  An approximate expression for $V(\hat{M}_{2m})$ can be obtained by substituting $\rho$ for $b$ in (7.56).  In that case

$$V(\hat{M}_{2m}) = \frac{\sigma^2}{n\lambda} + \rho^2\mu^2\sigma^2 \left( \frac{1}{n\lambda} + \frac{1}{n\mu} \right) - 2\mu\rho^2 \frac{\sigma^2}{n\lambda} = \frac{\sigma^2}{n\lambda}(1 - \mu\rho^2)$$

By weighting $\hat{M}_{2m}$ and $\hat{M}_{2u} = \bar{y}''$ inversely to their variances, the estimator obtained is

$$\hat{M}_2 = \frac{1}{1 - \rho^2\mu^2} [\lambda\mu b(\bar{x}'' - \bar{x}') + \lambda\bar{y}' + \mu(1 - \rho^2\mu)\bar{y}''] \qquad (7.57)$$

which agrees with the minimum-variance estimator (7.45) provided $b$ is replaced by $\rho$.  It is fairly obvious that the variance of $\hat{M}_2$ calculated under the assumption that $b = \rho$ will agree with the minimum variance given by (7.46) and that this will in turn lead to the same replacement policy.


### 7.11 SAMPLING ON MORE THAN TWO OCCASIONS

The results obtained in the previous sections can be extended to more than two occasions.  For simplicity of presentation we shall assume that the population variance remains constant and that the sample size and the proportion retained are the same on each occasion.  A further assumption will be made that correlations between observations on the same units one, two, three, . . . , occasions apart are $\rho$, $\rho^2$, $\rho^3$, . . . .  A more general notation will now have to be used.  The mean of the observations on occasion $h - 1$ associated with the $n\lambda$ units common with occasion $h$ will be denoted by $\bar{x}'_{h-1}$ and the mean on occasion $h$ of observations associated with the same $n\lambda$ units will be $\bar{y}'_h$.  Similarly, $\bar{x}''_{h-1}$ and $\bar{y}''_h$ will be the means of the $n\mu$ units not common to occasions $h$ and $h - 1$.  The minimum-variance estimate of $M_h$ will be of the form

$$\hat{M}_h = A\hat{M}_{h-1} + B\bar{x}''_{h-1} - (A + B)\bar{x}'_{h-1} + \phi_h\bar{y}''_h + (1 - \phi_h)\bar{y}'_h$$

where $\hat{M}_{h-1}$ is the minimum-variance estimate for $M_{h-1}$.  Applying the conditions that this is uncorrelated with every zero function, we have $\text{Cov}(\bar{x}''_{h-1}, \hat{M}_h) = \text{Cov}(\bar{x}'_{h-1}, \hat{M}_h)$.  Since $\text{Cov}(\hat{M}_{h-1}, \bar{x}''_{h-1} - \bar{x}'_{h-1})$ is zero, it is found that

$$B = \mu[\rho(1 - \phi_h) - A]$$

Using the conditions that $\hat{M}_h$ is uncorrelated with $\bar{x}''_{h-2} - \bar{x}'_{h-2}$ and that $\text{Cov}(\bar{x}'_{h-2}, \bar{y}'_h) = \rho \text{Cov}(\bar{x}'_{h-2}, \bar{x}'_{h-1})$, we get

$$B = 0 \qquad A = \rho(1 - \phi_h)$$

so that the minimum-variance estimator is of the form

$$\hat{M}_h = \phi_h \bar{y}_h'' + (1 - \phi_h)[\bar{y}_h' + \rho(\hat{M}_{h-1} - \bar{x}_{h-1}')] \qquad (7.58)$$

In the language of Sec. 7.10 this means that the estimator of $M_h$ is a linear function of two independent estimators $\bar{y}_h''$ and $\bar{y}_h' + \rho(\hat{M}_{h-1} - \bar{x}_{h-1}')$. The quantity $\phi_h$ will be determined from the condition that

$$\mathrm{Cov}\ (\bar{y}_h'', \hat{M}_h) = \mathrm{Cov}\ (\bar{y}_h', \hat{M}_h)$$

which gives

$$\phi_h \frac{\sigma^2}{n\mu} = (1 - \phi_h)\left[\frac{\sigma^2}{n\lambda} + \rho\ \mathrm{Cov}\ (\bar{y}_h', \hat{M}_{h-1}) - \rho^2 \frac{\sigma^2}{n\lambda}\right]$$

But $\quad \mathrm{Cov}\ (\bar{y}_h', \hat{M}_{h-1}) = \rho\ \mathrm{Cov}\ (\bar{x}_{h-1}', \hat{M}_{h-1}) = \rho V(\hat{M}_{h-1})$

This gives

$$\phi_h = \frac{\rho^2 V(\hat{M}_{h-1}) + \dfrac{\sigma^2}{n\lambda}(1 - \rho^2)}{\rho^2 V(\hat{M}_{h-1}) + \dfrac{\sigma^2}{n\lambda}(1 - \rho^2) + \dfrac{\sigma^2}{n\mu}} \qquad (7.59)$$

Further

$$V(\hat{M}_h) = \mathrm{Cov}\ (\bar{y}_h'', \hat{M}_h) = \phi_h \frac{\sigma^2}{n\mu} \qquad (7.60)$$

The question of the limiting value of $V(\hat{M}_h)$ when the optimum values of $\lambda_h$ and $\mu_h$ are used has been considered by Cochran (1963). Let

$$V(\hat{M}_h) = \frac{\sigma^2}{n} G_h \qquad G_1 = 1$$

From (7.59) and (7.60) we have

$$\frac{1}{G_h} = 1 - \lambda_h + \frac{1}{\rho^2 G_{h-1} + (1 - \rho^2)/\lambda_h} \qquad (7.61)$$

The variance of $\hat{M}_h$ will be a minimum when the quantity on the right-hand side of (7.61) is a maximum. Simple calculus methods give the best value of $\lambda_h$ as

$$\lambda_h = \frac{\sqrt{1 - \rho^2}}{G_{h-1}(1 + \sqrt{1 - \rho^2})} \qquad (7.62)$$

Substituting this value of $\lambda_h$ in Eq. (7.61), we get

$$\frac{1}{G_h} = 1 + \frac{(1 - \sqrt{1 - \rho^2})^2}{\rho^2 G_{h-1}}$$

Thus the limiting value of $G_h$ is

$$\lim_{h \to \infty} G_h = G = \frac{2[\sqrt{1 - \rho^2} - (1 - \rho^2)]}{\rho^2} \tag{7.63}$$

and hence $\qquad\qquad \lim \lambda_h = \tfrac{1}{2} = \lim \mu_h \tag{7.64}$

## 7.12  A USEFUL PROCEDURE

In some monthly surveys it may be possible to collect data from the respondents for the current month as well as for the previous month (for example, retail-trade sales of shops).   And it may be considered desirable not to rotate the same units month after month over the year but spread the burden of response evenly over the population.   The following sample design may then be adopted.   Every month an independent random sample of establishments is taken.   During the enumeration each member of the sample provides data both for the current month and the previous month (Eckler, 1955; Woodruff, 1963).

Let $\bar{y}_h$ and $\bar{x}_{h-1}$ denote the sample means for the $h$th and $(h - 1)$st occasions, respectively, based on the sample of $n$ units taken on occasion $h$. We shall assume that $V(\bar{y}_h) = \sigma^2/n$ on each occasion and that $\rho$ is the correlation coefficient between consecutive periods.   The best linear estimator $\hat{M}_h$ of the mean on occasion $h$ will be of the form

$$\hat{M}_h = \bar{y}_h - a_h \bar{x}_{h-1} + a_h \hat{M}_{h-1} \qquad a_1 = 0$$

and $\qquad \hat{M}_{h-1} = \bar{y}_{h-1} - a_{h-1} \bar{x}_{h-2} + a_{h-1} \hat{M}_{h-2}$

The condition for $\hat{M}_h$ to be minimum variance is

$$\text{Cov } (\bar{x}_{h-1}, \hat{M}_h) = \text{Cov } (\bar{y}_{h-1}, \hat{M}_h)$$

since both $\bar{x}_{h-1}$ and $\bar{y}_{h-1}$ refer to the same occasion.

But $\qquad \text{Cov } (\bar{x}_{h-1}, \hat{M}_h) = (\rho - a_h) \dfrac{\sigma^2}{n}$

And $\qquad \text{Cov } (\bar{y}_{h-1}, \hat{M}_h) = a_h \text{ Cov } (\bar{y}_{h-1}, \hat{M}_{h-1})$

$$= a_h(1 - \rho a_{h-1}) \dfrac{\sigma^2}{n}$$

Hence $\qquad a_h(1 - \rho a_{h-1}) = \rho - a_h$

which gives $\qquad a_h = \dfrac{\rho}{2 - \rho a_{h-1}} \qquad a_1 = 0$

The variance of $\hat{M}_h$ is given by

$$V(\hat{M}_h) = \mathrm{Cov}\ (\bar{y}_h, \hat{M}_h) = (1 - \rho a_h)\frac{\sigma^2}{n}$$

### Further reading

*1.* In Sec. 7.12 the sample numbers are the same on each occasion. If the sample sizes vary, the procedure indicated in Exercise 64 may be followed.

*2.* If the estimate for a month is made after data for the succeeding month have been collected, it is shown in Exercise 65 that this is equivalent to the procedures of Sec. 7.11 with 50 percent overlap.

*3.* If the sample contains unexpectedly large units, their inclusion as such will inflate the sampling error. In Exercise 67 is discussed a method of reducing the impact of large units on the sampling variance.

### REFERENCES

Cochran, W. G. (1963). "Sampling Techniques," 2d ed. John Wiley & Sons, Inc., New York.

Eckler, A. R. (1955). Rotation sampling. *Ann. Math. Stat.,* 26.

Jessen, R. J. (1942). Statistical investigation of a sample survey for obtaining farm facts. *Iowa Agr. Expt. Sta. Res. Bull.,* 304.

Lahiri, D. B. (1951). A method of sample selection providing unbiased ratio estimates. *Intern. Stat. Inst. Bull.,* 33.

Patterson, H. D. (1950). Sampling on successive occasions with partial replacement of units. *J. Roy. Stat. Soc.,* B 12.

Raj, D. (1954). Ratio estimation in sampling with equal and unequal probabilities. *J. Ind. Soc. Agr. Stat.,* 6.

—— (1964). On double sampling for pps estimation. *Ann. Math. Stat.,* 35.

—— (1965a). On a method of using multiauxiliary information in sample surveys. *J. Am. Stat. Assoc.,* 60.

—— (1965b). On sampling over two occasions with probability proportionate to size. *Ann. Math. Stat.,* 36.

Rao, C. R. (1952). Some theorems on minimum-variance unbiased estimation. *Sankhya,* 12.

Woodruff, R. S. (1959). The use of rotating samples in the Census Bureau's monthly surveys. *Proc. Soc. Stat. Sec.. Am. Stat. Assoc.*

Yates, F. (1949). "Sampling Methods for Censuses and Surveys." Charles Griffin & Company, Ltd., London.

# CHAPTER EIGHT

# NONSAMPLING ERRORS

## 8.1 INTRODUCTION

In the theory presented in the foregoing chapters it has been assumed that to each unit $U_i$ in the population is attached a value $y_i$, called the true value of the unit for the character $y$. It has also been assumed that whenever $U_i$ is in the sample the value of $y$ reported or observed on it is $y_i$. It is important to take a good look at these assumptions. With some characters, such as the age of a person, or number of fruits on a tree, the idea of a true value is not difficult to contemplate. In certain other situations, such as the attitude of a person towards remarriage, the concept of the true value is harder to define. But it is not senseless to contemplate it. However, the assumption that the value reported or observed on unit $U_i$ is always $y_i$, irrespective of who reports it and under what circumstances it is obtained, is an oversimplification of the problem. Actual survey experience does not support this assumption. To give an example, the author (Raj, 1965) made an investigation in Greece in which all the parcels of land situated in five communes were visited by agricultural officials and the name of the operator recorded. Later on, all farmers in the communes were asked how many parcels they operated in the five communes. With 87 percent of the farmers there was no agreement between the figure reported by the farmer and the value obtained by field-to-field enumeration. About 65 percent of the farmers declared less and 22 percent more than the number of parcels operated (as found by the ground survey). There is no dearth of examples to show that errors of measurement or observation, or errors of response, are present when a survey is carried out (or a census is taken). The reason for making the assumption of the absence of errors of response (in the previous chapters) was to focus attention on sampling errors alone. In this chapter we shall face the problem of the presence of response errors and devise methods for the measurement of these errors to the point that it is possible to decide what proportion of the total budget should be devoted to the control of response errors and what should be devoted to the control of sampling errors. In addition to response errors, surveys are subject to errors of coverage, processing errors, etc. A study will be made of some of these errors in the latter part of this chapter.

## 8.2 RESPONSE ERRORS

As stated before, it is useful to assume that there is a true value $y_i$ attached to the unit $U_i$ in the population. An interviewer assigned to collect information on $U_i$ plays the role of a person who is trying to shoot at a target. We all know that if the target is shot at a very large number of times, the hits (rather the deviations) form a distribution with a mean and a variance. Another marksman will generally produce another distribution, with a different mean and variance. We are going to carry this analogy over to the realm of collection of information. When an interviewer approaches a unit for collecting information on some item, we shall assume that the response obtained is an observation on a random variable with a certain distribution. Different interviewers will produce different distributions depending upon their skill, the interaction between the interviewer and the respondent, and so on. When it comes to interviewing two different units by the same person, experience shows that the responses obtained cannot be assumed to be uncorrelated. The interviewer's personality affects the observations he produces. The fact that he has made a particular observation on one unit seems to affect his observation on the other unit. The author noted during the post-census check of the 1958 Greek Census of Establishments that investigators who did not find many establishments missing during the early part of their assignment lost interest in their job and produced a very high rate of coverage as compared with that of others who had started differently. The responses observed by the same interviewer appeared to be correlated. We are thus going to recognize the presence of correlations within interviewer assignments. But it will be carrying matters too far (thereby making the analysis of data too complicated) if we assume correlations between the response obtained by one interviewer on one unit and that of another interviewer on another unit. A uniform system of training of the interviewers and other procedures may bring about such correlations, but we are going to ignore them. Another point to remember is that the distribution of responses produced by an interviewer is going to depend on what may be called the *essential conditions* of the survey. In a thorough survey with considerable resources, in which great attention is paid to the problems of training, interviewing etc., the distribution will be different from one in which all that is considered important is writing out a questionnaire and ordering some persons to fetch data at a moment's notice. Thus while speaking of the random variables involved, we shall always have in mind the essential conditions of the survey which determine these distributions.

## 8.3 RESPONSE BIAS

The reason that the interviewer is being brought into the picture for the study of response errors is that modern large-scale surveys are usually conducted with the help of interviewers specially trained for the purpose in order to get worthwhile results. We shall assume that a large number $M$ of interviewers is available for the survey (Hansen, et al., 1951). The response $x_{ijk}$ obtained by interviewer $i$ on unit $j$ is a random variable (this is the heart of the assumption), possessing a distribution with $E_2(x_{ijk}) = \bar{X}_{ij}$ and $V_2(x_{ijk}) = S_{ij}^2$. The average of responses obtained by interviewer $i$ on all the $N$ units in the population would be $\sum_j \bar{X}_{ij}/N = \bar{X}_i$, and the average obtained by all the $M$ interviewers available for the survey would be $\sum_i \bar{X}_i/M = \bar{X}$. This may be called the expected survey value, the true value being $\sum_j Y_j/N = \bar{Y}$. Our target is to estimate $\bar{Y}$ and hence the difference, $\bar{X} - \bar{Y}$, between the expected survey value and the true value, is called the response bias. The response bias would obviously depend upon interviewing procedures, the questionnaire, and the training of personnel. Unless proper procedures can be devised which would guarantee a small response bias, it would not be worthwhile to go ahead with the survey.

## 8.4 THE ANALYSIS OF DATA

Since the response is going to depend on who interviews whom, there should be proper randomization procedures for the allocation of the sample interviewers (selected out of the $M$ available) to the sample units (selected out of the $N$ units in the population). We shall be discussing the theoretically most simple situation, in which a random sample of $\bar{n} = n/m$ units is selected from the population of $N$ units and assigned to an interviewer selected at random from the $M$ available for the survey. Another independent random sample of $\bar{n}$ units is selected and assigned to another interviewer selected at random from the $M$. In all $m$ such subsamples, each of size $\bar{n}$, are selected and assigned to the $m$ interviewers. Calling this sampling scheme scheme $B$, we shall prove the following theorem.

### Theorem 8.1

Under scheme $B$, an unbiased estimator of $\bar{X}$ is provided by

$$\bar{x} = \frac{S\bar{x}_i}{m} = \frac{\underset{i}{S}\,\underset{j}{S}\,x_{ijk}}{\bar{n}m} \tag{8.1}$$

with

$$V(\bar{x}) = \frac{V(x)}{n} + \left(\frac{1}{m} - \frac{1}{n}\right)C(x,I) \tag{8.2}$$

where

$$V(x) = \frac{\sum_{i}\sum_{j} E(x_{ijk} - \bar{X})^2}{MN} \tag{8.3}$$

$$C(x,I) = \frac{\sum_{i}\sum_{j \neq j'} E(x_{ijk} - \bar{X})(x_{ij'k'} - \bar{X})}{MN(N - 1)} \tag{8.4}$$

PROOF   If a unit is selected at random from the population of $N$ units and an interviewer is picked up at random from the $M$ and assigned to the selected unit, the expected value of the response $x_{ijk}$ will be $\bar{X}$. This is so because for a given interviewer $i$ and a given unit $U_j$, $E_2(x_{ijk}) = \bar{X}_{ij}$. Hence for fixed $i$, $E_2(x_{ijk}) = \sum_{j} \bar{X}_{ij}/N$, and therefore

$$E(x_{ijk}) = \frac{1}{M}\sum_{i} \frac{\bar{X}_{ij}}{N} = \bar{X}$$

This proves that the sample mean $\bar{x}_i = \underset{j}{S}\,x_{ijk}/\bar{n}$ provided by the $i$th selection (of the interviewer) gives an unbiased estimate of $\bar{X}$. Hence $E(\bar{x}) = \Sigma E(\bar{x}_i)/m = \bar{X}$. The bias in $\bar{x}$ for estimating $\bar{Y}$ will be $B(\bar{x}) = \bar{X} - \bar{Y}$. In order to find the variance of $\bar{x}$ we shall make repeated use of Theorem 1.8. It is to be remembered that the probability that a pair of units is assigned to an interviewer is $n(n - 1)/N(N - 1)$ and the chance that a specified interviewer is selected at the $i$th selection is $1/M$. We shall begin by finding $V(\bar{x}_i)$ by making use of Theorem 1.8; that is,

$$V(\bar{x}_i) = E_1 V_2(\bar{x}_i) + V_1 E_2(\bar{x}_i)$$

where the conditional expectations are taken keeping the interviewer and the sample units assigned to him fixed. We have

$$E_2(\bar{x}_i) = \frac{\underset{j}{S} \bar{X}_{ij}}{\bar{n}}$$

$$V_2(\bar{x}_i) = \frac{\underset{j}{S} S_{ij}{}^2 + \underset{j \neq j'}{S} C_2(x_{ijk}, x_{ij'k'})}{\bar{n}^2}$$

$$E_1 V_2(\bar{x}_i) = \frac{1}{\bar{n}MN} \sum_i \sum_j S_{ij}{}^2 + \frac{\bar{n} - 1}{\bar{n}MN(N - 1)} \sum_i \sum_{j \neq j'} C_2(x_{ijk}, x_{ij'k'}) \quad (8.5)$$

Now, $\quad V E_2(\bar{x}_i) = V(\bar{h}_i) = E_1 V_2(\bar{h}_i) + V_1 E_2(\bar{h}_i) \qquad \bar{h}_i = E_2(\bar{x}_i)$

where the conditional expectations are taken assuming the interviewer fixed.

We have $\qquad E_2(\bar{h}_i) = \dfrac{\sum_j \bar{X}_{ij}}{N} = \bar{X}_i$

$$V_2(\bar{h}_i) = \frac{1}{\bar{n}N} \sum_j (\bar{X}_{ij} - \bar{X}_i)^2 + \frac{\bar{n} - 1}{\bar{n}N(N - 1)} \sum_{j \neq j'} (\bar{X}_{ij} - \bar{X}_i)(\bar{X}_{ij'} - \bar{X}_i)$$

$$EV_2(\bar{h}_i) = \frac{1}{M\bar{n}N} \sum_i \sum_j (\bar{X}_{ij} - \bar{X}_i)^2$$

$$+ \frac{\bar{n} - 1}{M\bar{n}N(N - 1)} \sum_i \sum_{j \neq j'} (\bar{X}_{ij} - \bar{X}_i)(\bar{X}_{ij'} - \bar{X}_i) \quad (8.6)$$

$$V E_2(\bar{h}_i) = \frac{\sum_i (\bar{X}_i - \bar{X})^2}{M} \quad (8.7)$$

Adding the terms given by (8.5), (8.6), and (8.7), we get $V(\bar{x}_i)$. Now $V(\bar{x}) = V(\bar{x}_i)/m$, since the random variables $\bar{x}_i$ $(i = 1, \ldots, m)$ are uncorrelated.  Hence we get

$$V(\bar{x}) = \frac{1}{nMN} \sum_i \sum_j (\bar{X}_{ij} - \bar{X}_i)^2$$

$$+ \frac{\bar{n} - 1}{nMN(N-1)} \sum_i \sum_{j \neq j'} (\bar{X}_{ij} - \bar{X}_i)(\bar{X}_{ij'} - \bar{X}_i) + \frac{\bar{n}\Sigma(\bar{X}_i - \bar{X})^2}{nM}$$

$$+ \frac{1}{nMN} \sum_i \sum_j S_{ij}^2 + (\bar{n} - 1)[nMN(N-1)]^{-1} \sum_i \sum_{j \neq j'} C_2(x_{ijk}, x_{ij'k'}) \quad (8.8)$$

We shall now define the variance of $x_{ijk}$ over the population of all inter-viewers and all units as

$$V(x) = \frac{1}{NM} \sum_i \sum_j E_2(x_{ijk} - \bar{X})^2 = \frac{\sum_i \sum_j (\bar{X}_{ij} - \bar{X}_i)^2}{NM}$$

$$+ \frac{\sum_i (\bar{X}_i - \bar{X})^2}{M} + \frac{\sum_i \sum_j S_{ij}^2}{NM} \quad (8.9)$$

And we define the covariance between responses obtained from different individuals by the same interviewer as

$$C(x,I) = \sum_i \sum_{j \neq j'} \frac{E_2(x_{ijk} - \bar{X})(x_{ij'k'} - \bar{X})}{MN(N-1)}$$

$$= \sum_i \sum_{j \neq j'} \frac{C_2(x_{ijk}, x_{ij'k'})}{MN(N-1)} + \frac{\sum_i (\bar{X}_i - \bar{X})^2}{M} + \frac{\sum_i \sum_{j \neq j'} (\bar{X}_{ij} - \bar{X}_i)(\bar{X}_{ij'} - \bar{X}_i)}{MN(N-1)}$$

$$(8.10)$$

Using (8.9) and (8.10) we find that

$$V(\bar{x}) = \frac{V(x)}{n} + \frac{(\bar{n} - 1)C(x,I)}{n}$$

$$= \frac{V(x) - C(x,I)}{n} + \frac{C(x,I)}{m}$$

$$= \frac{V(x)}{n} + \left(\frac{1}{m} - \frac{1}{n}\right) C(x,I) \qquad \blacksquare$$

**Corollary**

Defining by $\rho$ the intra-interviewer correlation coefficient of response, the variance of $\bar{x}$ may be written as

$$V(\bar{x}) = \frac{V(x)}{n} [1 + (\bar{n} - 1)\rho]$$

**Corollary**

$\text{MSE}(\bar{x}) = V(\bar{x}) + (\bar{X} - \bar{Y})^2$. Thus the mean square error of $\bar{x}$ around the true mean $\bar{Y}$ is the sum of the variance of $\bar{x}$ and the square of the response bias.

*Remark* The quantity $V(x)$ is the variance over all responses $x_{ijk}$ for all units to all interviewers. The quantity $C(x,I)$ is the covariance between responses obtained from different units by the same interviewer. With some characters, that is, in cases in which the interviewer is required to make an estimate, such as eye-estimation of area under a crop in a field, the covariance $C(x,I)$ may be substantial and may form an important part of $V(\bar{x})$. On the other hand, with factual items, such as the number of persons in the household, their distribution by age and sex, etc., the interviewer may have little to do with the response obtained from the members of the household and in this case $C(x,I)$ may be assumed to be an unimportant component of $V(\bar{x})$.

*Remark* If survey procedures are such that the response bias is quite large relative to $V(\bar{x})$, the variance of the sample mean will give a misleading picture of the accuracy attained by the survey. It is the total error of the estimate, measured by $\text{MSE}(\bar{x})$, which is to be made small and not simply the variance of $\bar{x}$.

*Remark* If $\bar{n} = 1$, that is if each interviewer enumerates just one unit, the covariance term drops from the expression for $V(\bar{x})$.

*Remark* Scheme $B$ of this section is due to Mahalanobis (1946) who calls it the method of interpenetrating subsamples. The $m$ subsamples are interpenetrating in the sense that each is a probability sample over the population.

*Further reading* See Exercise 71 for an extension to the situation in which a random sample taken from the entire population is allocated to strata.

### 8.5 THE OPTIMUM NUMBER OF INTERVIEWERS

By Theorem 8.1, the variance of the sample mean based on a survey employing interviewers is made up of two components. One component, $V(x)$, is the variability of all responses over all units to all interviewers. The other one, $C(x,I)$, is the covariance between responses obtained from different units within interviewer assignments (called interviewer covariance). If advance estimates of $V(x)$ and $C(x,I)$ are available which can be assumed to be usable over the range of $m$ (the number of interviewers) envisaged, it is possible to determine from (8.2) the optimum number of interviewers to employ for the collection of data. Assuming a simple cost structure, let $c_1$ be cost per unit in the sample and $c_2$ be the cost per interviewer, so that the total cost of the survey is given as $C = c_0 + c_1 n + c_2 m$. By the method of undetermined multipliers, the values of $n$ and $m$ can be found which minimize $V(\bar{x})$ for a given cost. The two equations obtained by equating to zero the derivatives of $V(\bar{x}) + \lambda(c_0 + c_1 n + c_2 m - C)$ with respect to $n$ and $m$ are:

$$\lambda c_1 = \frac{V(x) - C(x,I)}{n^2} \qquad \lambda c_2 = \frac{C(x,I)}{m^2}$$

Hence

$$\frac{m}{n} = \left(\frac{c_1}{c_2}\right)^{\frac{1}{2}} \frac{[C(x,I)]^{\frac{1}{2}}}{[V(x) - C(x,I)]^{\frac{1}{2}}} \tag{8.11}$$

The actual values of $n$ and $m$ are obtained by substitution in the cost equation the ratio of $m/n$ given by (8.11). Since $C(x,I)$ and $V(x)$ would ordinarily themselves depend on the number of interviewers used and the size of the interviewer assignment, the solution obtained should merely be used for getting an idea of the magnitudes involved. Speaking unprecisely, this section provides an illustration of the manner in which resources can be allocated toward the reduction of sampling errors (as judged by $n$) and nonsampling errors (interviewer errors in this case).

### 8.6 ESTIMATION OF VARIANCE COMPONENTS

The advantage of using the method of interpenetrating subsamples (Sec. 8.4) is that it is possible to obtain from the sample itself an estimate of $V(x)$, $C(x,I)$, and $V(\bar{x})$. These estimates are made in Theorem 8.2.

#### Theorem 8.2

*Under scheme B, unbiased estimates of $C(x,I)$, $V(x)$ and $V(\bar{x})$ are provided by*

$$C(x,I) \cong \frac{s_b^2 - s_w^2}{\bar{n}} \tag{8.12}$$

$$V(x) \cong s_w^2 + \frac{s_b^2 - s_w^2}{\bar{n}} \tag{8.13}$$

$$V(\bar{x}) \cong \frac{\underset{i}{S}(\bar{x}_i - \bar{x})^2}{m(m-1)} \tag{8.14}$$

*where*

$$s_b^2 = \underset{i}{S} \frac{\bar{n}(\bar{x}_i - \bar{x})^2}{m-1} \qquad s_w^2 = \underset{i}{S}\underset{j}{S} \frac{(x_{ijk} - \bar{x}_i)^2}{m(\bar{n}-1)}$$

PROOF  As $\bar{x} = \underset{i}{S} \bar{x}_i/m$, and since $\bar{x}_i$ are independently and identically distributed random variables, we prove by Theorem 3.4 that Eq. (8.14) holds. At the same time it follows that

$$E(s_b^2) = \bar{n}mV(\bar{x}) = nV(\bar{x})$$

$$= V(x) - C(x,I) + \frac{n}{m}C(x,I)$$

Now $\qquad \underset{i}{S}\underset{j}{S}(x_{ijk} - \bar{x}_i)^2 = SSx_{ijk}^2 - \frac{1}{\bar{n}}\underset{i}{S}\left(\underset{j}{S}x_{ijk}\right)^2$

$$ESSx_{ijk}^2 = ESS(\bar{X}_{ij}^2 + S_{ij}^2) = \frac{m}{M}\frac{\bar{n}}{N}\sum_i\sum_j (\bar{X}_{ij}^2 + S_{ij}^2)$$

Given the $i$th interviewer, $E\left(\underset{j}{S}x_{ijk}\right)^2 = (ESx_{ijk})^2 + V(Sx_{ijk})$

But $\qquad (ESx_{ijk})^2 = \left(\frac{\bar{n}}{N}\sum \bar{X}_{ij}\right)^2 = \bar{n}^2\bar{X}_i^2$

$$V(Sx_{ijk}) = E_1V_2(Sx_{ijk}) + V_1E_2(Sx_{ijk})$$

$$E_2(Sx_{ijk}) = \underset{j}{S} \bar{X}_{ij}$$

$$V_1E_2(Sx_{ijk}) = \frac{\bar{n}\Sigma(\bar{X}_{ij} - \bar{X}_i)^2}{N} + \frac{\bar{n}(\bar{n}-1)}{N(N-1)}\sum_{j'\neq j} (\bar{X}_{ij} - \bar{X}_i)(\bar{X}_{ij'} - \bar{X}_i)$$

$$V_2(Sx_{ijk}) = \underset{j}{S} S_{ij}^2 + \underset{j'\neq j}{S} C_2(x_{ijk}, x_{ij'k'})$$

$$E_1V_2(Sx_{ijk}) = \frac{\bar{n}}{N}\sum_j S_{ij}^2 + \frac{\bar{n}(\bar{n}-1)}{N(N-1)}\sum_{j'\neq j} C_2(x_{ijk}, x_{ij'k'})$$

Hence, given the $i$th interviewer

$$E(Sx_{ijk})^2 = \bar{n}^2\bar{X}_i^2 + \frac{\bar{n}\sum_j (\bar{X}_{ij} - \bar{X}_i)^2}{N}$$

$$+ \frac{\bar{n}(\bar{n}-1)}{N(N-1)}\sum_{j'\neq j} (\bar{X}_{ij} - \bar{X}_i)(\bar{X}_{ij'} - \bar{X}_i) + \frac{\bar{n}}{N}\sum_j S_{ij}^2$$

$$+ \frac{\bar{n}(\bar{n}-1)}{N(N-1)}\sum_{j'\neq j} C_2(x_{ijk}, x_{ij'k'})$$

Thus
$$E(Sx_{ijk})^2 = \frac{m}{M} \sum_i E[(Sx_{ijk})^2 | i]$$

Hence

$$E \underset{i}{S} \underset{j}{S} (x_{ijk} - \bar{x}_i)^2 = \frac{m\bar{n}}{NM} \sum_i \sum_j (\bar{X}_{ij}{}^2 + S_{ij}{}^2) - \frac{m}{M} \left[ \bar{n} \sum_i \bar{X}_i{}^2 \right.$$

$$+ \sum_i \sum_j \frac{(\bar{X}_{ij} - \bar{X}_i)^2}{N} + \frac{\bar{n} - 1}{N(N-1)} \sum_i \sum_{j' \neq j} (\bar{X}_{ij} - \bar{X}_i)(\bar{X}_{ij'} - \bar{X}_i)$$

$$+ \frac{1}{N} \sum_i \sum_j S_{ij}{}^2 + \frac{\bar{n} - 1}{N(N-1)} \sum_i \sum_{j' \neq j} C_2(x_{ijk}, x_{ij'k'}) \bigg]$$

$$= m(\bar{n} - 1) \left[ \sum \sum S_{ij}{}^2 + \frac{1}{NM} \sum_i \sum_j (\bar{X}_{ij} - \bar{X}_i)^2 \right.$$

$$- \frac{1}{MN(N-1)} \sum_i \sum_{j' \neq j} (\bar{X}_{ij} - \bar{X}_i)(\bar{X}_{ij'} - \bar{X}_i)$$

$$\left. - \frac{1}{MN(N-1)} \sum_i \sum_{j' \neq j} C_2(x_{ijk}, x_{ij'k'}) \right] = m(\bar{n} - 1)[V(x) - C(x,I)]$$

Thus
$$E(s_w{}^2) = V(x) - C(x,I)$$

Also
$$E(s_b{}^2) = V(x) - C(x,I) + \frac{n}{m} C(x,I)$$

Hence
$$C(x,I) \cong \frac{m}{n} (s_b{}^2 - s_w{}^2)$$

and
$$V(x) \cong s_w{}^2 + \frac{m}{n} (s_b{}^2 - s_w{}^2) \qquad \blacksquare$$

**Remark**  Having completed a survey employing $m$ interviewers, each investigating a random sample of $\bar{n}$ units, we can estimate $V(x)$ and $C(x,I)$ from the survey and determine the optimum number $(m_0)$ of interviewers and the total number of sample units $(n_0)$ to be used in a future survey. For the cost function of Sec. 8.5, an estimate of $m_0/n_0$ is given by

$$\frac{m_0}{n_0} = \frac{(c_1/c_2)^{1/2}[(s_b{}^2 - s_w{}^2)/\bar{n}]^{1/2}}{s_w}$$

**Remark**  It is a remarkable fact that an unbiased estimate of the sampling variance $V(\bar{x})$ of $\bar{x}$ can be made even in the presence of response errors.  The device of interpenetrating subsamples is indeed skillful.  And it provides estimates of interviewer correlations at the same time.

**Remark**  If each interviewer collects information on just one unit, an unbiased estimate of $V(\bar{x})$ would be $\underset{j}{S} (x_{ijk} - \bar{x})^2/n(n-1)$.  This coincides with the estimator of Theorem 3.3, used in wr simple random sampling. Thus the usual variance estimator is all right provided an interviewer investigates only one unit. But the estimator of the mean, $\bar{y}$ of Sec. 3.4, would be a biased one in the presence of response errors.

**Remark** In practice an interviewer collects information from several units. In this situation the estimator $S\limits_{j} (x_{ijk} - \bar{x})^2/n(n-1)$ would be inappropriate. The proper variance estimator is given by (8.14).

## 8.7 SOME RESTRICTED MODELS

The theory presented in the earlier sections is quite general, the main assumption made being that the response obtained by interviewer $i$ on unit $j$ is a random variable. We shall now discuss a particular case of this model. To start with, a check will be made of Formula (8.2) for the situation in which $x_{ijk} = y_j$ (the true value of unit $j$). We have

$$\bar{X}_{ij} = y_j \qquad S_{ij}{}^2 = 0 \qquad \bar{X}_i = \bar{X} = \bar{Y} \qquad E(\bar{x}) = \bar{Y}$$

$$V(x) = (N-1)\frac{S_y{}^2}{N} \qquad C(x,I) = \frac{-S_y{}^2}{N} \qquad C_2(x_{ijk},x_{ij'k'}) = 0$$

Hence
$$V(\bar{x}) = \frac{1}{m}\left(\frac{1}{\bar{n}} - \frac{1}{N}\right)S_y{}^2$$

This agrees with the sampling variance of $\bar{y} = (1/m)S\bar{y}_i$ in which $m$ independent samples each of size $\bar{n}$ are selected at random, and in which a unique value is attached to every unit. If the responses are subject to a constant bias so that $x_{ijk} = y_j + a$, $V(\bar{x})$ remains unchanged but $\bar{x}$ is subject to a bias of $a$ (Exercise 68).

The model we are now going to discuss is due to Sukhatme (1953). The response obtained by interviewer $i$ on unit $j$ is supposed to be $x_{ijk} = y_j + a_i + e_{ij}$, where $E_2(e_{ij}) = 0$, $V_2(e_{ij}) = S_e{}^2$. The quantity $a_i$ is the bias associated with interviewer $i$. The random variables $e_{ij}$ and $e_{ij'}$ are assumed to be uncorrelated. For this restricted model, we have

$$\bar{X}_{ij} = y_j + a_i \qquad \bar{X}_i = \bar{Y} + a_i \qquad \bar{X} = \bar{Y} + \bar{a} \qquad S_{ij}{}^2 = S_e{}^2$$

$$V(x) = \left(1 - \frac{1}{N}\right)S_y{}^2 + \left(1 - \frac{1}{M}\right)S_a{}^2 + S_e{}^2$$

$$C(x,I) = \left(1 - \frac{1}{M}\right)S_a{}^2 - \frac{1}{N}S_y{}^2$$

Hence
$$E(\bar{x}) = \bar{Y} + \bar{a}$$

$$V(\bar{x}) = \frac{1}{m}\left(\frac{1}{\bar{n}} - \frac{1}{N}\right)S_y{}^2 + \frac{1}{m}\left(1 - \frac{1}{M}\right)S_a{}^2 + \frac{1}{n}S_e{}^2$$

These results are illuminating. The sample mean does not give an unbiased estimate of $\bar{Y}$ unless the individual biases $a_i$ of the interviewers average to zero over the population of $M$ interviewers. Secondly, $V(\bar{x})$ is built up of three components. One component is the sampling variance obtained when there are no response errors whatsoever. The other factor (which is to be added) is a function of $S_a{}^2$, the variability of the biases of the interviewers. Also, there is the variance of individual response deviations. This points to the need that survey procedures be so designed as to ensure that $\bar{a}$ is about zero and $S_a{}^2$ is as small as possible.

*Further reading*   The optimum number of enumerators for a certain cost function is obtained in Exercise 70 when the additive model is assumed.

### 8.8  UNCORRELATED RESPONSE ERRORS

In certain types of surveys there may be evidence that errors of response can be assumed to be uncorrelated from one unit to another in the sample. For example, this may happen in surveys carried out by mail in which the sample units scattered far and wide are required to fill out certain question-naires. We will study in this situation the effect of response errors on the estimation procedures discussed in the previous chapters. A wtr simple random sample of $n$ units is taken. The model assumed is that the response on the $j$th unit in the sample may be exhibited as

$$x_{jk} = y_j + e_{jk} \tag{8.15}$$

where
$$E_2(e_{jk}) = 0 \qquad V_2(e_{jk}) = S_{ej}{}^2$$

The $e_{jk}$'s are uncorrelated from unit to unit. Denoting the sample mean by $\bar{x} = \underset{j}{S}\, x_{jk}/n$, we have

$$E_2(\bar{x}) = \bar{y} \qquad V_2(\bar{x}) = \underset{j}{S}\, \frac{S_{ej}{}^2}{n^2} \qquad E_1 V_2(\bar{x}) = \frac{1}{n}\frac{\Sigma S_{ej}{}^2}{N}$$

$$V_1 E_2(\bar{x}) = (1 - f)\frac{S_y{}^2}{n}$$

Hence
$$E(\bar{x}) = \bar{Y} \qquad V(\bar{x}) = (1 - f)\frac{S_y{}^2}{n} + \frac{1}{n}\frac{\Sigma S_{ej}{}^2}{N} \tag{8.16}$$

This shows that, provided the response errors average to zero, the sample mean is an unbiased estimate of the population mean. But its variance is not simply the customary sampling variance of the true values (see Theorem 3.1). It gets inflated by a quantity depending upon the variance

$S_{ej}^2$ of individual response errors. In order to estimate $V(\bar{x})$ from the sample, suppose we use the customary variance estimator $(1 - f)S(x_{jk} - \bar{x})^2/n(n - 1)$. We have

$$E \underset{j}{S} (x_{jk} - \bar{x})^2 = E_1 \underset{j}{S} (S_{ej}^2 + y_j^2) - nE(\bar{x}^2)$$

$$= \frac{n}{N} \sum_j (y_j^2 + S_{ej}^2) - n[\bar{Y}^2 + V(\bar{x})]$$

$$= \frac{n(n-1)V(\bar{x})}{1-f} - \frac{n(n-1)}{N^2(1-f)} \sum_j S_{ej}^2$$

Hence

$$E(1 - f) \frac{\underset{j}{S} (x_{jk} - \bar{x})^2}{n(n-1)} = V(\bar{x}) - \frac{\Sigma S_{ej}^2}{N^2} \qquad (8.17)$$

This shows that the customary variance estimator slightly understates the true variance.

The model (8.15) can be extended by assuming a systematic bias of $a_j$ associated with the $j$th unit.

Then $$x_{jk} = y_j + a_j + e_{jk} = y_j' + e_{jk}$$

where the $e_{jk}$'s are assumed to be uncorrelated. The new formulas are

$$E(\bar{x}) = \bar{Y} + \bar{a} \qquad V(\bar{x}) = (1 - f)\frac{S_{y'}^2}{n} + \frac{1}{n}\frac{\Sigma S_{ej}^2}{N} \qquad (8.18)$$

Thus the sample mean is subject to a response bias of $\bar{a}$. The new variance formula differs from (8.16) in that the variance of $y_j'$ is involved in place of the variance of $y_j$, the true values. Regarding the estimator of the variance, formula (8.17) continues to hold. It must be pointed out here that actual survey experience in certain fields shows that biases are exceptionally stable. As a result, when surveys are regularly conducted over the same population, it should be possible to make estimates of change (Sec. 7.9) with very small response bias provided the essential conditions of the survey are about the same at the two periods (see also Exercise 77).

## 8.9 ESTIMATION OF RESPONSE BIAS

As stated in Sec. 8.4 the response bias, $\bar{X} - \bar{Y}$, may be an important component of the mean square error of the sample estimate. If this component is large, it is not worthwhile trying to reduce the other components. The problem is how to make an estimate of the response bias.

Since it involves $\bar{Y}$, the mean of the true values, the response bias cannot be measured as such from the survey. If an estimate of $\bar{Y}$ is available from another source which is believed to be very accurate, the response bias can then be estimated. But often it is difficult to make sure that the other source is very accurate. Another approach in recent years has been to conduct a small-scale study after the main survey in which "star" interviewers are used and the procedures employed are more careful and detailed. The differences of the estimates based on the main survey and the small-scale survey throw some light on the response biases involved. At least one can find what difference more careful procedures will make in the results. This method is being increasingly used to estimate the response bias of census data. The small-scale studies are called post-enumeration surveys. Occasionally it is possible to match the survey data with figures believed to be true values of the units involved. Such comparisons throw light on the size and direction of response errors. The present author (Raj, 1965) made such a comparison between farmer's reports on the number of parcels operated along with their areas and the corresponding data gathered through a ground survey. The so-called true average size of a holding was found to be 8.7 parcels, while the reports produced a figure of 6.6 parcels, the response bias being $-2.1$ parcels. For areas, the averages were 42.2 and 37.8, giving a response bias of $-4.4$ (measured in stremmas). The responses were found to be correlated with the true values, the correlation coefficient being $-0.39$ for the number of parcels and $-0.23$ for areas. In surveys of this type it would be far better to concentrate efforts toward the reduction of response bias (by improving survey procedures) rather than increase the size of the sample. Among other studies of this kind, one has been made by Kish and Lansing (1954), the item considered being the selling price of homes (see also Exercises 75 and 76).

*Further reading* See Exercise 77 where the standard error of the esti-mated bias is obtained when the survey is repeated on the same sample for estimating a population proportion.

## 8.10 EXTENSION TO OTHER SAMPLING DESIGNS

For simplicity of presentation the analysis of response errors has been restricted to the situation in which a simple random sample has been selected from the entire population. The method can be easily extended to other sampling designs. If stratification has been employed we shall assume that a large number $M_h$ of interviewers is available for work in the $h$th stratum from which $m_h$ are selected at random. These interviewers are allocated at random to $m_h$ psu's, one to each, and selected, say, with replacement with pp to $z$. From the $j$th psu in stratum $h$ a sample of $m_{hj}$ second-stage units (say, households) is selected at random from the $M_{hj}$ in the psu. Denoting by $x_{hijku}$ the response obtained by interviewer $i$ on the $k$th household in the $j$th psu, the population total $Y = \Sigma Y_h$ would be estimated by

$$\hat{X} = \sum_h \frac{I}{m_h} S_j \frac{I}{p_{hj}} \frac{M_{hj}}{m_{hj}} S_k x_{hijku} = \sum_h \frac{I}{m_h} S_j \hat{X}_{hj}$$

We shall assume that given the stratum $h$, the interviewer $i$, the psu $j$ and the household $k$,

$$E_2(x_{hijku}) = \bar{X}_{hijk} \quad \text{and} \quad V_2(x_{hijku}) = S^2{}_{hijk}$$

and that responses taken by the same interviewer on two different households are not necessarily uncorrelated. But we shall assume that the random variables $x_{hijku}$ and $x_{hi'j'k'u'}$ are uncorrelated. In stratum $h$ there will be $m_h$ interpenetrating subsamples, each providing an unbiased estimate of $X_h = \sum_i \sum_j \sum_k \bar{X}_{ijk}/M_h$, the expected survey value for stratum $h$, the true value being $Y_h = \sum_i \sum_j \sum_k y_{jk}/M_h$. The estimator of $X_h$ based on the $i$th interviewer would be

$$\hat{X}_{h,i} = \frac{1}{p_{hj}} \frac{M_{hj}}{m_{hj}} S_k x_{hijku} \qquad \hat{X} = \sum_h \frac{1}{m_h} S_i \hat{X}_{h,i}$$

And an unbiased estimator of $V(\hat{X})$ would be given by

$$V(\hat{X}) \hat{=} \sum_h \frac{1}{m_h(m_h - 1)} S_i \left( \hat{X}_{h,i} - \frac{1}{m_h} S\hat{X}_{h,i} \right)^2$$

## 8.11 RESPONSE AND SAMPLING VARIANCE

We shall now make a more detailed examination of the mean square error of a survey estimate when response errors are present. An attempt will be made to separate the response variance from the sampling variance (Hansen et al., 1964). Suppose a unit is selected at random from a population of $N$ units in order to estimate the population mean $\bar{Y}$. Let the response on the selected unit $U_j$ on trial $t$ be $x_{jt}$. Given this unit, let $E(x_{jt}|j) = X_j$ and further let $E(X_j) = \Sigma X_j/N = \bar{X}$. We shall then define:

Response deviation: $\quad d_{jt} = x_{jt} - X_j$

Sampling deviation: $\quad \delta_j = X_j - \bar{X}$

It is easy to see that $E(x_{jt}) = \bar{X}$, so that $B = \bar{X} - \bar{Y}$ is the amount of bias present in $x_{jt}$ for estimating $\bar{Y}$. For the mean square error of $x_{jt}$

we have

$$\begin{aligned}
\mathrm{MSE}(x_{jt}) &= E(x_{jt} - \bar{Y})^2 \\
&= E(x_{jt} - X_j + X_j - \bar{X} + \bar{X} - \bar{Y})^2 \\
&= E(d_{jt} + \delta_j + B)^2 \\
&= E(d_{jt}{}^2) + E(\delta_j{}^2) + 2E(d_{jt}\delta_j) + B^2 \\
&= V(d_{jt}) + V(\delta_j) + 2\sigma(d_{jt})\sigma(\delta_j)\rho(\delta_j,d_{jt}) + B^2 \quad (8.19)
\end{aligned}$$

The first term in Eq. (8.19) will be called the response variance; the second, the sampling variance; and the third, the covariance between response and sampling deviations.

### Theorem 8.3

*Let a simple random sample of n units be selected with replacement from a population, giving rise to responses at trial t as*

$$x_{1t}, x_{2t}, \ldots, x_{nt} \qquad \bar{x} = \frac{Sx_{jt}}{n}$$

*Then* $\qquad E(\bar{x}) = \bar{X} \qquad B(\bar{x}) = \bar{X} - \bar{Y}$

*and the mean square error of $\bar{x}$ around $\bar{Y}$ is*

$$\mathrm{MSE}(\bar{x}) = \frac{1}{n} V(d_{jt})[1 + (n-1)\rho(d_{jt},d_{kt})] + V\frac{S\delta_j}{n}$$

$$+ 2 \operatorname{Cov}\left(\frac{Sd_{jt}}{n}, \frac{S\delta_j}{n}\right) + (\bar{X} - \bar{Y})^2$$

PROOF   Using the expression for $\mathrm{MSE}(x_{jt})$ from Eq. (8.19), we have

$$\mathrm{MSE}(\bar{x}) = V\frac{Sd_{jt}}{n} + V\frac{S\delta_j}{n} + 2\operatorname{Cov}\left(\frac{Sd_{jt}}{n}, \frac{S\delta_j}{n}\right) + (\bar{X} - \bar{Y})^2 \quad (8.20)$$

Furthermore

$$\begin{aligned}
V\frac{Sd_{jt}}{n} &= E\left(\frac{Sd_{jt}}{n}\right)^2 = E\frac{Sd_{jt}{}^2}{n^2} + 2E\frac{S'd_{jt}d_{kt}}{n^2} \\
&= \frac{1}{n}V(d_{jt}) + \frac{n-1}{n}\operatorname{Cov}(d_{jt},d_{kt}) \\
&= \frac{1}{n}V(d_{jt})[1 + (n-1)\rho(d_{jt},d_{kt})] \quad (8.21)
\end{aligned}$$

The proof of Theorem 8.3 now follows.                                       ■

*Remark*   The quantity $n^{-1}V(d_{jt})$ in Eq. (8.21) is the simple variance of the response deviations and is called the simple response variance. The second term reflects any correlations among the response deviations from one unit to another within the survey trial.

*Remark*   The first term in Eq. (8.20) will be called the response variance; the second, the sampling variance; and the third, the covariance between response and sampling deviations.

*Remark*   The precision of the estimate depends on the sampling variance, the response variance, the covariance between sampling and response deviations, and the bias.   In case response deviations are all zero, the precision will be governed simply by the sampling variance and the bias.

*Further reading*   See Exercise 79 for an extension to pps sampling.

### 8.11.1   APPLICATION TO ESTIMATING PROPORTIONS

The results obtained in the previous section will now be applied to the problem of estimating the proportion $P$ of units belonging to the class $A$, when a wr simple random sample of $n$ units is taken.   Suppose the response obtained on unit $U_j$ is a random variable which classifies the unit to the class $A$ or not $A$ according as $x_{jt} = 1$ (with probability $P_j$) or zero (with probability $Q_j$).

Then   $p = \dfrac{Sx_{jt}}{n}$   $E(x_{jt}|j) = P_j$   $E(P_j) = \dfrac{\Sigma P_j}{N} = \bar{P} = E(p)$

$$V(d_{jt}) = E(d_{jt}{}^2) = \frac{\Sigma[(1 - P_j)^2 P_j + P_j{}^2(1 - P_j)]}{N} = \frac{\Sigma P_j(1 - P_j)}{N}$$

$$V(\delta_j) = \frac{\Sigma(P_j - \bar{P})^2}{N}$$

Hence the simple response variance is $\Sigma P_j(1 - P_j)/nN$, and the sampling variance is $\Sigma(P_j - \bar{P})^2/nN$.   If we further assume that the within-trial response deviations are uncorrelated and so are the sampling and response deviations,

$$\text{MSE}(p) = \frac{\bar{P}(1 - \bar{P})}{n} + (\bar{P} - P)^2 \tag{8.22}$$

*Remark*   The sum of the simple response variance and the sampling variance equals $\bar{P}(1 - \bar{P})/n$, which is analogous to the well-known expression $P(1 - P)/n$ taken as the sampling variance of the estimate $p$ (see Exercise 69).   This shows that, in this case, the customary expression for the sampling variance includes the simple response variance.

*Remark*   The simple response variance has an upper limit, namely,

$$\frac{1}{n} V(d_{jt}) \leq \frac{\bar{P}(1 - \bar{P})}{n} \tag{8.23}$$

Since a large value of the response variance should indicate greater inconsistency of classification of the units to the class $A$, we may use $V(d_{jt})/\bar{P}(1 - \bar{P})$ as an index of inconsistency of classification.

### 8.11.2 ESTIMATION OF SIMPLE RESPONSE VARIANCE

We will now present a method of estimating the simple response variance when the survey is repeated, and the purpose is to estimate the population proportion $P$. Let the survey be repeated independently under identical conditions using the same sample on both trials $t$ and $t'$. The following four-fold table of frequencies will then be observed (Hansen, et al., 1964).

*Original*

|  |  | $x_{jt} = 1$ | $x_{jt} = 0$ |  |
|---|---|---|---|---|
| *Repetition* | $x_{jt'} = 1$ | $a$ | $b$ | $a + b$ |
|  | $x_{jt'} = 0$ | $c$ | $d$ | $c + d$ |
|  |  | $a + c$ | $b + d$ | $n$ |

Consider the statistic $g = S(x_{jt} - x_{jt'})^2/n$. We have

$$E(g) = E(x_{jt} - x_{jt'})^2 = V(x_{jt} - x_{jt'})$$
$$= V(d_{jt} - d_{jt'}) = 2V(d_{jt})$$

Thus $g/2$ is an unbiased estimate of $V(d_{jt})$.

Since $g = (b + c)/n$, the estimate of the simple response variance is given by $(b + c)/2n$. Further, an estimate of the index of inconsistency is provided by $(b + c)/2np(1 - p)$.

### 8.12 THE PROBLEM OF NONRESPONSE

Another source of error in large-scale surveys is the nonavailability of information from some units included in the sample. If a questionnaire is mailed to a sample of establishments, some establishments will fail to respond. If visits are made to a sample of households, some households will be found to be away from home and others may refuse to cooperate. An obvious solution in the first case would be to continue issuing reminders. If this does not remedy the situation, actual visits may be made again and again. Or, a subsample of the nonrespondents may be taken (Sec. 4.9 and Exercise 73) and all attention directed toward them. The same procedure can be used in the second case. We continue recalling and recalling until it is found that it is no use making further calls. Or, further calls are made on a subsample only. In case the cost per completed schedule based on recalling is far higher than that based on the first call, an ingenious device has been proposed by Hartley (1946) and developed by Politz and Simmons (1949, 1950). It is used when the major cause of noninterviews is the absence of the respondents from home when the interviewer knocks at the door. The interviewer makes only one call at each sample household, the time of call being considered random within interviewing hours. If the household is available, the desired information is collected and it is also asked whether the household was at home on the previous six days at the same time. This information is used to estimate $p$, the probability of availability at home. If the household is found to have been away, no information is collected.

Assume that a wr simple random sample of $n$ households has been selected. Then the $i$th selection can be used to give an estimate of $\bar{Y}$ as

$$\hat{y}_i = \frac{y_i}{\hat{p}_i} \qquad \text{if the household is available}$$

$$\hat{y}_i = 0 \qquad \text{if the household is not available}$$

where $\hat{p}_i$ is an estimate of $p_i$. Assuming that the at-home probability is estimated from $s$ moments, we note that $\hat{p}_i$ is a random variable taking up the value $j/s$ $(j = 1, 2, \ldots, s)$ with probability $\binom{s-1}{j-1} p_i{}^{j-1}(1 - p_i)^{s-j}$ if the sample unit is available. Hence, for a specified unit, the expected value of $\hat{y}_i$ would be (given availability)

$$y_i \sum_{j=1}^{s} (j/s)^{-1} \binom{s-1}{j-1} p_i{}^{j-1}(1 - p_i)^{s-j} = \frac{y_i}{p_i}(1 - q_i{}^s)$$

$$q_i = 1 - p_i$$

Thus $\qquad E(\hat{y}_i) = \frac{1}{N} \sum y_i(1 - q_i{}^s) = \bar{Y} - \frac{1}{N} \sum q_i{}^s y_i$

At the same time

$$E(\hat{y}_i{}^2) = \frac{s}{N} \sum_i y_i{}^2 \sum_{j=1}^{s} \frac{1}{j}\binom{s}{j} p_i{}^j q_i{}^{s-j} = \frac{s}{N} \sum y_i{}^2 P_i$$

where $\qquad P_i = \sum_{j=1}^{s} (j)^{-1} \binom{s}{j} p_i{}^j q_i{}^{s-j}$

Hence, $\qquad V(\hat{y}_i) = \frac{s}{N} \sum_{i=1}^{N} y_i{}^2 P_i - \left[\frac{1}{N} \sum y_i(1 - q_i{}^s)\right]^2$

Finally, let

$$\hat{M} = S\hat{y}_i/n \qquad (8.24)$$

Then

$$E(\hat{M}) = \bar{Y} - \frac{1}{N} \sum q_i{}^s y_i \qquad (8.25)$$

$$V(\hat{M}) = \frac{1}{n} V(\hat{y}_i)$$

and

$$V(\hat{M}) \cong \frac{S(\hat{y}_i - S\hat{y}_i/n)^2}{n(n-1)}$$

Although the sample estimate (8.24) is not strictly unbiased, it does seek to remove the major part of bias. The following results were obtained by the author in a health survey carried out in a part of Beirut, in which this technique was applied. In order to test this method, further calls were made again and again on the nonrespondents to obtain complete response. The column "first call adjusted" in Table 8.1 gives the figures obtained by using the at-home probabilities. The results are interesting.

**Table 8.1  Estimates based on recalls**

| | Estimates in %, based on | | |
| Item | First call | First call adjusted | All calls |
|---|---|---|---|
| Unmarried | 45.5 | 59.5 | 61.7 |
| Literate | 48.1 | 75.4 | 61.7 |
| Earner | 24.7 | 33.5 | 34.2 |
| Nonearning dependent | 52.0 | 65.9 | 65.1 |
| Having refrigerator | 61.4 | 63.3 | 65.9 |
| Having servants | 35.5 | 36.1 | 42.3 |

### Further reading

**1.** See Exercise 74 for another procedure in which calls are made on each person in the sample and information collected from those who are available at least once.

**2.** Bounds for the bias due to noninterview when the object is to obtain a population proportion are derived in Exercise 72.

### 8.12.1  PRACTICAL PROCEDURES

In spite of best efforts to track down the nonrespondents, some nonresponse will always remain. A good practice is to get some kind of information from those who do not cooperate. A comparison can then be made with the respondents of the survey to assess the probable effect of the exclusion of nonrespondents on the results of the survey. For example, it may be found that the results of the survey relate to 98 percent of the population, two percent belonging to the nonresponse stratum. If it has been possible to collect some information, such as the size of the household, from the nonrespondents, comparative figures on the average size of a household for the two strata would be useful in interpreting the results. The situation becomes more serious when the object is to estimate totals on a regular basis. It is inconvenient to publish differing totals simply because the response rate has changed during the two periods. A practice generally followed is to make substitutions at random from the completed schedules paying due regard to certain known characteristics of the non-respondents. This will help reduce the bias involved although no method can eliminate the bias altogether. (See Exercise 81.)

*Further reading* If the respondents are unlikely to cooperate in the survey because the question asked is too personal, it should be possible to win their cooperation by asking them to furnish information on a probability basis only. This is discussed in Exercise 94.


## 8.13 SOME EXAMPLES OF SOURCES OF ERROR

For the benefit of readers not connected with data collection, some examples will now be presented of the sources of error involved when information is collected. Take the problem of the collection of information on consumer expenditure by the method of interview. It has been found (Neter, et al., 1964) that there is a tendency on the part of respondents to allocate expenditures either to earlier or later time periods than when the expenditures actually occurred. This phenomenon is called "telescoping" (of expenditures, in this case). If telescoping exists on a substantial scale, estimates made for a given time period might be seriously biased. Another source of error here is the failure of respondents to report some of the expenditures that were actually made. This (Exercise 80) may be called "memory failure" or "recall lapse." A third source of error is the so-called "conditioning" effect. If one member of a household is interviewed today and another the following day, the intervening conversations might condition the responses on the second interview. The presence of the interviewer by itself might condition the response in the sense that the response obtained otherwise might be different. It may be mentioned that these errors are not peculiar to expenditure data only. To take another example, suppose data are to be collected on food consumption. For this purpose the households selected at random are asked to maintain account books in which records are kept of the food consumed. Many households will refuse to cooperate, and this will vitiate the random character of the sample. If the interview method is used instead, there will be much less nonresponse but many households will not know what they consumed, especially when they happen to be farmers using home-grown foods for which they can give no numerical estimates. If the alternative method of weighing all food consumed is considered, other types of errors come in. As a matter of prestige, the sample households may begin to consume more food than is usual and use more expensive food, at least for the first few days. The normal course of life in the household is disturbed. Altogether, it may be found to be an exceedingly difficult task to collect usable data on food consumption through house-hold surveys. We shall give another example from the field of agriculture. The object is to estimate the total production of a crop by harvesting a sample cut (or plot) taken at random from each field (or parcel) selected in the sample. Owing to high correlation between yields in adjoining parts of the same field and for reasons of convenience and economy, it is desired to keep the size of the cut small. But actual survey experience shows (Mahalanobis, 1946; Sukhatme, 1947) that cuts of a small size tend to overstate the true yield persistently. One explanation that is usually offered is the "boundary effect." There is a tendency on the part of the investigator to include rather than exclude plants which stand near the boundary or perimeter of the sample cut. Naturally this effect becomes less and less important as the size of the cut is increased. Another explanation given is that in locating the sample cut the investigator may unconsciously tend to favor fertile patches in the field by shifting about the random point to some extent.

REFERENCES

Hansen, M. H., et al. (1951). Response errors in surveys. *J. Am. Stat. Assoc.*, 46.

——— (1964). The estimation and interpretation of gross differences and the simple response variance. *Contributions to Statistics*, Calcutta.

Hartley, H. O. (1946). Discussion of paper by F. Yates. *J. Roy. Stat. Soc.*, 109.

Kish, L. and J. B. Lansing (1954). Response errors in estimating the value of homes. *J. Am. Stat. Assoc.*, 49.

Mahalanobis, P. C. (1946). Recent experiments in statistical sampling in the Indian Statistical Institute. *J. Roy. Stat. Soc.*, 109.

Neter, J. and J. Waksberg (1964). A study of response errors in expenditures data from household surveys. *J. Am. Stat. Assoc.*, 59.

Politz, A. N. and W. R. Simmons (1949, 1950).   An attempt to get the "not at homes" into the sample without call-backs.   *J. Am. Stat. Assoc.*, 44 and 45.

Raj, D. (1965).   Farmers reporting at the Census.   *Sankhya*, B 27.

Sukhatme, P. V. (1947).   The problem of plot size in large-scale yield surveys. *J. Am. Stat. Assoc.*, 42.

―――― (1953).   Sampling theory of surveys with applications.   *Ind. Soc. Agr. Stat.*, New Delhi.

# CHAPTER NINE

# OTHER DEVELOPMENTS

## 9.1 INTRODUCTION

A number of important topics were not included in the previous chapters at their proper place because they might have retarded the flow of discussion. They will all be discussed now under the following headings: variance estimation, estimation for subpopulations, the best linear estimator, the method of overlapping maps, two-way stratification with small samples, the performance of systematic sampling in different situations, the method of controlled selection, a general rule for variance estimation in multistage sampling, sampling from imperfect frames, and sampling inspection.

## 9.2 VARIANCE ESTIMATION

In all the sampling systems discussed in this book, estimators of population characteristics (such as means, proportions, etc.), and their variances and variance estimators have always been given. But the question of the stability of the variance estimator was left untouched. This question becomes important if the variance estimated from a sample is to be used for comparing one method with another, if it is to be used for estimating the sample size needed to achieve a specified degree of precision, or if it is to be used for making a firm estimate of the precision actually attained in the survey. We shall agree to judge the stability of a variance estimator $u$ by its coefficient of variation, $CV(u) = \sigma(u)/E(u)$. We begin by proving the following theorem (Raj, 1958).

### Theorem 9.1

Let $t_1, t_2, \ldots, t_k$ be $k$ independently and identically distributed random variables and let $u = \Sigma(t_i - \Sigma t_i/k)^2/(k - 1)$. Then

$$CV^2(u) = \frac{\beta_2(t_i) - (k - 3)(k - 1)^{-1}}{k} \tag{9.1}$$

where $\beta_2(t_i) = M_4(t_i)/M_2^2(t_i)$ and $CV^2(u)$ denotes the square of the coefficient of variation of $u$, $M$ standing for the central moment.

PROOF   Let $v_i = t_i - E(t_i)$ so that $E(v_i) = 0$. Now

$$u = \frac{\Sigma(v_i - \bar{v})^2}{k - 1} = \frac{\Sigma v_i^2}{k} - 2\frac{\sum_i \sum_{j>i} v_i v_j}{k(k - 1)}$$

$$E(u^2) = \frac{1}{k^2}\sum E(v_i^4) + \frac{2}{k^2}\sum_i \sum_{j>i} E(v_i^2 v_j^2) + \frac{4}{k^2(k - 1)^2}\sum_i \sum_{j>i} E(v_i^2 v_j^2)$$

since other terms will have zero expectation. Hence,

$$E(u^2) = \frac{1}{k^2}\sum M_4(t_i) + \frac{2}{k^2}\left(1 + \frac{2}{(k - 1)^2}\right)\sum_i \sum_{j>i} M_2(t_i)M_2(t_j)$$

or     $$V(u) = \frac{1}{k}M_4(t_i) + \frac{k - 1}{k}\frac{k^2 - 2k + 3}{(k - 1)^2}M_2^2(t_i) - E^2(u)$$

Hence,   $$CV^2(u) = \frac{1}{k}\beta_2(t_i) + \frac{k^2 - 2k + 3}{k(k - 1)} - 1 = \frac{1}{k}\left[\beta_2(t_i) - \frac{k - 3}{k - 1}\right]\ \blacksquare$$

### Corollary

If a wr simple random sample of size $n$ is selected and the population total is estimated by $\hat{Y} = N\bar{y}$, we have

$$V(\hat{Y}) = N^2V(\bar{y})    \qquad V(\hat{Y}) \cong \frac{N^2(1 - f)S(y_i - \bar{y})^2}{n(n - 1)} = u$$

Since the $y$'s are independently and identically distributed, Theorem 9.1

gives (Hansen, et al., 1953)

$$CV^2(u) = \frac{\beta_2(y) - \dfrac{n-3}{n-1}}{n} \qquad (9.2)$$

Thus the precision of the variance estimator depends, apart from the sample size, on the $\beta_2$ of the distribution of $y$. If the parent population is peaked, giving a high value of $\beta_2$, the variance estimator will be of low precision. Given the value of $\beta_2(y)$ for a population, it is possible to find from (9.2) the sample size $n$ for which the variance estimate would be satisfactory (having a coefficient of variation of, say, 20 percent or less). In case the object is to estimate a population proportion $P$,

$$\beta_2(y) = P^{-1}(1 - P)^{-1} - 3$$

Hence $\qquad CV^2(u) = \dfrac{1}{n}\left[\dfrac{1}{P(1-P)} - 4\,\dfrac{n - \frac{3}{2}}{n-1}\right]$

If $n$ is large so that $(n - 1.5)/(n - 1) \doteq 1$, the sample size is given by

$$n = \frac{\dfrac{1}{P(1-P)} - 4}{CV^2(u)}$$

### Corollary

If we are dealing with wr pps sampling, the random variables $y_i/p_i$ will be independently and identically distributed. Denoting by $u$ the variance estimator $S[y_i/p_i - (1/n)Sy_i/p_i]^2/n(n - 1)$, we have

$$CV^2(u) = \frac{\beta_2(y_i/p_i) - (n - 3)(n - 1)^{-1}}{n} \qquad (9.3)$$

Thus the stability of the variance estimator in this case depends on the fourth moment of $y_i/p_i$. If the ratio of $y$ to $x$ departs considerably from the average for some of the units, $y/p$ for these units will fall in the tails, which will inflate the fourth moment. Even a few extreme values of $y/p$ may bring about a very high value of $\beta_2$.

### 9.2.1 VARIANCE ESTIMATION IN STRATIFIED SAMPLING

Let there be $L$ strata with $n_h$ units selected from stratum $h$ with replacement with pp to $x$. Then

$$\hat{Y} = \sum \hat{Y}_h = \sum \frac{1}{n_h} S_j \frac{y_{hj}}{p_{hj}} = \sum \frac{1}{n_h} S_j z_{hj}$$

An unbiased estimator of $V(\hat{Y})$ is given by

$$u = \sum_h \frac{S(z_{hj} - \bar{z}_h)^2}{n_h(n_h - 1)}$$ (9.4)

By Theorem 9.1, we have

$$V(u) = \sum_h \frac{1}{n_h{}^3} [M_4(z_h) - (n_h - 3)(n_h - 1)^{-1} M_2{}^2(z_h)]$$

Since $E(u) = \Sigma(1/n_h) M_2(z_h)$, we have

$$CV^2(u) = \sum_h \frac{1}{n_h{}^3} \frac{M_4(z_h) - (n_h - 3)(n_h - 1)^{-1} M_2{}^2(z_h)}{\left[ \sum \frac{1}{n_h} M_2(z_h) \right]^2}$$

If the sample size is the same within each stratum, that is $n_h = k$, we get

$$CV^2(u) = \frac{1}{k} \frac{\Sigma M_4(z_h)}{[\Sigma M_2(z_h)]^2} - \frac{k - 3}{k(k - 1)} \frac{\Sigma M_2{}^2(z_h)}{[\Sigma M_2(z_h)]^2}$$

To examine a few particular cases, let there be $L = 100$ strata with $k = 2$ sample units from each stratum. Assuming the distribution of $z_h$ to be rectangular with a range of $r$ in each stratum, we get $M_2(z_h) = r^2/12$, $M_4(z_h) = r^4/80$. Hence

$$CV^2(u) = \frac{1}{kL} \left( 1.8 - \frac{k - 3}{k - 1} \right) = 0.014$$

If the distribution is normal within strata

$$M_2(z_h) = \sigma^2 \qquad M_4(z_h) = 3\sigma^4 \qquad CV^2(u) = \frac{1}{kL} \left( 3 - \frac{k - 3}{k - 1} \right) = 0.02$$

There is a quicker method of estimating $V(\hat{Y})$ in stratified sampling when a constant sample size is taken from each stratum. We form $t_1 = \Sigma_h \hat{Y}_{h1}$ as an estimate of the population total based on the first selection from each stratum. The second selection from each stratum gives $t_2$, and so on. Thus we have $k$ independently and identically distributed random variables. Hence, an estimate of the population total is given by $t = \Sigma t_i/k$, $V(t) = V(t_i)/k$, and

$$u = \hat{V}(t) = \frac{\Sigma(t_i - \bar{t})^2}{k(k - 1)}$$ (9.5)

The estimator $u$ given by (9.5) is quicker to calculate than that given by (9.4), since variances are not to be estimated within strata. From Theorem

9.1, its precision is given by $CV^2(u) = (1/k)[\beta_2(t_i) - (k-3)/(k-1)]$. If the number of strata is large, the $t_i$ will be normally distributed. This follows from the central-limit theorem (Sec. 1.12). Hence $\beta_2(t_i) = 3$. This gives $CV^2(u) = 2/(k-1)$. Thus the precision of the variance estimator in this case depends entirely on the sample size within one stratum. If there are two units taken per stratum, $CV^2(u) = 2$ as compared with 0.014 and 0.02 when the more laborious estimator (9.4) is used. Calling the first selection from each stratum the first interpenetrating subsample, etc., we may state the following result.

**Theorem 9.2**

*Let there be a stratified sampling design in which $k$ units are selected from each stratum following the* wr pps *scheme. If the variance estimator $u$ is based on the $k$ interpenetrating subsamples involved, we have*

$$\hat{Y} = \sum_{i=1}^{k} \frac{t_i}{k} \qquad t_i = \sum_h \hat{Y}_{hi}$$

$$V(\hat{Y}) \cong u = \sum_{i=1}^{k} \frac{(t_i - t)^2}{k(k-1)}$$

$$CV^2(u) = \frac{\beta_2(t_i) - \dfrac{k-3}{k-1}}{k}$$

*If the number of strata is large, $\beta_2(t_i) \doteq 3$ and $CV^2(u) \doteq 2/(k-1)$.*

**Remark**   In this case the precision of the variance estimator depends entirely on the number of degrees of freedom.

**Further reading**   See Exercise 20 for sample allocation to strata in order to have a reasonably stable variance estimator.

### 9.2.2 THE NUMBER OF DEGREES OF FREEDOM

In the general estimation theory the stability of a variance estimator is judged by the number of degrees of freedom. This is so because normality is the basic assumption made.

If the distribution is not necessarily normal, the stability of the variance estimator is a function of the $\beta_2$ of the distribution [Formula (9.2)]. Some authors have given formulas ascribed to Satterthwaite (1946), by which the number of degrees of freedom can be calculated approximately when the sample design used is stratified simple random sampling. The reasoning appears to take the following form. The population total is estimated by $\hat{Y} = \sum_i N_i \bar{y}_i$ and the variance estimator $u$ is

$$u = \sum \frac{N_i(N_i - n_i)}{n_i} s_i^2 = \sum g_i s_i^2$$

Assuming normality within strata, it is easy to see that

$$V(u) = 2 \sum \frac{g_i^2 \sigma_i^4}{n_i - 1}$$

and
$$\mathrm{CV}^2(u) = \frac{2\Sigma[g_i^2\sigma_i^4/(n_i - 1)]}{(\Sigma g_i \sigma_i^2)^2}$$

We can say that the variance estimator is based on the number of degrees of freedom given by $(\Sigma g_i \sigma_i^2)^2/\Sigma[g_i^2\sigma_i^4/(n_i - 1)]$. Just as we can with normal distribution in which the number of degrees of freedom equals $2/\mathrm{CV}^2(u)$. But this result must be interpreted with great caution. In the absence of normality, the number of degrees of freedom as such may not give the true picture about the precision of the variance estimator. Consider, for example, the situation in which with-replacement pps sampling is used for selecting the sample within strata. We have the variance estimator $u$ given by (9.4), for which

$$\mathrm{CV}^2(u) = \frac{\sum_h M_2^2(z_h)[\beta_2(z_h)/n_h^3 - (n_h - 3)(n_h - 1)^{-1}]}{\left\{\sum_h [M_2(z_h)/n_h]\right\}^2} \tag{9.6}$$

Thus the stability of the variance estimator depends upon the $\beta_2(z_h)$ within strata, the variances $M_2(z_h)$, and the sample sizes $n_h$. There is no simple quantity to calculate which will at once guide us regarding the stability of $u$. In case, however, the number of strata is large and the variance estimator is based on interpenetrating subsamples, there is an almost exact relationship between the stability of the variance estimator and the number of degrees of freedom involved (Theorem 9.2).

### 9.2.3 THE METHOD OF RANDOM GROUPS

In large-scale work involving the estimation of several characters, the calculation of standard errors is a laborious process. Methods in which errors can be calculated more quickly with the attendant risk of some loss of efficiency are being increasingly used. Theorem 9.2 is an illustration of such a method in stratified sampling. We shall now consider an unstratified case. Suppose a simple random sample of $n$ units is selected for estimating the population mean. If the customary variance estimator $s^2$ (Sec. 3.3) is used, we have

$$\text{CV}^2(s^2) = \frac{1}{n} [\beta_2(y) - 3] + \frac{2}{n - 1} \tag{9.7}$$

where $n$ is considered to be very small relative to $N$ so that we may assume wr sampling. Instead of calculating $s^2$, we may divide the sample into $k$ random groups, each group containing $m = n/k$ units. Denoting by $t_i$ the sample mean based on the $i$th group, we have $\hat{M} = \Sigma t_i/k$, and a quicker estimator of variance is provided by

$$v^2 = \sum \frac{(t_i - \bar{t})^2}{k(k - 1)}$$

Assuming wr sampling, we have, by Theorem 9.1,

$$\text{CV}^2(v^2) = \frac{1}{k} \left( \beta_2(t_i) - \frac{k - 3}{k - 1} \right)$$

Using the fact that $t_i$ is the mean of $m$ observations on the variable $y$, a simple calculation shows that (Raj, 1964)

$$\beta_2(t_i) = \frac{\beta_2(y)}{m} + \frac{3(m - 1)}{m}$$

Hence

$$\text{CV}^2(v^2) = \frac{1}{n} [\beta_2(y) - 3] + \frac{2}{k - 1} \tag{9.8}$$

A comparison of (9.8) and (9.7) gives

$$\text{CV}^2(v^2) - \text{CV}^2(s^2) = 2 \left( \frac{1}{k - 1} - \frac{1}{n - 1} \right) = \frac{2(n - k)}{(n - 1)(k - 1)} > 0$$

Denoting by $a$ and $a'$ the coefficients of variation when no grouping is made and when $k$ groups are formed, we have for large $n$:

$$a' = \left( a^2 + \frac{2}{k - 1} \right)^{\frac{1}{2}}$$

Thus with a small number of random groups the precision of the variance estimator may be extremely low.

### 9.2.4 VARIANCE ESTIMATION IN WTR SAMPLING

It was a simple matter to get usable results on the variance of the variance estimator when sampling was done with replacement. In case of wtr sampling it is not difficult to put down formal expressions for the variance of the estimator of variance, but their simplication for actual use is a herculean task. Only two sample designs, for which the author has been able to get simplified results, will be considered. The problem is important, since it is generally believed that variance estimation is a hazardous task when sampling is without replacement with unequal probabilities. Only the case of two sample units within a stratum will be discussed, but luckily this is a situation of considerable practical interest. The results for one particular design (Sec. 3.24) are given (Raj, 1966$a$) below.

### Theorem 9.3

*Let the first member of the sample be selected with probabilities*

$$p_i \ (i = 1, \ldots, N)$$

*proportional to measures of size $x_i$ of the units, the second unit being selected with pp to $x_i$ of the remaining units. Then $t_1 = y_1/p_1$,*

$$t_2 = y_1 + (1 - p_1) \frac{y_2}{p_2}$$

*$t = (t_1 + t_2)/2$ are unbiased estimators of the stratum total, the variance estimator being*

$$u = \frac{(t_1 - t_2)^2}{4}$$

*and the coefficient of variation of $u$ is given by*

$$1 + \mathrm{CV}^2(u) = \frac{E(u^2)}{[E(u)]^2}$$

*where*                                 $E(u) = V(t)$

$$E(u^2) = \frac{1}{16} \sum_i (1 - p_i)^3 \left[ p_i \left( \frac{y_i}{p_i} - Y \right)^4 + 6(A_{21} - Y^2) \frac{y_i^2}{p_i} \right.$$
$$\left. - 4(A_{32} - Y^3)y_i + (A_{43} - Y^4)p_i \right] \quad (9.9)$$

*with $A_{lm} = \sum_i (y_i^l/p_i^m)$.*

PROOF    The only result to be proved is (9.9). We have

$$16E(u^2) = E(t_1^4) - 4E(t_1^3 t_2) + 6E(t_1^2 t_2^2) - 4E(t_1 t_2^3) + E(t_2^4)$$

Now,                       $E(t_1^4) = \sum \left( \frac{y_1^4}{p_1^3} \right) = A_{43}$

$$E(t_1^3 t_2) = E_1[E_2(t_2 t_1^3)]$$

where $E_2$ denotes the conditional expectation given the first selection.

But $E_2(t_2t_1{}^3) = t_1{}^3E_2(t_2) = t_1{}^3Y$. Hence

$$E(t_1{}^3t_2) = YE(t_1{}^3) = Y \sum \left(\frac{y_1{}^3}{p_1{}^2}\right) = YA_{32}$$

Proceeding on the same lines, it is not difficult to establish that

$$E(t_1{}^2t_2{}^2) = (A_{21})^2 - A_{42} - A_{21}A_{20} + 2YA_{31}$$
$$E(t_1t_2{}^3) = A_{32}\Sigma(1 - p_i)^2y_i + 3A_{21}(A_{20} - \Sigma p_iy_i{}^2) - A_{41} - A_{42} + 3YA_{30}$$
$$\text{and} \quad E(t_2{}^4) = A_{43}\Sigma p_i(1 - p_i)^3 + 4A_{32}\Sigma p_i(1 - p_i)^2y_i$$
$$+ 6A_{21}\Sigma p_i(1 - p_i)y_i{}^2 - A_{42} - A_{41} - A_{40} + 4Y\Sigma p_iy_i{}^3$$

After considerable rearrangement of terms we get (9.9).    ∎

**Remark**  In the notation of Theorem 9.3, the expected value of the square of the variance estimator $u$ in wr pps sampling (corollary, Theorem 9.1) can be written as $[A_{43} + 3(A_{21})^2 - 4YA_{32}]/8$.

### 9.2.5 VARIANCE ESTIMATION IN RANDOMIZED PPS SYSTEMATIC SAMPLING

With this procedure (Sec. 3.18) an unbiased estimator of the stratum total is $\hat{Y} = y_i/\pi_i + y_j/\pi_j$ with

$$V(\hat{Y}) = \Sigma'(\pi_i\pi_j - \pi_{1j})\left(\frac{y_i}{\pi_i} - \frac{y_j}{\pi_j}\right)^2$$

an unbiased estimator of the variance being

$$v = (\pi_i\pi_j - \pi_{1j})\frac{(y_i/\pi_i - y_j/\pi_j)^2}{\pi_{ij}} \tag{9.10}$$

Hartley and Rao (1962) have obtained an approximate expression for $\pi_{ij}$ when the units in the stratum are randomized before selection. Correct to $0(N^{-4})$, they find that

$$\pi_{ij} \doteq \tfrac{1}{2}\pi_i\pi_j\{1 + \tfrac{1}{2}(\pi_i + \pi_j) + \tfrac{1}{2}(\pi_i{}^2 + \pi_j{}^2 + \pi_i\pi_j)$$
$$- \tfrac{1}{4}S_2[1 + \tfrac{3}{2}(\pi_i + \pi_j)] + \tfrac{3}{16}S_2{}^2 - \tfrac{1}{4}S_3\}$$

where $S_k = \Sigma\pi_i{}^k$. Substituting this value of $\pi_{ij}$ in (9.10) it can be shown (Raj, 1965) that to $0(N^3)$

$$E(v^2) = F - 3G \tag{9.11}$$

where $\quad F = B_{43} - 2YB_{32} + \tfrac{3}{2}(B_{21})^2$

$$G = \tfrac{1}{2}B_{42} - B_{32}\Sigma\pi_jy_j + \tfrac{1}{2}YS_2B_{32} - YB_{31} - \tfrac{3}{8}S_2(B_{21})^2 + \tfrac{3}{2}B_{21}B_{20}$$

and $\qquad\qquad B_{lm} = \sum \left(\frac{y_i{}^l}{\pi_i{}^m}\right)$

If we use the simpler, but biased, variance estimator

$$w = \left(\frac{y_i}{\pi_i} - \frac{y_j}{\pi_j}\right)^2 \tag{9.12}$$

it can be shown that, correct to $0 \ (N^3)$,

$$E(w^2) = F + G \tag{9.13}$$

where $F$ and $G$ have been defined before.  If the estimator $w$ is used in wr pps sampling in which $\pi_i = 2p_i$, we have already noted that in this case

$$E(w^2) = F \tag{9.14}$$

An example will now be given to show what these formulas are expected to give in some practical situations.  The data are taken from studies by Horvitz and Thompson (1952), in which the object is to estimate from a sample of two blocks the total number of households in an area containing 20 blocks.  The $x_i$ are eye-estimates of the number of households (Table 9.1) and the $y_i$ are the actual number of households.

Table 9.1   Eye-estimated $(x_i)$ and actual $(y_i)$ number of households in twenty blocks

| $i$ | 1 | 2 | 3 | 4 | 5 | 6 | 7 | 8 | 9 | 10 |
|-----|---|---|---|---|---|---|---|---|---|----|
| $y_i$ | 19 | 9 | 17 | 14 | 21 | 22 | 27 | 35 | 20 | 15 |
| $x_i$ | 18 | 9 | 14 | 12 | 24 | 25 | 23 | 24 | 17 | 14 |

| $i$ | 11 | 12 | 13 | 14 | 15 | 16 | 17 | 18 | 19 | 20 |
|-----|----|----|----|----|----|----|----|----|----|----|
| $y_i$ | 18 | 37 | 12 | 47 | 27 | 25 | 25 | 13 | 19 | 12 |
| $x_i$ | 18 | 40 | 12 | 30 | 27 | 26 | 21 | 9 | 19 | 12 |

Table 9.2 gives results for this data, as well as for the modified data, in which the sizes $(x_i)$ of the 5th and 14th blocks are changed to 34 and

Table 9.2   Coefficients of variation of variance estimators

| Sampling scheme | Original data | | | Modified data | | |
|---|---|---|---|---|---|---|
| | Variance to be estimated (000) | Variance of variance estimator (000) | CV % | Variance to be estimated (000) | Variance of variance estimator (000) | CV % |
| Simple random | 17,122 | 704,319 | 1.55 | 17,122 | 704,319 | 1.55 |
| wr pps | 3,247 | 21,259 | 1.42 | 9,435 | 435,129 | 2.21 |
| wtr pps: | | | | | | |
| Estimator $u$ | | | | | | |
| (Theorem 9.3) | 3,045 | 16,748 | 1.34 | 8,886 | 483,437 | 2.47 |
| Estimator $v$ (9.10) | 3,014 | 15,862 | 1.32 | 8,848 | 354,952 | 2.13 |
| Estimator $w$ (9.12) | 3,014 | 22,330 | 1.56 | 8,848 | 456,844 | 2.41 |

20, respectively, so that we may study the effect of the presence of extreme values of $y/x$ in the data. It will be found that with the original data (with good measures of size) the stability of the variance estimators did not deteriorate when one passed on from sampling with equal probabilities to sampling with unequal probabilities. With poorer measures of size the variance estimators became less stable in the case of sampling with unequal probabilities.

## 9.3 ESTIMATION FOR SUBPOPULATIONS

Ordinarily data are required not only for the entire population but also for its subdivisions, which may be called subpopulations, or domains of study. For example, in a labor-force survey, estimates may be wanted not only for the total number employed, but separately for those working in agriculture by sex. Out of all males working in agriculture we may wish to know what proportion worked for less than 20 hours during the week of the survey, and we may be interested in comparing the average earnings of these with those working in industry, and so on. In these cases we are estimating totals, means, ratios and proportions in subpopulations. The question arises: Do we require new theory for this purpose? The general answer is: No, no new principles are involved. A probability sample taken from the entire universe would serve as a probability sample taken from the subpopulation provided that units in the sample not belonging to the subpopulation are assumed to have a value of zero for the character under study. This is like taking a sample from a frame which is known to include extra units not belonging to the population under consideration. If we make sure that such units are given a value of zero, we can make estimates as before. The only difference is that the number of units in the sample belonging to the subpopulation is a chance variable.

To take an example, let a simple random sample of $n$ persons be selected from a population containing $N$ persons. If we are interested in estimating the total earnings of males, the females in the population (and therefore in the sample) will be assumed to have $y_i$ equal to zero. With this definition, $Y_g = \sum_1^N y_i$, where $Y_g$ is the total of the subpopulation for $y$. Hence, $\hat{Y}_g = NSy_i/n$ is an unbiased estimator of $Y_g$ and the population mean is estimated by $\bar{y}_g = Sy_i/n_g$, where $n_g$ is the number of males in the sample. Given $n_g > 0$, the expected value of $\bar{y}_g$ is $\bar{Y}_g = Y_g/N_g$ and hence $E(\bar{y}_g) = \bar{Y}_g$. Regarding the variance of $\hat{Y}_g$, we immediately have

$$V(\hat{Y}_g) = \frac{N^2}{n}(1-f)S_y'^2 \cong \frac{N^2}{n}(1-f)s_y'^2$$

where $S_y'^2, s_y'^2$ are defined as $S_y^2, s_y^2$, the only difference being that units not belonging to the subgroup are assumed to have a value of zero. Coming now to the variance of $\bar{y}_g$, we find that given $n_g$,

$$E_2(\bar{y}_g) = \bar{Y}_g \qquad V_2(\bar{y}_g) = \left(\frac{1}{n_g} - \frac{1}{N_g}\right) S_g^2$$

Hence $\qquad V(\bar{y}_g) = E_1 V_2(\bar{y}_g) = -\frac{1}{N_g} S_g^2 + E\left(\frac{1}{n_g}\right) S_g^2$

As an estimator of its variance, we may take $(1 - n/N)s_g^2/n_g$. Strictly speaking, we should apply the methods of ratio estimation to the estimator of the mean, since it is the ratio of two random variables. If the size of the group $N_g$ is known, it is possible to achieve higher precision by making use of this information. A better estimate of the subpopulation total $Y_g$ would be $\hat{Y}_g = N_g \bar{y}_g$ whose variance could be developed by methods given in Chap. 5. The same remarks apply to the estimation of proportions in the subpopulation.

### 9.3.1 SUBPOPULATION ANALYSIS FOR OTHER DESIGNS

Consider a population divided up into $L$ strata for which a random sample of $n_h$ units has been selected from stratum $h$ $(h = 1, 2, \ldots, L)$ containing $N_h$ units. The total of a subpopulation for a character $y$ will be $\sum_h \sum_i y_{ih}$, where $y_{ih}$ is zero for all units in the population not belonging to the subpopulation. A sample estimate of it will be $\Sigma N_h S y_{ih}/n_h$. Since this is of the form $\Sigma N_h \bar{y}_h$, with $y_{ih}$ properly defined, the formulas given in Theorem 4.2 can be used for obtaining its variance or estimating the variance from the sample. For this subpopulation, the average would be given by

$$\bar{Y}_g = \frac{\displaystyle\sum_h \sum_i y_{ih}}{\displaystyle\sum_h \sum_i x_{ih}}$$

where $x_{ih}$ takes the value 1 if the unit belongs to the subpopulation and zero otherwise. A sample estimate of it would be

$$\bar{y}_g = \frac{\displaystyle\sum_h N_h \sum_i y_{ih}/n_h}{N_h \sum_i x_{ih}/n_h}$$

This estimator has the same form as the combined ratio estimator of Sec. 5.18, so that no new formulas are required for its bias and variance.

Again, consider a two-stage design in which $n$ psu's have been selected following scheme $B$ of Sec. 6.5, and a random sample of $m_i$ subunits has been taken from the $M_i$ in the $i$th psu. Defining $x_{ij}$ as 1 if the $j$th subunit in the $i$th psu belongs to the subpopulation and zero otherwise, and letting $y_{ij}$ be zero for the subunit if it does not belong to the subpopulation, we immediately see that the subpopulation mean per subunit will be estimated by

$$\frac{(1/n) \underset{i}{S} (M_i/p_i) \underset{j}{S} y_{ij}/m_i}{(1/n) \underset{i}{S} (M_i/p_i) \underset{j}{S} x_{ij}/m_i}$$

The bias, variance, and other particulars of this estimator follow readily from the theory developed in Sec. 6.8.2.


### 9.4 THE BEST LINEAR ESTIMATOR

As pointed out in Sec. 2.8, it is possible to consider very general estimators in sampling theory. Let there be a sampling scheme in which the units are selected with equal or unequal probabilities and sampling is with or without replacement. The sampling scheme generates the totality of samples $s$, each sample having a probability of $p(s)$, $\sum_s p(s) = 1$. Let the unit $U_i$ be included in $H_i$ samples so that $\pi_i = \overset{H_i}{\underset{s}{\sum}} p(s)$ is the probability that $U_i$ occurs in the sample. Further, let $a_i(s)$ be a coefficient attached to $U_i$ when it occurs in sample $s$. A fairly general linear estimator may then be written as

$$t = Sy_i a_i(s) = \sum_{i=1}^{N} y_i a_i'(s) \tag{9.15}$$

in which $a_i'(s)$ takes the value 0 if $U_i$ is not in $s$ and the value $a_i(s)$ if $U_i$ is in $s$. The problem is to determine the coefficients $a_i(s)$ such that $t$ is unbiased and is uniformly better than any other unbiased estimator of $Y$ (Godambe, 1955). The expected value of $t$ would be

$$E(t) = \sum_i y_i \overset{H_i}{\underset{s}{\sum}} a_i(s)p(s)$$

In order that $t$ be an unbiased estimator of $Y = \Sigma y_i$, the coefficients $a_i(s)$ must satisfy the conditions

$$\overset{H_i}{\underset{s}{\sum}} a_i(s)p(s) = 1 \qquad (i = 1, 2, \ldots, N) \tag{9.16}$$

We shall now determine the $a_i(s)$ such that $V(t) = \sum_s t^2 p(s) - Y^2$ is a minimum subject to the conditions given by (9.16). For getting stationary values, we differentiate with respect to $a_i(s)$ the function

$$V(t) + \sum_i \lambda_i \left[ \sum^{H_i} a_i(s)p(s) - 1 \right]$$

and equate the resulting expression to zero. We have $2y_i t = -\lambda_i$. This means that the estimator $t$ must be a constant whenever $U_i$ is in the sample. And this should hold no matter what $y$'s are. Obviously enough, it is impossible to choose the coefficients $a_i(s)$ such that the resulting estimator is a constant whatever the $y$'s be. This proves that a uniformly best unbiased estimator does not exist. An admissible estimator, however, is obtained in the following theorem (Roy and Chakravarty, 1960). By an admissible estimator we mean one for which it can be shown that there is no estimator which is uniformly better.

**Theorem 9.4**

*Under the sampling scheme of Sec. 9.4, let there be the estimator*

$$t^* = \Sigma y_i \frac{v_i(s)}{\pi_i} = \Sigma y_i a_i^*(s) \tag{9.17}$$

*where $v_i(s) = 1$ if $U_i$ belongs to $s$ and $0$ otherwise. Then there does not exist a $t$ belonging to the class (9.15) and satisfying (9.16) such that $V(t) \leq V(t^*)$, the sign of inequality holding for at least one set of $y$'s.*

PROOF   We have

$$E(t^*) = \sum \frac{y_i \overset{H_i}{\underset{}{\sum}} p(s)}{\pi_i} = \sum y_i = Y$$

so that $t^*$ is an unbiased estimator of $Y$. And

$$V(t^*) = \Sigma \Sigma y_i y_j \, \text{Cov} \, (a_i^*, a_j^*) = \Sigma \Sigma y_i y_j \delta_{ij}^*$$

Now, let there exist an estimator $t = \Sigma y_i a_i'(s)$, which is unbiased for $Y$ and for which $V(t^*) - V(t) \geq 0$. Since

$$V(t) = \Sigma \Sigma y_i y_j \, \text{Cov} \, (a_i', a_j') = \Sigma \Sigma y_i y_j \delta_{ij}$$

the inequality $\Sigma \Sigma y_i y_j (\delta_{ij}^* - \delta_{ij}) \geq 0$ must hold, which means that $\|\delta_{ij}^* - \delta_{ij}\|$ be positive definite. But

$$\delta_{ii}^* - \delta_{ii} = V(a_i^*) - V(a_i') = E(a_i^{*2}) - E(a_i'^2)$$
$$= -[E(a_i'^2) - E(a_i^{*2})] = -Ea_i^* - a_i'^2$$

since $$E(a_i^* a_i') = \sum^{H_i} \frac{a_i(s)p(s)}{\pi_i} = \frac{1}{\pi_i} = \sum_s^{H_i} \frac{p(s)}{\pi_i^2} = E(a_i^{*2})$$

Hence the matrix $\| \delta_{ij}^* - \delta_{ij} \|$ is not positive definite, which leads to the result that there is no $t$ which is better than $t^*$. ∎

### Corollary

In sampling with replacement with probabilities proportionate to size, an admissible estimator of $Y$ would be $\sum_i y_i \nu_i(s)/[-(1 - p_i)^n + 1]$. Note that this estimator is based on the distinct units in the sample. The reason that the admissible estimator is not used in large-scale surveys is the complexity of its calculation along with its standard deviation.

### Corollary

In wtr sampling with unequal probabilities, the estimator $S(y_i/\pi_i)$ of Sec. 3.19 is admissible.

*Remark* Koop (1963) considers estimators more general than (9.15). He makes the coefficient $a_i'(s)$ to be attached to $y_i$ depend on the order in which $y_i$ is selected in the sample. We know, however, that the admissible estimator makes no use of the order of selection.

### Further reading

*1.* We have restricted ourselves to unbiased linear estimators for estimating population means or totals. It does not, however, imply that, given any nonlinear unbiased estimator, there exists a linear unbiased estimator which is uniformly better (see Exercise 97).
*2.* There does not necessarily exist a linear unbiased estimator for every general sampling design (see Exercise 91).
*3.* If there is further information available (for example, the value of the coefficient of variation of a population), it is possible to improve upon the admissible estimator of this section (see Exercise 90).
*4.* For a formal definition of sample design and its relationship to a sampling scheme, see Exercise 85.

### 9.5 THE METHOD OF OVERLAPPING MAPS

In multipurpose surveys involving the estimation of several characters, it is usually found desirable to select the units with one set of probabilities for estimating one group of characters and with a different set of probabilities for estimating another group of characters. For example, in the National Sample Survey of India, population is made the basis for selection (of psu's) for the household enquiry and area is made the basis of selection for the land utilization survey. Thus there are two overlapping maps for the universe (Lahiri, 1954). A problem arising in such a situation is that of designing a suitable selection procedure such that the sample units (psu's) for the two types of enquiry are identical or near to one another. Such a procedure will greatly reduce the cost of operations in the field. Let there be a stratum containing $N$ psu's. We are required to select a pair of psu's, one with probabilities $a_1/G$, $a_2/G$, . . . , $a_N/G$ proportional to area and the other with probabilities $b_1/G$, $b_2/G$, . . . , $b_N/G$ proportional to population. Let $c_{ij}$ be the distance (in some sense) between the $i$th area psu and the $j$th population psu. Let $x_{ij}/G$ be the probability with which the corresponding pair of psu's is selected (see Table 9.3). The problem is to find $x_{ij}$ such that

$$\sum_j x_{ij} = a_i \qquad \sum_i x_{ij} = b_j \qquad \sum_i a_i = \sum_j b_j = G \qquad x_{ij} \geq 0$$

and $Z = \Sigma\Sigma c_{ij}x_{ij}$, the expected distance, is minimized. Stated thus, this is the familiar "transportation problem" (Koopmans, 1951) in linear programming, which may be solved by the simplex method (Raj, 1956).

**Table 9.3  Probability mass to be distributed**

|  | Psu no. | *By population* | | | | | | |
|---|---|---|---|---|---|---|---|---|
|  |  | 1 | 2 | $\cdots$ | $j$ | $\cdots$ | $N$ | *Total* |
|  | 1 | $x_{11}$ | $x_{12}$ | $\cdots$ | $x_{1j}$ | $\cdots$ | $x_{1N}$ | $a_1$ |
|  | 2 | $x_{21}$ | $x_{22}$ | $\cdots$ | $x_{2j}$ | $\cdots$ | $x_{2N}$ | $a_2$ |
| *By area* | $i$ | $x_{i1}$ | $x_{i2}$ | $\cdots$ | $x_{ij}$ | $\cdots$ | $x_{iN}$ | $a_i$ |
|  | $N$ | $x_{N1}$ | $x_{N2}$ | $\cdots$ | $x_{Nj}$ | $\cdots$ | $x_{NN}$ | $a_N$ |
| *Total* |  | $b_1$ | $b_2$ | $\cdots$ | $b_j$ | $\cdots$ | $b_N$ | $G$ |

## 9.5.1  CHANGING SELECTION PROBABILITIES

The method of overlapping maps is a useful application in the following problem (Keyfitz, 1951). From a stratum a psu is selected with pp to some measures of size $x$. In due course we get better measures of size of the psu's (based, say, on the latest census). The problem is to make use of the new measures of size for the new survey but to change as few sample psu's (one in each stratum) as possible. Thus the problem is the same as that discussed in Sec. 9.5. The object now is to maximize the probability of getting identical psu's at the two surveys. This is the same as minimizing $Z = \Sigma\Sigma c_{ij}x_{ij}$, where the cost matrix $(c_{ij})$ is given by Table 9.4.

**Table 9.4  Cost matrix in Keyfitz' problem**

| Psu | New survey | | | | |
|---|---|---|---|---|---|
| no. | 1 | 2 | 3 | $\cdots$ | N |
| 1 | 0 | 1 | 1 | $\cdots$ | 1 |
| 2 | 1 | 0 | 1 | $\cdots$ | 1 |
| 3 | 1 | 1 | 0 | $\cdots$ | 1 |
| N | 1 | 1 | 1 | $\cdots$ | 0 |

*Old survey* (left margin)

The optimum solution will consist in putting as much mass as possible in the diagonals, that is, min $(a_i,b_i)$ in the $(i,i)$ cell of Table 9.3. Other cells are then filled out so that the row totals and the column totals add to the desired figures (Table 9.3) specified in the margins. As an illustration, let $N = 5$ and $a_1 > b_1$, $a_2 > b_2$, $a_3 > b_3$, $a_4 < b_4$ and $a_5 < b_5$. Then the probability of getting identical psu's is given by

$$\frac{\sum_i \min (a_i,b_i)}{G} = \frac{b_1 + b_2 + b_3 + a_4 + a_5}{G}$$

It must be pointed out that the probability table 9.3 associated with this problem cannot be made until after the new sizes $(b_1,b_2, \ldots)$ are known. For the initial survey a psu is selected with pp to $a$'s. Let the selected psu be the $i$th one with a size of $a_i$. When the new sizes are available, Table 9.3 is completed, and another psu is selected with probabilities $x_{i1}/a_i$, $x_{i2}/a_i$, $\ldots$, $x_{iN}/a_i$. With this procedure the chance that the pair $(i,j)$ be selected is $(a_i/G)$ times $(x_{ij}/a_i) = x_{ij}/G$, as required.

The solution to this problem as given by Keyfitz (1951) is the following for the case of the above five units $U_1$, $U_2$, $U_3$, $U_4$, and $U_5$. If the original selection is $U_4$ or $U_5$, it is retained. If not, some chance of change is introduced. The chance of rejecting $U_1$ would be $(a_1 - b_1)/a_1$ if $U_1$ is the original selection, that of $U_2$ is $(a_2 - b_2)/a_2$, and so on. If we have determined that $U_1$ (or $U_2$ or $U_3$) is to be rejected, the next problem is to choose between $U_4$ and $U_5$. This choice will be made with probabilities proportionate to $b_4 - a_4$ and $b_5 - a_5$ respectively. It is easy to show that with this procedure the probabilities of selection for the new survey are proportionate to $b_i$ and that the chance of getting identical psu's is $(b_1 + b_2 + b_3 + a_4 + a_5)/G$.

## 9.6 TWO-WAY STRATIFICATION WITH SMALL SAMPLES

In some surveys it may be considered very important to employ two criteria of stratification (like altitude and size of locality) which may give rise to a large number of substrata. But the total sample size $n$ (the number of localities) is not large enough to provide an allocation to each cell of the two-way table of substrata. The problem then is how to design the sample in this situation and make proper estimates. A particular case of this problem, when the number of subclasses for each of the criteria of stratification is the same, was considered in Sec. 4.10. A more general treatment of the problem will now be presented (Bryant, et al., 1960). To fix ideas let there be three altitude groups $A_i$ and five size groups $B_j$, so that there are in all 15 substrata. Let the total number of sample localities be 10 only. The proportions of the localities in the three altitude groups are $P_{i.}$ ($i = 1, 2, 3$) while those in the size groups are $P_{.j}$ ($j = 1, \ldots, 5$). On the basis of these proportions, it is decided to have $n_i = nP_{i.}$ sample localities for the $i$th altitude group and $n_{.j} = nP_{.j}$ sample localities for the $j$th size group. In this example let the desired sample numbers be 5,2,3 and 1,3,2,1,3, respectively. Denoting by $n_{ij}$ the number of sample localities in the cell $(i,j)$, the following sampling scheme ensures that $E(n_{ij}) = nP_{i.}P_{.j} = n_{i.}n_{.j}/n$. In order to select a sample of 10 localities we construct a square with 10 rows and 10 columns and select 10 cells at random using the Latin square principle (Sec. 4.10).

Table 9.5  Latin square selection

| | 1 | 2 | 3 | 4 | 5 | 6 | 7 | 8 | 9 | 10 |
|---|---|---|---|---|---|---|---|---|---|---|
| 1 | | ✓ | | | | | | | | |
| 2 | ✓ | | | | | | | | | |
| 3 | | | ✓ | | | | | | | |
| 4 | | | | ✓ | | | | | | |
| 5 | | | | | ✓ | | | | | |
| 6 | | | ✓ | | | | | | | |
| 7 | | | | | | | | ✓ | | |
| 8 | | | | | | | ✓ | | | |
| 9 | | | | | | | ✓ | | | |
| 10 | | | | | | | ✓ | | | |

Table 9.6  Sample numbers

| | $B_1$ | $B_2$ | $B_3$ | $B_4$ | $B_5$ | |
|---|---|---|---|---|---|---|
| $A_1$ | 1 | 2 | 2 | 0 | 0 | 5 |
| $A_2$ | 0 | 1 | 0 | 0 | 1 | 2 |
| $A_3$ | 0 | 0 | 0 | 1 | 2 | 3 |
| | 1 | 3 | 2 | 1 | 3 | 10 |

The selected cells are shown as $(\checkmark)$ in Table 9.5.   Based on the numbers $n_i.$ and $n_{.j}$ lines are drawn parallel to the sides of the square to determine the $n_{ij}$ for each substratum.   The $n_{ij}$ so obtained are shown in Table 9.6. The specified number $n_{ij}$ of localities is selected at random from the total number $N_{ij}$ in the cell $(i,j)$.

Let $\bar{y}_{ij}$ be the sample mean based on the $n_{ij}$ localities in this cell. Then, as an estimate of the population total $Y$, we use the estimator

$$\hat{Y} = n \sum_i \sum_j \frac{n_{ij}}{n_i.n_{.j}} N_{ij}\bar{y}_{ij} \tag{9.18}$$

Given $n_{ij}$, $E(N_{ij}\bar{y}_{ij}) = Y_{ij}$.   But $E(n_{ij}) = n_i.n_{.j}/n$.   Hence

$$E(\hat{Y}) = \sum_i \sum_j Y_{ij} = Y$$

Thus we have an unbiased estimator of $Y$.   To develop the variance of $\hat{Y}$, we introduce the following lemmas.

**Lemma 1**

*In Table 9.5 let $u_{rs}$ be a random variable associated with cell $(r,s)$ defined as: $u_{rs} = 1$ if the cell contains an $(\checkmark)$ and 0 otherwise.   Then $E(u_{rs}) = 1/n$,*

$$V(u_{rs}) = \frac{n-1}{n^2} \qquad \mathrm{Cov}\,(u_{rs},u_{rs'}) = -\frac{1}{n^2}$$

$$\mathrm{Cov}\,(u_{rs},u_{r's}) = -\frac{1}{n^2} \qquad \mathrm{Cov}\,(u_{rs},u_{r's'}) = \frac{1}{n^2(n-1)}$$

Using the fact that the variances and covariances of $n_{ij}$ (Table 9.6) are the sums of the variances and covariances of $u_{rs}$, we prove the following lemma.

**Lemma 2**

$$E(n_{ij}) = \frac{n_i.n_{.j}}{n}$$

$$V(n_{ij}) = \frac{n_i.n_{.j}(n - n_i.)(n - n_{.j})}{n^2(n-1)}$$

$$\mathrm{Cov}\,(n_{ij},n_{ij'}) = \frac{n_i.n_{.j}n_{.j'}(n_i. - n)}{n^2(n-1)}$$

$$\mathrm{Cov}\,(n_{ij},n_{i'j}) = \frac{n_i.n_{.j}n_{i'.}(n_{.j} - n)}{n^2(n-1)}$$

$$\mathrm{Cov}\,(n_{ij},n_{i'j'}) = \frac{n_i.n_{.j}n_{i'.}n_{.j'}}{n^2(n-1)}$$

### Lemma 3

*Let $w = \Sigma\Sigma c_{ij}n_{ij}$ where $c_{ij}$'s are constants.   Then*

$$V(w) = \sum_i \sum_j c_{ij}{}^2 V(n_{ij}) + \sum_i \sum_j \sum_{j' \neq j} c_{ij}c_{ij'} \, \mathrm{Cov}\,(n_{ij},n_{ij'})$$
$$+ \sum \sum_{i' \neq i} \sum c_{ij}c_{i'j} \, \mathrm{Cov}\,(n_{ij},n_{i'j}) + \sum \sum_{i' \neq i} \sum_{j' \neq j} c_{ij}c_{i'j'} \, \mathrm{Cov}\,(n_{ij},n_{i'j'})$$

*In particular, for $c_{ij} = Y_{ij}(n_{i.}n_{.j})^{-1}$, we have*

$$V(w) = \frac{1}{n^2(n-1)} \sum \sum \left\{ \left(\frac{n}{n_{i.}} - 1\right)\left(\frac{n}{n_{.j}} - 1\right) Y_{ij}{}^2 \right.$$
$$+ \left(1 - \frac{n}{n_{i.}}\right) Y_{ij}(R_i - Y_{ij}) + \left(1 - \frac{n}{n_{.j}}\right) Y_{ij}(C_j - Y_{ij})$$
$$+ Y_{ij}[Y - (R_i - Y_{ij}) - (C_j - Y_{ij}) - Y_{ij}] \Big\}$$
$$= \frac{1}{n^2(n-1)} \sum \sum Y_{ij}\left(\frac{n^2}{n_{i.}n_{.j}} Y_{ij} - \frac{n}{n_{i.}} R_i - \frac{n}{n_{.j}} C_j + Y\right)$$

where $R_i$ and $C_j$ are totals of the $i$th row and $j$th column in Table 9.6. With this background, we prove the following theorem.

### Theorem 9.5

*Assuming the sample sizes within substrata small enough to make the finite population corrections negligible, the variance of the estimator (9.18) is given by*

$$V(\hat{Y}) = n \sum \sum \frac{N_{ij}{}^2 S_{ij}{}^2}{n_{i.}n_{.j}} + \frac{1}{n^2(n-1)} \sum \sum n_{i.}n_{.j}\left(\frac{n^2}{n_{i.}n_{.j}} Y_{ij}\right.$$
$$\left. - \frac{n}{n_{i.}} R_i - \frac{n}{n_{.j}} C_j + Y\right)^2 \quad (9.19)$$

PROOF    Given $n_{ij}$

$$E_2(\hat{Y}) = n \sum \sum \frac{n_{ij}}{n_{i.}n_{.j}} Y_{ij} \qquad V_2(\hat{Y}) = n^2 \sum \sum \left(\frac{n_{ij}}{n_{i.}{}^2 n_{.j}{}^2} N_{ij}{}^2 S_{ij}{}^2\right)$$

Hence                      $$E_1 V_2(\hat{Y}) = n \sum \sum \frac{N_{ij}{}^2 S_{ij}{}^2}{n_{i.}n_{.j}}$$

$$V_1 E_2(\hat{Y}) = n^2 V(w) \qquad w = \sum \sum \frac{n_{ij}Y_{ij}}{n_{i.}n_{.j}}$$

By Lemma 3, we have

$$
V_1 E_2(\hat{Y}) = \frac{1}{n-1} \sum \sum Y_{ij} \left( \frac{n^2}{n_{i.}n_{.j}} Y_{ij} - \frac{n}{n_{i.}} R_i - \frac{n}{n_{.j}} C_j + Y \right)
$$

$$
= \frac{1}{n-1} \left( \sum \sum \frac{n^2}{n_{i.}n_{.j}} Y_{ij}^2 - \sum \frac{n}{n_{i.}} R_i^2 - \sum \frac{n}{n_{.j}} C_j^2 + Y^2 \right)
$$

$$
= \frac{1}{n^2(n-1)} \sum \sum n_{i.}n_{.j} \left( \frac{n^2}{n_{i.}n_{.j}} Y_{ij} - \frac{n}{n_{i.}} R_i - \frac{n}{n_{.j}} C_j + Y \right)^2
$$

This proves the theorem.                                              ∎

**Remark**  Owing to the dependence of the sample sizes $n_{ij}$, the variance of $\hat{Y}$ is not simply a function of variances $S_{ij}^2$ within substrata.

**Remark**  If only one-way stratification be employed, the estimator would be $\hat{Y} = N_i.\bar{y}_i.$ with a variance of

$$
\sum_i \frac{N_{i.}^2}{n_{i.}} \sum_j \frac{N_{ij}S_{ij}^2}{N_{i.}} + \sum \frac{N_{i.}^2}{n_{i.}} \sum \frac{N_{ij}}{N_i} (\bar{Y}_{ij} - \bar{Y}_i)^2
$$

approximately.  If the allocation is proportional, $n_{i.} = nN_{i.}/N$.  Then

$$
V(\hat{Y}) = \frac{N}{n} [\Sigma\Sigma N_{ij}S_{ij}^2 + \Sigma\Sigma N_{ij}(\bar{Y}_{ij} - \bar{Y}_i)^2]
$$

Based on these results it is possible to write down the condition that two-way stratification be better than one-way stratification.


## 9.7  SYSTEMATIC SAMPLING

In Sec. 3.8 systematic sampling was introduced to the reader as one of the basic methods of sample selection.  It was stated that the performance of this technique depends on the relationship of the variate with the order in which units are listed in the population.  We shall now give a number of examples of this phenomenon.


### 9.7.1  DATA EXHIBITING PERIODICITY

Suppose we want to make an estimate of the number of vehicles passing over a bridge during a certain month.  We expect that traffic over the bridge exhibits periodicity during the day, there being hours that are very busy and others when there is very little traffic.  If we were to select an hour at random from the first day and examine the traffic over this hour and subsequent 24-hour periods (i.e., take a systematic sample of hours over the month), sample-to-sample variation would be very large. If the hour selected at random happens to be the peak hour, the sample will contain all peaks and this will produce a very high figure. On the other hand, if the first hour selected shows poor traffic, all observations taken at this time during the subsequent days are expected to be well below the average, thereby producing a very low figure. Thus, if there is periodicity present in the data and the sampling interval $k$ coincides with the period, it will be unwise to take a systematic sample with this value of $k$. It is not uncommon to come across populations with periodic features. Temperatures over a 24-hour period, sales of stores over a week, and postal articles received in a post office over the week are some other examples of the occurrence of periodicity. One has to be sufficiently acquainted with the data on hand in order to be able to decide upon the sampling interval if systematic sampling is to be used. There will be no such problem involved if a random sample is taken or different random starts are used within strata.

### 9.7.2 POPULATIONS SHOWING TREND

When there is trend present in the data (for example, when households are listed by income and the character $y$ varies with income) substantial gains can be achieved by taking a systematic sample which will give an even spread over the population. A stratified design with one sample unit per stratum will be still better. This may be shown with the help of an example in which the $y$ for a unit depends linearly on the order in which it is placed in the universe, that is, $y_j = j$ $(j = 1, 2, \ldots, N)$. Let $N = nk$ where $k$ is the sampling interval. The population variance $S_y^2$ will be found to be $N(N + 1)/12$. If the first $k$ units form one stratum, the next $k$ units form another stratum, and so on, the variance $S_{wy}^2$ within a stratum would be $k(k + 1)/12$. A one-in-$k$ systematic sample will give observations on $y$ as $j, k + j, 2k + j, \ldots, (n - 1)k + j$, giving a sample mean of $j + k(n - 1)/2$. The variance of the means of the $k$ systematic samples will be $V_2 = (k^2 - 1)/12$. Denoting by $V_1$ and $V_3$ the variance of the sample estimate of the mean in the case of simple random sampling and stratified random sampling with one sample unit per stratum, we have

$$V_1 = \frac{(k - 1)(N + 1)}{12} \qquad V_3 = V\left(\frac{1}{N} \sum_{j=1}^{k} k y_j\right) = \frac{k^2 - 1}{12n}$$

This shows that in this case stratification with one unit per stratum is superior to systematic sampling, which in turn is better than simple random sampling. Madow and Madow (1944) provide further information on this point.

**Further reading**   If the population is monotone, it is shown in Exercise 15 that centered systematic sampling is more efficient than random start systematic sampling.

### 9.7.3  AUTOCORRELATED POPULATIONS

We shall now consider populations in which there is higher correlation between adjacent units than between units further apart, the correlations decreasing as the interval between units increases. Cochran (1946) has investigated the relative performance of systematic and stratified random sampling for such populations. Due to the finiteness of the population, the model that $\rho_u \geq \rho_v$ whenever $u < v$ will not hold exactly with a given population. As a result, the model is assumed to hold over an infinite superpopulation, and the finite population at hand is supposed to have been selected at random from this superpopulation. In fact we shall assume that

$$E(y_i) = \mu \qquad E(y_i - \mu)^2 = \sigma^2 \qquad E(y_i - \mu)(y_{i+u} - \mu) = \rho_u \sigma^2$$

where $\rho_u \geq \rho_v \geq 0$ whenever $u < v$. Now, for a specific finite population $y_1, y_2, \ldots, y_N$ where $N = nk$, the variance of the mean based on a random sample of size $n$ is given by $V_1 = (1 - 1/k)[1/n(N - 1)]\Sigma(y_i - \bar{Y})^2$ and the variance of the stratified sample estimate (taking one unit per stratum of $k$ units) is $V_3 = \sum_i \sum_j (y_{ij} - \bar{Y}_i)^2/kn^2$. Using the algebraic identity

$$N \sum (y_i - \bar{Y})^2 = \sum_i \sum_{j>i} (y_i - y_j)^2 = \sum \sum [(y_i - \mu) - (y_j - \mu)]^2$$

we have   $E \sum (y_i - \bar{Y})^2 = \dfrac{\sigma^2}{N} \left[ N(N - 1) - 2 \sum_{u=1}^{N-1} (N - u)\rho_u \right]$

$$= (N - 1)\sigma^2 \left[ 1 - 2N^{-1}(N - 1)^{-1} \sum_{u=1}^{N-1} (N - u)\rho_u \right]$$

Hence

$$E(V_1) = \left( 1 - \frac{1}{k} \right) \frac{\sigma^2}{n} \left[ 1 - 2N^{-1}(N - 1)^{-1} \sum_{u=1}^{N-1} (N - u)\rho_u \right] \quad (9.20)$$

$$E(V_3) = \frac{1}{nk} (k - 1)\sigma^2 \left[ 1 - 2k^{-1}(k - 1)^{-1} \sum_{u=1}^{k-1} (k - u)\rho_u \right] \quad (9.21)$$

Denoting by $\bar{y}_i$ the mean based on the $i$th systematic sample of size $n$, the variance of the systematic sample mean would be

$$V_2 = \frac{\Sigma(\bar{y}_i - \bar{Y})^2}{k} = \frac{\Sigma n(\bar{y}_i - \bar{Y})^2}{N}$$

$$= \frac{\text{total sum of squares} - \text{sum of squares within samples}}{N}$$

Hence $\quad NE(V_2) = (N-1)\sigma^2 \left[ 1 - 2N^{-1}(N-1)^{-1} \sum_{u=1}^{N-1} (N-u)\rho_u \right]$

$$- k(n-1)\sigma^2 \left[ 1 - 2n^{-1}(n-1)^{-1} \sum_{u=1}^{n-1} (n-u)\rho_{ku} \right]$$

or

$$E(V_2) = \left(1 - \frac{1}{k}\right) \frac{\sigma^2}{n} \left[ 1 - 2N^{-1}(k-1)^{-1} \sum_{u=1}^{N-1} (N-u)\rho_u \right.$$

$$\left. + 2k(n)^{-1}(k-1)^{-1} \sum_{u=1}^{n-1} (n-u)\rho_{ku} \right] \quad (9.22)$$

Thus the comparison involved is among (9.20), (9.21), and (9.22). We shall first prove the following lemma.

### Lemma

*If the $\rho$'s are positive and $\rho_i - \rho_{i+1} = \delta_i \geq 0$, a necessary and sufficient condition that $L = \sum_{i=1}^{m} a_i\rho_i \geq 0 \left(\sum a_i = 0\right)$ is that $A_i = \sum_{j=1}^{i} a_j \geq 0$ for every $i = 1, 2, \ldots, m-1$.*

PROOF

$$L = \delta_1 a_1 + \delta_2(a_1 + a_2) + \cdots + \delta_{m-1}(a_1 + a_2 + \cdots + a_{m-1})$$

Since the $\delta$'s are positive, the condition that $A_i \geq 0$ is sufficient to establish that $L \geq 0$. Also, if for any $i$ the coefficient of $\delta_i$ is negative, we can make $L$ negative by making $\delta_i$ positive and all the other $\delta$'s zero. This proves that the condition $A_i \geq 0$ is necessary. ∎

This lemma will be used in proving that

$$L(k) = 1 - 2[k(k-1)]^{-1} \sum_{u=1}^{k-1} (k-u)\rho_u$$

is a monotonically increasing function of $k$.   We have

$$L(k) - L(k + 1) = -2[k(k^2 - 1)]^{-1} \sum_{u=1}^{k} (k + 1 - 2u)\rho_u$$

Since $\sum_{u=1}^{k} (k + 1 - 2u) = 0$, the lemma applies.   As

$$\sum_{u=1}^{i} (k + 1 - 2u) = i(k - i) \geq 0$$

it follows that $L(k) \leq L(k + 1)$.   This establishes that $E(V_3) \leq E(V_1)$. Thus the average variance based on the stratified sample is less than or equal to that of the random sample.   No such general result can be proved about the efficiency of systematic sampling relative to random sampling, unless further restrictions are imposed on the correlations $\rho_u$.   We shall in fact prove the following theorem.

**Theorem 9.6**

*If*

$$\rho_i \geq \rho_{i+1} \geq 0 \qquad i = 1, 2, \ldots, N - 1$$

*and*

$$\delta_i^2 = \rho_{i-1} + \rho_{i+1} - 2\rho_i \geq 0 \qquad i = 2, 3, \ldots, N - 2 \qquad (9.23)$$

*then*

$$E(V_2) \leq E(V_3) \leq E(V_1)$$

PROOF   Just as the variance $V_2$ was developed as [total sum of squares (s.s.)]$/N$ − (average s.s. within systematic samples)$/n$, the variance $V_3$ can be expressed as (total s.s.)$/N$ − (average s.s. within stratified samples)$/n$.   Hence, in order to prove the theorem, we shall prove that

$E$ (average s.s. within systematic samples)
$$\geq E \text{ (average s.s. within stratified samples)}$$

Now given a set of values $a_1, a_2, \ldots, a_n$, it is easily seen that

$$n \sum (a_i - \bar{a})^2 = \sum_i \sum_{j>i} (a_i - a_j)^2 = \frac{n(n-1)}{2} E'(a_i - a_j)^2$$

where $E'$ denotes averaging over the different pairs, so that

$$\sum (a_i - \bar{a})^2 = \frac{n-1}{2} E'(a_i - a_j)^2$$

Denoting by $y_{ij}$ and $y_{lj}$ the elements in the sample from the $i$th and $l$th strata, the average sum of squares within a sample would be given by

$[(n - 1)/2]E'(y_{ij} - y_{lj})^2$, where $E'$ is over different pairs of strata. Consider now a fixed pair of strata with $l - i = u$. In the case of the systematic sample, the elements in the two strata are always at a distance of $ku$. Hence $E(y_{ij} - y_{lj})^2 = 2\sigma^2(1 - \rho_{ku})$. For the stratified sample there are $k^2$ possible pairs of elements from the two strata. One pair is $(ku - k + 1)$ elements apart, two pairs are $(ku - k + 2)$ elements apart, and so on. Hence for the stratified sample we have

$$E(y_{ij} - y_{lj})^2 = 2\sigma^2 \left[ 1 - \frac{1}{k^2} \sum_{i=-(k-1)}^{k-1} (k - |i|)\rho_{ku+i} \right]$$

Thus, to prove the theorem, it is sufficient to show that

$$\frac{1}{k^2} \sum (k - |i|)\rho_{ku+i} \geq \rho_{ku}$$

or $$\sum (k - |i|)\rho_{ku+i} - k^2\rho_{ku} \geq 0$$

or $$\sum_{i=1}^{k-1} (k - i)(\rho_{ku+i} + \rho_{ku-i} - 2\rho_{ku}) \geq 0$$

Now $$\rho_{ku+i} + \rho_{ku-i} - 2\rho_{ku} = \sum_{j=-(i-1)}^{i-1} (i - |j|)\delta_{ku+j}^2 \geq 0$$

which proves that $E(V_2) \leq E(V_3)$. As it has already been shown that $E(V_3) \leq E(V_1)$, the theorem is proved. ∎

**Remark** It has been proved that systematic sampling is superior to stratified random sampling if condition (9.23) holds, i.e., if the correlogram is concave upwards. This condition does not appear to be an impossible one to fulfill so far as practical applications are concerned. Several authors, including Wold (1938), Osborne (1942), and Fisher and Mackenzie (1922), have proposed such correlograms as models for specific natural populations.

### 9.8 CONTROLLED SELECTION

The idea of using controls in selecting a sample may be viewed conceptually as an extension of the method of purposive selection. The extension involved is that we consider not just one purposive sample but many purposive samples, until every unit in the universe is included in one or more samples. The number of samples in which each unit occurs must be exactly proportionate to its assigned probability of selection. After the complete set of purposive samples has been established, the random selection of one of them constitutes a probability sample. In the subjective approach many samples are examined and discarded arbitrarily; with this technique the preferred and other samples are recorded and assigned probabilities of selection, the final choice being a probability selection from the totality recorded. An example of the use of this method has already been given in Sec. 4.8.3. The following simple example will be presented to make the ideas clear. The universe consists of nine schools; four $(L_1, L_2, L_3, L_4)$ of them are large and the other five $(S_1, S_2, S_3, S_4, S_5)$ are small. Two of the large schools, namely $L_1$ and $L_2$, are state-controlled, and the other two are under private management. In the case of small schools, $S_1$ and $S_2$ are state-owned, and the others are run privately. The problem is to select a sample of two schools, one large and one small. Each large school should have a $\frac{1}{4}$ chance of being included in the sample and each small school should have a $\frac{1}{5}$ chance of being included. Preferably, the sample should contain schools of either type (state-owned and privately managed). We may then list the following eight samples and select one of them with the probabilities specified below.

| *Sample* | $L_1S_3$ | $L_2S_4$ | $L_3S_1$ | $L_4S_2$ | $L_1S_5$ | $L_2S_5$ | $L_3S_5$ | $L_4S_5$ |
|---|---|---|---|---|---|---|---|---|
| *Probability of sample* | 0.20 | 0.20 | 0.20 | 0.20 | 0.05 | 0.05 | 0.05 | 0.05 |
| *Cumulative probability* | 0.20 | 0.40 | 0.60 | 0.80 | 0.85 | 0.90 | 0.95 | 1.00 |

It can be verified that the large and small schools have a chance of 0.25 and 0.20, respectively, of being selected in the sample. And the probability of selecting a preferred sample (containing schools of either type) is 0.90. In case a school is selected at random from the four large ones and another one is selected independently from the five small ones, the chance of a preferred sample would be only 0.50. Thus the method of controlled selection has enabled us to increase the probability of a preferred combination from 0.50 to 0.90. This problem can also be solved by the methods of linear programming (see Sec. 9.5 and Exercises 92 and 93).

## 9.9 A GENERAL RULE FOR VARIANCE ESTIMATION IN MULTISTAGE SAMPLING

Suppose $n$ psu's are selected from the $N$ without replacement with unequal probabilities. To begin with, we shall assume that the sample psu's are completely enumerated (single-stage sampling). In order to estimate the stratum total, the very general estimator $\sum_{i=1}^{N} a_{is}y_i$ will be used, where $a_{is}$ $(i = 1, \ldots, N)$ are real numbers predetermined for every sample $s$, with the restriction that $a_{is} = 0$ whenever the sample $s$ does not contain the $i$th psu. In order that the estimator be unbiased whatever the $y$'s, the condition is that $E(a_{is}) = 1$ for every $i$. The variance of the estimator would be

$$V\left(\sum a_{is}y_i\right) = \sum_i y_i{}^2 V(a_{is}) + \sum_{j>i} y_i y_j \operatorname{Cov}(a_{is}, a_{js}) \qquad (9.24)$$

Let

$$f(y) = \sum_i b_{is} y_i{}^2 + \sum_{j>i} d_{ijs} y_i y_j \qquad (9.25)$$

be an unbiased estimator of $V(\Sigma a_{is} y_i)$, where, like $a_{is}$, the real numbers $b_{is}, d_{ijs}$ are predetermined for every sample $s$. It follows that

$$E(b_{is}) = V(a_{is}) \qquad (9.26)$$

Now consider the multistage case in which the psu's are subsampled independently in a known manner. Given the $i$th psu, let $t_i$ (based on sampling at the second and subsequent stages) be an unbiased estimator of $y_i$. Further, let $V(t_i|i) = \sigma_i{}^2$ and $E(\hat{\sigma}_i{}^2|i) = \sigma_i{}^2$.

As an unbiased estimator of the stratum total we shall use

$$\hat{Y} = \sum_{i=1}^{N} a_{is} t_i \qquad (9.27)$$

where

$$V(\hat{Y}) = V\left(\sum a_{is} y_i\right) + \sum_i E(a_{is}{}^2)\sigma_i{}^2 \qquad (9.28)$$

Then we shall prove the result:

$$E[f(t) + \Sigma a_{is}\hat{\sigma}_i{}^2] = V(\hat{Y}) \qquad (9.29)$$

where $f(t) = \sum_i b_{is} t_i{}^2 + \sum_{j>i} d_{ijs} t_i t_j$ is obtained from $f(y)$ by substituting $t_i$ for $y_i$.

**PROOF**

$$\begin{aligned} Ef(t) &= Ef(y) + E\Sigma b_{is}\sigma_i{}^2 \\ &= Ef(y) + \Sigma V(a_{is})\sigma_i{}^2 \\ &= V(\hat{Y}) - \Sigma\sigma_i{}^2 \end{aligned}$$

But $\Sigma a_{is}\hat{\sigma}_i{}^2$ is an unbiased estimator of $\Sigma\sigma_i{}^2$, from which the result follows (Raj, 1966$b$). ∎

The rule for estimating the variance in multistage sampling may then be stated as follows. "Get an unbiased estimator of the variance in single-stage sampling. Obtain a copy of it by substituting for $y_i$ its estimate $t_i$. Also get the copy of the estimator of the stratum total in single-stage sampling by substituting $\hat{\sigma}_i{}^2$ for $y_i$. The sum of the two copies is an unbiased estimator of the variance in the multistage case."

It may be noted that this rule is slightly different from that given by Durbin (Exercise 56). This rule will be more handy when the estimators are based on conditional probabilities, in which case it may be difficult to calculate $\pi_i$, the probability with which the $i$th psu is selected in the entire sample. This rule was noticed by the author (1954, 1956) in connection with two different sampling schemes. As an example, consider the two-stage design of Theorem 6.2. The population total estimator in single-stage sampling is

$$\frac{N}{n} Sy_i$$

and the variance estimator is

$$\frac{N^2}{n}\left(1 - \frac{n}{N}\right)\frac{1}{n-1} S(y_i - \bar{y})^2$$

The copies of the two are

$$\frac{N}{n} S \frac{M_i^2}{m_i}\left(1 - \frac{m_i}{M_i}\right) s_{wi}^2$$

and
$$\frac{N^2}{n}\left(1 - \frac{n}{N}\right)\frac{1}{n-1} S\left(M_i\bar{y}_i - \frac{1}{n} SM_i\bar{y}_i\right)^2$$

Hence the sum of the two copies is an unbiased estimator of the variance in the two-stage design.

To take another example, consider the sample design (Sec. 6.10.3) in which the stratum is divided up into $n$ substrata by allocating the psu's at random to them and in which one psu is selected with pps from each substratum. It is known that in single-stage sampling the stratum total estimator is (see Exercises 16 and 54)

$$\sum_{i=1}^{n} \frac{y_{ij}}{p'_{ij}} \tag{9.30}$$

and the variance estimator is

$$\frac{\sum_{1}^{n} N_i^2 - N}{N^2 - \sum_{1}^{n} N_i^2}\left[\sum_{1}^{n} \frac{y_{ij}^2}{p_{ij}p'_{ij}} - \left(\sum_{1}^{n} \frac{y_{ij}}{p'_{ij}}\right)^2\right] \tag{9.31}$$

Hence an unbiased variance estimator in the multistage case is given by our rule as:

$$\hat{V}(\hat{Y}) = \frac{\Sigma N_i^2 - N}{N^2 - \Sigma N_i^2}\left[\sum_{1}^{n} \frac{t_{ij}^2}{p_{ij}p'_{ij}} - \left(\sum_{1}^{n} \frac{t_{ij}}{p'_{ij}}\right)^2\right] + \sum_{1}^{n} \frac{\hat{V}_3(t_{ij})}{p'_{ij}} \tag{9.32}$$

## 9.10 SAMPLING FROM IMPERFECT FRAMES

We have by and large assumed that given a target population with reporting units

$$U_1, U_2, \ldots, U_N \qquad (9.33)$$

there exists a perfect frame (or list) of these units from which to select the sample. In practice such frames rarely exist and one has to fall back on imperfect frames. The frame may be imperfect in that it does not contain all the units of the target population, or some units may occur more than once, or some particulars (e.g., measures of size) of the listed units are inaccurate, or that certain units in the frame do not belong to the target population. Thus the frame has on it the units

$$f_1, f_2, \ldots, f_m \qquad (9.34)$$

and the sample is to be selected from this and not from (9.33). The problem is to establish rules of association between the listed units $f_k$ and the reporting units $U_j$ such that the selection of units $f_k$ with known probabilities leads to the selection of units $U_j$ also with known probabilities. The selection mechanism should give rise to known nonzero probabilities $\pi_i$ and $\pi_{ij}$ for the units in the target population. This is not always easy. Suppose the target population (9.33) consists of all individuals currently resident in a city, whereas the listed units in (9.34) are addresses taken at the time of the last census. It may be found that some houses have been demolished since the last census, others have come up since then, some single units at listed addresses have been converted into multiple units, and so on. All this will have to be taken into account when (9.34) is used for sampling from (9.33). A general discussion of some of the problems involved is given here.

*Extraneous units*  If the frame contains some units which are not in the target population, their selection in the sample will give rise to a value of zero for the characteristic $y$ under study. No bias is involved thereby, although the variance will increase somewhat. As far as practicable, such units should be removed from the frame before sample selection.

*Duplications*  If some units occur more than once in the frame, this will affect their probability of selection. No real problem is involved when these probabilities can be ascertained. To the extent possible, the frame should be unduplicated before selecting the sample. When the extent of duplications is not known, it is possible to estimate it on the basis of a sample taken from the frame (Exercise 101). If there are two frames available, sampling methods will help in estimating the number of units common to the two (see Exercises 87 and 88).

*Inaccurate sizes*  If the sizes of some of the units in the frame are inaccurate and this information has been used for sample selection, it may happen that some unexpectedly large or small units appear in the stratum. This will increase the variance of the estimates made. When the survey is repeated over a period of time, the surprise stratum technique (Exercise 67) may be used in order to reduce the impact of the unusual units on the variance.

*Incomplete lists* If the list is incomplete (i.e., if some units in the target population do not find a place on it), it should be supplemented by other lists or area samples in order to take in units not on the list. (In an area sample the sampling units are land areas and the reporting units in the sample are identified through geographic rules in the field.) The area sample may contain some units which are on the list. One procedure is to remove such units from the area sample, since these have a chance of selection through the list. A better method is not to exclude them from the area sample but to use the procedures indicated in Exercise 89 and Exercise 96(*a*). Sometimes it is possible to locate the successor of each unit in the target population. In that case a sample taken from the list will lead to a sample from the target population if the method indicated in Exercise 96(*b*) is used.

## 9.11 SAMPLING INSPECTION

A large-scale survey is an exercise in statistical engineering. Each step in the production line is a potential source of error. The sample units may not be identified correctly, enumerators may make errors in the field, there may be errors of coding or punching the cards in the office, and so on. Thus it becomes important to ensure that the production process is under control and that the outgoing quality is acceptable. Sampling methods can play an important part in achieving this. The problem of control of clerical errors by inspection on a sampling basis will be discussed here.

Suppose punched cards are being received in lots of $N$. We agree to call a card defective if it contains one or more errors of punching. Let the sampling plan consist in selecting a sample of $n$ cards from the lot for verification. If the sample contains $c$ or fewer defective cards, the lot is accepted; otherwise it is verified on a 100 percent basis. In either case the cards found to be defective are corrected. If the proportion of defective cards is $P$, the probability of accepting the lot will be

$$L(P) = \sum_{d=0}^{c} \frac{\binom{NP}{d}\binom{N - NP}{n - d}}{\binom{N}{n}} \tag{9.35}$$

Assuming that the lot size $N$ is very large as compared with $n$,

$$L(P) = \sum_{d=0}^{c} \binom{n}{d} P^d (1 - P)^{n-d} \qquad (9.36)$$

The graph of $L(P)$ against $P$, $0 \leq P \leq 1$ is called the operating characteristic (OC) curve of the sampling plan $(n,c)$, and $c$ is called the acceptance number. The OC curve gives the probabilities with which lots of different quality are accepted.

Let the lot be considered satisfactory if the proportion defective is $P_1$ or lower and unsatisfactory if the proportion defective is $P_2$ or higher. The proportion $P_1$ is called the acceptable quality level (AQL) and $P_2$ the lot tolerance percent defective (LTPD). Obviously, $L(P_2)$ is the chance of accepting a lot at the LTPD level and $1 - L(P_1)$ is the chance of rejecting a lot at the AQL.

Since rejected lots are to be inspected on a 100 percent basis, the expected amount of inspection will be

$$C(P) = nL(P) + N[1 - L(P)] \qquad (9.37)$$

The quantity $C(P)$ is called the average sample number (ASN) of the sampling plan. Since all cards found to be defective are corrected, the proportion defective in the outgoing product (after sample inspection) will be smaller than $P$. Its expected value will be given by

$$P_A = \sum_{d=0}^{c} \frac{NP - d}{N} \frac{\binom{NP}{d}\binom{N - NP}{n - d}}{\binom{N}{n}} \qquad (9.38)$$

which can be approximated as

$$P_A = \frac{NP - PC(P)}{N} = P\left[1 - \frac{1}{N}C(P)\right] \qquad (9.39)$$

This is called the average outgoing quality (AOQ) of the sampling plan. The maximum value of $P_A$ for variations in $P$ is known as the average outgoing quality limit (AOQL). The proportion of defectives in the sampled material will not exceed this value, whatever the true proportion in the original material be.

How to choose a sampling plan $(n,c)$ will depend on what risks it is intended to cover. For example, if good lots at AQL are to be rejected with a frequency of just $\alpha$ and bad lots at LTPD be accepted with a frequency of $\beta$ and no more, the parameters of the plan will be so determined that

$$L(P_1) = 1 - \alpha$$
$$L(P_2) = \beta$$

**Further reading**   See Exercise 103, in which the two parameters of the sampling plan are obtained.

Alternatively, lots at LTPD may be accepted with a frequency of $\beta$, and the cost of inspection be made a minimum for lots of expected quality $\bar{P}$. In this case

$$C(\bar{P}) = nL(\bar{P}) + N[1 - L(\bar{P})]$$

is to be minimized, subject to the constraint that $L(P_2) = \beta$. Finally, the AOQL of the plan may be specified as $P_0$, whatever the proportion of defectives in the incoming lots be. The sampling plan chosen is one which minimizes the cost of inspection for product of expected quality (Exercise 104).

### 9.11.1   DOUBLE-SAMPLING PLANS

The plan considered in Sec. 9.11 is an example of a single-sampling plan characterized by the sample size $n$ and the acceptance number $c$. However, we may accept exceptionally good lots and reject exceptionally bad ones outright and give a second chance to lots of intermediate quality. Such plans are called double-sampling plans. A sample of $n_1$ cards is selected and the lot is accepted or rejected depending on whether the number of defectives does not exceed $c_1$ or exceeds $c_2$. If the number of defectives lies between $c_1 + 1$ and $c_2$, a further sample of $n_2$ cards is taken. The lot is accepted if the number of defectives does not exceed $c_2$ in the combined sample of $n_1 + n_2$. Otherwise, it is rejected. The operating characteristic (OC) of the plan will be given by

$$L(P) = \sum_{d_1=0}^{c_1} \binom{n_1}{d_1} P^{d_1}(1 - P)^{n_1-d_1}$$

$$+ \sum_{d_1=c_1+1}^{c_2} \sum_{d_2=0}^{c_2-d_1} \binom{n_1}{d_1} P^{d_1}(1 - P)^{n_1-d_1} \binom{n_2}{d_2} P^{d_2}(1 - P)^{n_2-d_2} \quad (9.40)$$

$$= \sum_{d_1=0}^{c_1} (n_1,d_1) + \sum_{d_1=c_1+1}^{c_2} \sum_{d_2=0}^{c_2-d_1} (n_1,d_1)(n_2,d_2) \quad (9.41)$$

where

$$(n,d) = \binom{n}{d} P^d(1 - P)^{n-d}$$

The expected cost of inspection will be

$$C(P) = n_1 \sum_0^{c_1} (n_1,d_1) + N \sum_{c_2+1} (n_1,d_1)$$

$$+ (n_1,c_1 + 1) \left[ (n_1 + n_2) \sum_0^{c_2-c_1-1} (n_2,d_2) + N \sum_{c_2-c_1} (n_2,d_2) \right]$$

$$+ \cdots + (n_1,c_2) \left[ (n_1 + n_2)(n_2,0) + N \sum_1 (n_2,d_2) \right]$$

$$= n_1 \sum_0^{c_1} (n_1,d_1) + (n_1 + n_2) \sum_{d_1=c_1+1}^{c_2} \sum_{d_2=0}^{c_2-d_1} (n_1,d_1)(n_2,d_2)$$

$$+ N \left[ \sum_{d_1=c_2+1} (n_1,d_1) + \sum_{d_1=c_1+1}^{c_2} \sum_{d_2=c_2-d_1+1} (n_1,d_1)(n_2,d_2) \right]$$

$$= n_1 L(P) + n_2 \left[ L(P) - \sum_0^{c_1} (n_1,d_1) \right] + N[1 - L(P)] \quad (9.42)$$

The expected value of the proportion defective in the outgoing product can be approximated as

$$P_A = \frac{NP - PC(P)}{N} = \frac{P}{N} \left\{ (N - n_1)L(P) - n_2 \left[ L(P) - \sum_0^{c_1} (n_1,d_1) \right] \right\}$$
$$(9.43)$$

Now the problem is to choose the parameters $(n_1,n_2,c_1,c_2)$ of the sampling plan in a suitable manner. The protection sought may be in terms of AOQL or LTPD. In either case, the parameters of the plan can be so determined that the cost of inspection for product of expected quality be made a minimum. Such plans have been worked out by Dodge and Romig (1959).

## REFERENCES

Bryant, E. C., H. O. Hartley, and R. J. Jessen (1960). Design and estimation in two-way stratification. *J. Am. Stat. Assoc.*, 55.

Cochran, W. G. (1946). Relative accuracy of systematic and stratified random samples for a certain class of populations. *Ann. Math. Stat.*, 17.

Dodge, H. F. and H. G. Romig (1959). "Sampling Inspection Tables," 2d ed. John Wiley & Sons, Inc., New York.

Fisher, R. A. and W. A. Mackenzie (1922). The correlation of weekly rainfall. *Quart. J. Roy. Met. Soc.*, 48.

Godambe, V. P. (1955). A unified theory of sampling from finite populations. *J. Roy. Stat. Soc.*, B 17.

Hansen, M. H., W. N. Hurwitz, and W. G. Madow (1953). "Sample Survey Methods and Theory." John Wiley & Sons, Inc., New York.

Hartley, H. O. and J. N. K. Rao (1962). Sampling with unequal probabilities and without replacement. *Ann. Math. Stat.*, 33.

Horvitz, D. G. and D. J. Thompson (1952). A generalization of sampling without replacement from a finite universe. *J. Am. Stat. Assoc.*, 47.

Keyfitz, N. (1951). Sampling with probabilities proportional to size-adjustment for changes in the probabilities. *J. Am. Stat. Assoc.*, 46.

Koop, J. C. (1963). On the axioms of sample formation and their bearing on the construction of linear estimators in sampling theory for finite universes. *Metrika*, 7.

Koopmans, T. C. (1951). "Activity Analysis of Production and Allocation." John Wiley & Sons, Inc., New York.

Lahiri, D. B. (1954). Technical paper on some aspects of the development of the sample design. "The National Sample Survey," No. 5. Government of India, New Delhi.

Madow, W. G. and L. H. Madow (1944). On the theory of systematic sampling. *Ann. Math. Stat.*, 15.

Osborne, J. G. (1942). Sampling errors of systematic and random surveys of cover-type areas. *J. Am. Stat. Assoc.*, 37.

Raj, D. (1956). On the method of overlapping maps in sample surveys. *Sankhya*, 17.

——— (1958). On the estimate of variance in sampling with probabilities proportionate to size. *J. Soc. Sci.*, 1.

——— (1964). Some apparently unconnected problems encountered in sampling work. *Contributions to Statistics*. Calcutta.

——— (1965). Variance estimation in randomized systematic sampling with probability proportionate to size. *J. Am. Stat. Assoc.*, 60.

——— (1966a). On a method of sampling with unequal probabilities. *Ganita*, 17.

——— (1966b). Some remarks on a simple procedure of sampling without replacement. *J. Am. Stat. Assoc.*, 61.

Roy, J. and I. M. Chakravarty (1960). Estimating the mean of a finite population. *Ann. Math. Stat.*, 31.

Satterthwaite, F. E. (1946). An approximate distribution of estimates of variance components. *Biometrics*, 2.

Wold, H. (1938). "A Study of the Analysis of Stationary Time Series." Uppsala.

# EXERCISES

## METHODS OF SAMPLE SELECTION

**1.** In order to estimate the mean of a finite population, sampling with replacement with equal probabilities is continued till the sample contains $n$ distinct units. Let $v$ be the total number of selections made, $k_r$ ($\Sigma k_r = v$) being the frequency of appearance of the $r$th distinct unit in the sample. Defining $\bar{y}_v = S k_r y_r / v$ and $\bar{y}_n = S y_r / n$, prove that

*a.* $\bar{y}_v$ and $\bar{y}_n$ are unbiased

*b.* $V(\bar{y}_v) = E \dfrac{1}{v} \sigma_y{}^2$

*c.* $E(v) = N \left( \dfrac{1}{N} + \dfrac{1}{N-1} + \cdots + \dfrac{1}{N-n+1} \right)$

*d.* $E \dfrac{1}{v} > \dfrac{1}{E(v)} > (N-n)[n(N-1)]^{-1}$

Hence or otherwise prove that $V(\bar{y}_v) \geq V(\bar{y}_n)$.

*2.* A population contains $N$ units, the variate-value of one unit being known to be $y_1$. A wtr random sample of $n$ units is selected from the remaining $(N - 1)$ units. Show that the estimator $y_1 + (N - 1)\bar{y}_n$ has a smaller variance than $N\bar{y}_n$ based on a wtr random sample of size $n$ taken from the entire population.

*3.* For the general sampling scheme of Sec. 9.4 consider the estimator

$$T = \sum_{i=1}^{N} a_i(s)y_i \text{ for estimating the population mean } \Sigma Y_i/N. \text{ Suppose } T$$

is unbiased and belongs to the class for which $V(T) = k\sigma^2$, where $k$ is a constant. Then prove that

*a.* $Ea_i(s) = \dfrac{1}{N}$

*b.* $E[a_i(s)a_j(s)] = \dfrac{1}{N^2} + \dfrac{k(N - 1)}{N^2} \qquad i = j$

and $\qquad\qquad\qquad E[a_i(s)a_j(s)] = \dfrac{1 - k}{N^2} \qquad i \neq j$

*c.* $V\Sigma a_i(s) = 0 \qquad$ so that $\Sigma a_i(s) = 1$

By computing $M = E\Sigma[a_i(s) - \nu_i(s)/\Sigma\nu_i(s)]^2$ show that there exists a lower bound for $V(T)$, namely $V(T) \geq K\sigma^2$ where

$$K = (N - 1)^{-1}N\left[E\left(\frac{1}{\nu(s)}\right) - \frac{1}{N}\right]$$

*4.* We shall denote by $V_1$ the variance of the with-replacement pps estimator $(1/n)S(y_i/p_i)$, and by $V_2$ the variance of $NSy_i/n$ in wr sampling with equal probabilities. The finite population of $y$ is supposed to be a random sample from an infinite population, the model assumed being $y = Bx + e$, where for a given $x$, $E(e) = 0$, $E(e^2) = \sigma^2$. Show that $E(V_1) = N^2\sigma^2[(\bar{X}/\tilde{X}) - 1/N]/n$, $E(V_2) = N[B^2 N\sigma_x^2 + (N - 1)\sigma^2]/n$. Hence prove that $E(V_1) < E(V_2)$ if $\sigma^2 < B^2\sigma_x^2(\bar{X} - \tilde{X})^{-1}\tilde{X}$. Assuming that cubes and higher powers of $(x_i - \bar{X})/\bar{X}$ can be neglected, prove that $E(V_1) < E(V_2)$ if $\rho^2 > C_x^2/(1 + C_x^2)$ where $C_x^2 = \sigma_x^2/\bar{X}^2$ and $\tilde{X} = N/\Sigma(1/X_i)$.

*5.* Assume that the finite population $(y_1, y_2, \ldots, y_N)$ is a random sample from an infinite superpopulation in which $y_i = Bx_i + e_i$, $E(e_i|x_i) = 0$, $V(e_i|x_i) = ax_i^g$, $g \geq 0$. Denoting by $V_1$ and $V_2$ the variances of the with-replacement pps estimator $[1/(nN)]S(y_i/p_i)$ and the wr equal probability estimator $Sy_i/n$, show that

$$E(V_1) = (nN^2)^{-1}a(X\Sigma x_i^{g-1} - \Sigma x_i^g)$$
$$E(V_2) = (nN^2)^{-1}(N - 1)(a\Sigma x_i^g + B^2 NS_x^2)$$

Hence prove that the pps estimator is superior to the equal probability estimator if $\rho(x,x^{g-1}) > -(N-1)B^2S_x/(NaS_x{}^{g-1})$. Hence for $g \geq 1$ the pps estimator is always superior.

**6.** In a wtr sampling scheme with unequal probabilities, let $V_1$ be the variance of the estimator $S(y_i/\pi_i)$ and let $v = S[y_i/p_i - (1/n)S(y_i/p_i)]^2/[n(n-1)]$ be used as an estimator of $V_1$. Then prove that $E(v) - V_1 = (V_2 - V_1)n/(n-1)$, where $V_2$ is the variance of $(n^{-1})S(y_i/p_i)$ in wr pps sampling with $\pi_i = np_i$.

**7.** In samples of size $n$, in which the first member of the sample is selected with probabilities $p_i$ $(i = 1, \ldots, N)$, $\Sigma p_i = 1$ and the remaining $(n-1)$ members with equal probability without replacement, prove that

$$\pi_i\pi_j - \pi_{ij} = (N-1)^{-2}(N-n)\left[(N-n)p_ip_j + \frac{(n-1)(1-p_i-p_j)}{N-2}\right]$$

Hence or otherwise prove that Yates and Grundy's variance estimator $S'[(\pi_i\pi_j - \pi_{ij})(y_i/\pi_i - y_j/\pi_j)^2/\pi_{ij}]$ would be positive in this situation.

**8.** It is proposed to select two different units from a stratum in order to estimate the stratum total $Y$. The probability of including $U_i$ in the sample is desired to be $\pi_i = 2x_i/X$ $(i = 1, \ldots, N)$. Assuming that the relationship between $y$ and $x$ is linear, prove that the variance of $S(y_i/\pi_i)$ would be a minimum if the $\pi_{ij}$ are so chosen that $\pi_{ij} \geq 0$, $\sum_{j \neq i} \pi_{ij} = \pi_i$

$(i = 1, \ldots, N)$ and $\sum' [\pi_{ij}/(\pi_i\pi_j)]$ is minimized.

**9.** **a.** In sampling with unequal probabilities for samples of size two, when the first unit is selected with pps and the second unit with pps of the remaining units, prove that Yates and Grundy's variance estimator would be positive.

**b.** If the first unit in the sample is selected with pps, the second with pps of the remaining units, and the other $(n-2)$ units selected with equal probabilities without replacement, prove that Yates and Grundy's variance estimator would be positive for this sampling system.

**10.** From a population of $N$ units a sample of two different units is selected in the following way. The first member of the sample is selected with probabilities $p_i$ $(i = 1, \ldots, N)$, $\Sigma p_i = 1$, based on measures of size $x_i$. The second selection is made with probabilities proportionate to $q_i$, $\Sigma q_i = 1$, leaving out the unit already selected. The $q_i$ are so determined that $p_i = \sum_{j \neq i} [p_jq_i/(1-q_j)]$ $(i = 1, \ldots, N)$. Prove that

**a.** The chance that $U_i$ is selected in the sample equals $2p_i$.

**b.** The variance of the estimator $S[y_i/(2p_i)]$ appropriate to this sampling scheme is less than or equal to the variance of the same estimator in the case of wr sampling with pp to $x$.

**11.** From a stratum two clusters are selected by the following procedure. Two independent selections are made with probability $q_i = N_i/N$, where $N_i$ is the number of elements in cluster $i$. If the same cluster is chosen twice, both selections are rejected and two further ones made, the process being continued until two different clusters are chosen. If the clusters are enumerated completely, show that the bias of the simple estimator $t = (\bar{y}_i + \bar{y}_j)/2$ is given by $(\Sigma q_i^2 \Sigma q_i \bar{Y}_i - \Sigma q_i^2 \bar{Y}_i)/(1 - \Sigma q_i^2)$, where $\bar{y}_i, \bar{y}_j$ are the means per element of the sample clusters and the purpose of the sample is to estimate the stratum mean per element. If the mean square error of $t$ around the stratum mean is estimated by $u = (\bar{y}_i - \bar{y}_j)^2/4$, show that $u$ will overstate the MSE and $B(u) = \Sigma q_i^2 (\bar{Y}_i - \bar{Y})^2/(1 - \Sigma q_i^2)$.

**12.** From a population of $N$ units a wtr sample of $n$ units is selected following the general scheme of Sec. 3.17. Defining $t'_n$ as

$$t'_n = [(N - 1)(N - 2) \cdots (N - n + 1)]^{-1} \frac{y_n}{p_{i1} p_{j2} \cdots p_{tn}}$$

prove that $t' = \sum_1^n c_i t'_i$, $\Sigma c_i = 1$ is an unbiased estimator of the population total $Y$. Derive expressions for $V(t'_n)$ and $\mathrm{Cov}\ (t'_\lambda, t'_\mu)$. Hence find the variance of $t'$. [Note that $p_{j2} = \Pr(U_j | U_1)$ and so on.]

**13.** In wtr random sampling from a population containing $N$ units, there will be $\binom{N}{n}$ different samples of size $n$, each sample ordered in $n! = M$ ways. Let $t = t(s,i)$ be an estimator of the population parameter based on the sample $s$ and order $i$. Denote by $p(s,i)$ the probability of the ordered sample, $p_s = \sum_i p(s,i)$ and $p'(s,i) = p(s,i)/p_s$. Prove that

$$V[t(s,i)] = \sum_s \sum_i t^2 p(s,i) - \left[ \sum \sum tp(s,i) \right]^2$$

$$V\left[ \sum_i tp'(s,i) \right] = \sum_s \left[ \sum tp'(s,i) \right]^2 p_s - \left[ \sum \sum tp(s,i) \right]^2$$

Hence or otherwise prove that the unordered estimator $\Sigma tp'(s,i)$ is superior to the ordered estimator $t(s,i)$ from the viewpoint of giving a lower variance.

**14.** Let a systematic sample of every hundredth household be taken with random start $j$ between 1 and 100 from a population containing $100h + k$ households, where $h$ and $k$ are integers with $0 \le k \le 99$. The number of households in the sample will be $h$, with a chance of $1 - k/100$, and $h + 1$, with a chance of $k/100$. Show that the expected sample size will be $h + k/100$, the variance of the sample size being $(1 - k/100)k/100$.

If the distribution of $k$ can be taken to be uniform over the range 0 to 99, show that the average variance would be very nearly $\frac{1}{6}$. Instead of taking $j$'s independently at random, we may select them in complementary pairs such that $j + j' = 101$. Assuming the distributions of $k$ and $k'$ to be independent and uniform, show that the average variance now reduces to $\frac{1}{12}$.

**15.** A population contains $N = nk$ units where $k$ is odd. We shall denote by $\bar{y}_i$ the mean of the systematic sample based on the random start $i$ taken between 1 and $k$. The centered systematic sample estimate will be obtained by taking the mean of the central units [numbered $(k + 1)/2$, $k + (k + 1)/2, \ldots$] from each of the $n$ strata formed when a random-start systematic sample is selected. If the population is monotone increasing, the centered systematic sample mean $\bar{y}_c$ will be the median of the $k$ random-start systematic sample means $\bar{y}_1 < \bar{y}_2 < \cdots < \bar{y}_k$. The mean square error of $\bar{y}_c$ will be $(\bar{y}_c - \bar{Y})^2$ while the variance of $\bar{y}_i$ would be $\Sigma(\bar{y}_i - \bar{Y})^2/k$. Use the result, (mean $-$ median)$^2$ < variance, to prove that centered systematic sampling is more efficient than random-start systematic sampling in the case of monotone populations.

**16.** **a.** In simple random sampling the variance of the sample mean is given by $V(\bar{y}) = \left(\dfrac{1}{n} - \dfrac{1}{N}\right)\dfrac{1}{N-1}\left(\sum y_i^2 - N\bar{Y}^2\right)$. Denoting by $v$ an unbiased estimate of $V(\bar{y})$ and noting that

$$E\frac{N}{n}Sy_i^2 = \sum y_i^2 \qquad E(\bar{y}^2 - v) = \bar{Y}^2$$

show that

$$E(v) = \left(\frac{1}{n} - \frac{1}{N}\right)\frac{1}{N-1}E\left[\frac{N}{n}Sy_i^2 - N(\bar{y}^2 - v)\right]$$

Use this equation to arrive at an expression for $v$.

**b.** In the case of with-replacement pps sampling, the variance of $\hat{Y} = \dfrac{1}{n}S(y_i/p_i)$ is given by $(1/n)[\Sigma(y_i^2/p_i) - Y^2]$. With $(1/n)S(y_i^2/p_i^2)$ as an unbiased estimator of $\Sigma(y_i^2/p_i)$, use the above technique to obtain an unbiased estimator of $V(\hat{Y})$.

**c.** For the sample design in which the population is split at random into $n$ substrata containing $N_i$ $(i = 1, \ldots, n)$ units, and one unit is selected with pp to $x$ from each substratum (Sec. 6.10.3), the variance of $\hat{Y}$ is given by

$$V(\hat{Y}) = \frac{\Sigma N_i^2 - N}{N(N-1)}\left(\sum_i \sum_j \frac{y_{ij}^2}{p_{ij}} - Y^2\right)$$

Using $\displaystyle\sum_1^n \frac{y_{ij}^2}{p_{ij}p'_{ij}}$ as an unbiased estimator of $\displaystyle\sum_i\sum_j (y_{ij}^2/p_{ij})$, show that an unbiased estimator of $V(\hat{Y})$ is given by

$$\frac{\Sigma N_i^2 - N}{N^2 - \Sigma N_i^2}\left(\sum_1^n \frac{y_{ij}^2}{p_{ij}p'_{ij}} - \hat{Y}^2\right) \qquad p'_{ij} = \frac{x_{ij}}{\displaystyle\sum_{j=1}^{N_i} x_{ij}} \qquad p_{ij} = \frac{x_{ij}}{X}$$

**17.** In order to estimate the mean of a finite population a sample of size $n$ is selected with replacement and the number $u$ of distinct units determined. Let the estimator used be

$$\bar{y}' = \frac{1}{n_0}f(u)\frac{Sy}{u} \qquad n_0 = Ef(u)$$

Show that $\bar{y}'$ is unbiased, with variance given by

$$V(\bar{y}') = \left[E\frac{f^2(u)/u}{n_0^2} - \frac{1}{N}\right]S^2 + \left(\bar{Y}^2 - \frac{S^2}{N}\right)\frac{Vf(u)}{n_0^2}$$

Compare it with the without-replacement sampling scheme in which a sample of size $E(u)$ is selected and the estimator used is $\bar{y} = Sy/E(u)$. Show that $V(\bar{y})$ is always smaller than $V(\bar{y}')$ provided $S^2/\bar{Y}^2 < N$.

**18.** A population containing $N$ units is sampled with replacement with probabilities $P_i$ $(i = 1, \ldots, N)$, $\Sigma P_i = 1$. Selection is terminated at the $(r + 1)$st draw when the sample first contains $n + 1$ different units. The last unit is rejected, and the recorded sample consists of the $n$ different units selected. (This procedure is called inverse sampling with unequal probabilities.) An observed sample of $r$ units is recorded as $s = (u_1, u_2, \ldots, u_r)$, where $u_1, u_2, \ldots, u_r$ are respectively the 1st, 2d, $\ldots$, $r$th sample units. Show that the probability of selecting $s$ is

$$Pr(s) = \text{const} \times p_1 p_2 \cdots p_r(1 - p'_1 - p'_2 - \cdots - p'_n)$$

where $p_i$ denotes the probability of selecting $u_i$, and $p'_1, \ldots, p'_n$ are respectively the probabilities of selection associated with the $n$ different population units $u'_1, \ldots, u'_n$ selected in the sample in that order. Given $r$, show that the random variables $u_1, u_2, \ldots, u_r$ are interchangeable in the sense that their joint distribution is invariable under any permutation of $u_1, u_2, \ldots, u_r$. Prove further that the probability of the sample $(u'_1, u'_2, \ldots, u'_n)$ of $n$ different units is given by

$$p'_1 \frac{p'_2}{1 - p'_1} \cdots \frac{p'_n}{(1 - p'_1 - \cdots - p'_{n-1})}$$

Hence prove that the procedure of inverse sampling with unequal probabilities is equivalent to selecting the first unit with pps, the second with pps of the remaining units and so on.

**19.** In the sampling scheme of Exercise 18 let the sample of $r$ units be $(u_1, u_2, \ldots, u_r)$ and let $z$ denote $y/p$ where $y$ is the characteristic of the unit and $p$ is its probability of selection at any draw. Using the fact that the random variables $z_1, z_2, \ldots, z_r$ are interchangeable, prove that $\bar{z} = Sz_i/r$ is an unbiased estimator of the population total $Y$ and that $v(\bar{z}) = S(z_i - \bar{z})^2/[r(r-1)]$ is an unbiased estimator of $V(\bar{z})$. Prove that

$$V(\bar{z}) = E[v(\bar{z})] = E\,\frac{(z_1 - z_2)^2}{2r}$$

$$= \sum{}' P_j P_{j'}(z_j - z_{j'})^2 E\left[\frac{1}{r} \,\middle|\, u_1 = U_j, u_2 = U_{j'}\right]$$

and for $n = 2$

$$E\left[\frac{1}{r} \,\middle|\, u_1 = U_j, u_2 = U_{j'}\right] = \frac{1 - P_j - P_{j'}}{(P_j + P_{j'})^2}\,[\log(1 - P_j - P_{j'}) + P_j + P_{j'}]$$

Consider the alternative estimator $\bar{t} = (t_1 + t_2)/2$

where $\qquad t_1 = \dfrac{y_1'}{p_1'} \quad t_2 = y_1' + \dfrac{y_2'(1 - p_1')}{p_2'} \qquad n = 2$

Show that in this case

$$V(\bar{t}) = \frac{1}{4}\sum{}' (z_j - z_{j'})^2 P_j P_{j'}(2 - P_j - P_{j'})$$

Hence obtain the condition that $\bar{t}$ has a smaller variance.


**STRATIFICATION**

**20.** In stratified random sampling the population mean is estimated by $\Sigma N_h \bar{y}_h/N$ with a variance of $N^{-2}\Sigma(N_h^2 S_h^2/n_h)$ when the finite multipliers within strata are ignored. If $S_h^2$ is estimated by $s_h^2 = S(y_{hi} - \bar{y}_h)^2/(n_h - 1)$, show that the variance of the variance estimator would be given by $N^{-4}\Sigma N_h^4 S_h^4 n_h^{-3}(\beta_{2h} - 1)$. Hence prove that under the cost function $C = \Sigma c_h n_h$, the allocation of the total sample of size $n$ to the strata for minimizing the variance of the variance estimator would be

$$n_h \propto N_h S_h(\beta_{2h} - 1)^{1/4} c_h^{-1/4}$$

Under what conditions is the optimum allocation for variances the same as that for the means?

**21.** A population consists of $k$ strata of sizes $N_j$ and mean values $\bar{Y}_j$ $(j = 1, \ldots, k)$. We are interested in estimating $r$ linear functions $L_i = \sum_j l_{ij}\bar{Y}_j$ $(i = 1, \ldots, r)$ of the strata means by selecting $n_j$ units at random from within the strata. Assuming the cost function to be $C = \Sigma c_j n_j{}^g$, $g > 0$, obtain the values of the $n_j$ such that for a fixed cost the expected loss given by $\sum_i \mu_i V(\hat{L}_i)$ be minimized. ($\hat{L}_i$ is an estimate of $L_i$ and $\mu_i$, $l_{ij}$ are known constants.)

**22.** A random sample of size $n$ is selected from a population and the sample units are allocated to $L$ strata on the basis of information collected about them. Denoting by $n_h$ (a random variable) the number of sample units falling in stratum $h$, show that the variance of $\Sigma W_h \bar{y}_h$ (with $W_h$ known) would be given approximately by $(1/n - 1/N)\Sigma W_h S_h{}^2 + (1/n^2)\Sigma(1 - W_h)S_h{}^2$. Compare this variance with the one obtained in stratified random sampling with proportionate allocation when it is feasible to select units within strata.

**23.** A population is divided up into two strata with $N_1/N_2 = d$, $S_1/S_2 = \lambda$. Let $\mu$ denote $[n_1/n_2]/[n_1'/n_2']$, where $n_1$, $n_2$ is a general allocation of the total sample size $n$, and $n_1'$, $n_2'$ is the optimum allocation for purposes of estimating the population mean in stratified simple random sampling. Show that the relative precision $\alpha$ of a general allocation to the optimum allocation is given by

$$\alpha = \mu(\lambda d + 1)^2 (\lambda \mu d + 1)^{-1} (\lambda d + \mu)^{-1}$$

By tabulating $\alpha$ agains $\mu$ for different values of $\lambda d$, show that the optimum is flat in the sense that there is no appreciable loss of precision for $\frac{1}{2} \leq \mu \leq 2$.

**24.** The variate $y$ is uniformly distributed in the range $a, a + c$. The range is cut in $L$ equal parts to make $L$ strata of equal size. From each stratum a simple random sample of $n/L$ units is taken. Denoting by $V_2$, $V_1$ the variances based on stratified and unstratified samples of size $n$ respectively, prove that $V_2 = V_1/L^2$.

**25.** For the normal distribution with zero mean and unit variance, let $l(x)$ denote the ordinate at $x$ and $W(x_1, x_2)$ the relative frequency between $x_1$ and $x_2$. If this distribution is truncated at $x_1$ and $x_2$, show that the mean $\mu$ and the variance $\sigma^2$ of the truncated distribution are given by $\mu = [l(x_1) - l(x_2)]/W(x_1, x_2)$,

$$\sigma^2 = 1 + \frac{x_1 l(x_1) - x_2 l(x_2)}{W(x_1, x_2)} - \frac{[l(x_1) - l(x_2)]^2}{W^2(x_1, x_2)}$$

Hence divide the positive half of the normal population into $L = 2, 3, 4$ strata of equal aggregate output $W_h\mu_h$. If the total sample size is allocated equally to the strata, show that the variances of the mean are proportional to 0.036, 0.023, 0.016, respectively, the corresponding figure for unstratified sampling being 0.091.

**26.** A population is divided up into $L$ strata, $N_i$ being the number of units in stratum $i$. Information on an auxiliary character $x$ is known for each unit. A sample of size $n$ is selected from the entire population such that the probability that $s_n$ be selected is proportional to $\left(\sum_1^L N_i\bar{x}_i\right)_{s_n}$, where $\bar{x}_i$ is the mean of $x$ based on the $n_i$ sample units taken from stratum $i$. Prove that $\bar{y}_{st} = X(\Sigma N_i\bar{y}_i)/\Sigma N_i\bar{x}_i$ is an unbiased estimator of the population total $Y$. Obtain an expression for the variance of $\bar{y}_{st}$ and an unbiased estimator of $V(\bar{y}_{st})$.

**27.** A population is divided up into $L$ strata, the imputed size of a unit in the $i$th stratum being $x_i$. Assume that $y_{ij} = \alpha + \beta x_i + e_{ij}$ where $E(e_{ij}|x_i) = 0$, $V(e_{ij}|x_i) = ax_i^g$. Denoting by $V_p$, $V_0$, and $V_{pps}$ the variances of the stratified proportionate, stratified optimum and unstratified with-replacement pps estimates of the population mean, show that

$$E(V_p) = \frac{a}{nN} \sum x_i^g - \frac{a}{N^2} \sum x_i^g$$

$$E(V_0) = \frac{a}{nN^2} \left(\sum x_i^{g/2}\right)^2 - \frac{a}{N^2} \sum x_i^g$$

$$E(V_{pps}) = \frac{a}{nN^2} \left(X \sum x_i^{g-1} - \sum x_i^g\right)$$

Hence prove that the stratified optimum estimator is superior to the pps estimator. Further prove that the condition for the pps estimator to be superior to the stratified proportionate estimator is $\rho(x,x^{g-1}) > 0$, provided that $(n-1)/N$ is negligible relative to unity.

**28.** A population is divided into $L$ strata, stratum $h$ containing $N_h$ units from which $n_h$ ($h = 1, \ldots, L$) are to be taken into the sample. The following procedure is used. One unit is selected with pp to $x$ from the entire population. If this unit comes from stratum $h$, a simple random sample of further $n_h - 1$ units is taken from the $N_h - 1$ units that remain. From the other strata simple random samples of specified sizes are taken. Show that $\Sigma N_h\bar{y}_h/\Sigma N_h\bar{x}_h$ is an unbiased estimator of $R = Y/X$.

**29.** There is a symmetric continuous bivariate distribution with frequency function $f(x,y)$, $a \le x \le b$, $c \le y \le d$. The problem is to divide this population into four strata by drawing lines parallel to the axes through the point $(x_0, y_0)$. If sample allocation is proportional, show that the double dichotomy point $(x_0, y_0)$, for which the generalized variance

$$\begin{vmatrix} V(\bar{x}) & \text{Cov } (\bar{x}, \bar{y}) \\ \text{Cov } (\bar{x}, \bar{y}) & V(\bar{y}) \end{vmatrix}$$

is a minimum, is the center of gravity of the distribution.

**30.** In a stratified design it is required to estimate the means $\bar{Y}_i$ of $k$ characteristics $(i = 1, 2, \ldots, k)$. The problem is to allocate the total sample of $n$ units to the $L$ strata in an optimum manner. In order to achieve this, the weighted sum of the variances $\Sigma \alpha_i V(\hat{M}_i)$, $\alpha_i \geq 0$, $\Sigma \alpha_i = 1$, is minimized subject to the constraint $\Sigma n_h - n = 0$. Show that

$$n_h \propto n N_h (\Sigma \alpha_i S_{ih}^2)^{\frac{1}{2}}$$

This gives a set $C$ of allocations $\mu(n_1, n_2, \ldots, n_L)$ for different vectors $\alpha$. Show that this set is complete in the sense that given any allocation $\lambda(n'_1, n'_2, \ldots, n'_L)$ not belonging to $C$, there is an allocation $\mu^0(n_1, \ldots, n_L)$ in $C$ which is better than $\lambda$. The term "better" is understood in the sense that

$$[V(\hat{M}_i)]_{\mu^0} \leq [V(\hat{M}_i)]_\lambda \qquad \text{for all } i$$

and $\qquad [V(\hat{M}_k)]_{\mu^0} < [V(\hat{M}_k)]_\lambda \qquad \text{for at least one } k$

**31.** A population is stratified in two directions with $N_{ij}$ units in the $(i, j)$ cell, $\sum_j N_{ij} = N_i$, $\sum_i N_i = N$ $(i = 1, 2, \ldots, L; j = 1, 2, \ldots, M)$. It is, however, not possible to select the sample from within substrata, since it is not known which units make up the substrata. Thus a wtr simple random sample of $n$ units is selected from the entire population and the sample units are allocated to the substrata on the basis of information collected about them. For a unit in the sample, we define

$$y' = y \qquad x = 1 \qquad \text{if the unit is in cell } (i, j)$$
$$y' = 0 \qquad x = 0 \qquad \text{if the unit is not in cell } (i, j)$$

Then $Sy'/Sx$ is a ratio estimate of the average $\bar{Y}_{ij}$ of cell $(i, j)$. Hence, by Theorem 5.3, we have approximately

$$V \frac{Sy'}{Sx} \doteq \left( \frac{N}{N_{ij}} \right)^2 V \left[ \frac{1}{n} S(y' - \bar{Y}_{ij} x) \right]$$

Since $y' - \bar{Y}_{ij} x = y - \bar{Y}_{ij}$ if the unit belongs to cell $(i, j)$ and zero otherwise, it is easy to see that

$$V \frac{Sy'}{Sx} \doteq \left( \frac{N}{N_{ij}} \right)^2 \left( \frac{1}{n} - \frac{1}{N} \right) \frac{1}{N - 1} (N_{ij} - 1) S_{ij}^2$$

Hence show that under certain conditions (to be stated),

$$V(\hat{Y}) \doteq \left(\frac{1}{n} - \frac{1}{N}\right) \frac{N^2}{N-1} \sum_i \sum_j (N_{ij} - 1)S_{ij}^2$$

where

$$\hat{Y} = \sum \sum \frac{N_{ij}Sy'}{Sx}$$

Consider another situation in which the stratification in direction $j$ is ignored so that $N_i$ units belong to the stratum $i$ ($i = 1, 2, \ldots, L$). Prove that the variance of $\hat{Y} = \Sigma(N_iSy'/Sx)$ in this case is given by

$$V(\hat{Y}) \doteq \left(\frac{1}{n} - \frac{1}{N}\right) \frac{N^2}{N-1} \sum_i (N_i - 1)S_i^2$$

Prove that, correct to the approximations used, the latter estimator which makes use of smaller information on the population has a larger variance as compared with the former estimator.

### RATIO AND REGRESSION ESTIMATION

**32.** In wtr simple random sampling it is usual to use $\bar{y}/\bar{x}$ as an estimate of $R = Y/X$. Obtaining an exact expression for the variance of $\bar{y}/\bar{x}$, show that a sufficient condition for the usual approximation $V(\bar{y} - R\bar{x})/(\bar{X})^2$ to be an understatement for $V(\bar{y}/\bar{x})$ is that

$$\rho\left[\frac{1}{\bar{x}}, (\bar{y} - R\bar{x})^2\right] \geq 0$$

where $\rho$ stands for the correlation coefficient.

**33.** Let $y_i$, $x_i$ ($i = 1, \ldots, m$) be unbiased estimators of $Y$ and $X$ respectively, based on $m$ interpenetrating subsamples of the same size. Prove that $\bar{r}X + m(\bar{y} - \bar{r}\bar{x})/(m - 1)$, where $\bar{r} = m^{-1}S(y_i/x_i)$, is an unbiased estimator of $Y$.

**34.** If the regression of $y$ on $x$ is linear, that is, $E(y|x) = ax + b$, show that in simple random sampling the estimator $\bar{y}/\bar{x}$ will give a smaller large sample variance than the ratio-type estimator $\bar{r} + (N - 1)n(\bar{y} - \bar{r}\bar{x})[N(n - 1)\bar{X}]^{-1}$ where $\bar{r} = n^{-1}S(y_i/x_i)$. Prove this result by using the corollary to Theorem 5.8, showing that $R - \beta = b/\bar{X}$, $\bar{R} - \beta = bE(1/x)$ and using $E(x)E(1/x) > 1$.

**35.** Let $y_i, x_i$ ($i = 1, \ldots, n$) be unbiased estimators of $Y$ and $X$, respectively, based on $n$ interpenetrating subsamples. Consider the following two estimators of $R = Y/X$: $\hat{R}_1 = \Sigma y_i/\Sigma x_i$, $\hat{R}_2 = n^{-1}\Sigma(y_i/x_i)$. Using

Theorem 5.2, show that approximately

$$B(\hat{R}_1) = n^{-2} \sum B\left(\frac{y_i}{x_i}\right) = n^{-1}B(\hat{R}_2)$$

Hence show that an estimator of $B(\hat{R}_1)$ is given by $(\hat{R}_2 - \hat{R}_1)/(n - 1)$, so that $\hat{R}_1 - (\hat{R}_2 - \hat{R}_1)/(n - 1) = (n\hat{R}_1 - \hat{R}_2)/(n - 1)$ is an almost unbiased estimator of $R$.

**36.** Defining the difference estimator as $t_1 = \bar{y} + \beta(\bar{X} - \bar{x})$ and the regression estimator as $t_2 = \bar{y} + b(\bar{X} - \bar{x})$, we have $t_2 = t_1 + (b - \beta)(\bar{X} - \bar{x})$ and hence $\text{MSE}(t_2) = V(t_1) + E(b - \beta)^2(\bar{X} - \bar{x})^2 + 2E[(b - \beta)(\bar{X} - \bar{x})(t_1 - \bar{Y})]$. Using Theorem 1.4, show that $E[(b - \beta)^2(\bar{X} - \bar{x})^2] = 0(n^{-2})$ and $E[(b - \beta)(\bar{X} - \bar{x})(t_1 - \bar{Y})]$ is of order lower than $n^{-1}$, whereas $V(t_1)$ is of order $n^{-1}$. Hence prove that for sufficiently large $n$, $\text{MSE}(t_2) \doteq V(t_1) = \sigma_y^2(1 - \rho^2)/n$.

**37.** A population containing $N$ units is split at random into $s$ mutually exclusive groups each of size $n/k$, where $N = sn/k$. A wtr sample of $k$ groups is taken with equal probabilities. We shall denote by $\bar{y}_i, \bar{x}_i$ the means of the $n/k$ units in the $i$th selection (of the group) and $b_i$ shall be any function of the $y$'s and the $x$'s of that group. Then prove that for a given split of the population, $\bar{y}_i, \bar{x}_i$ are unbiased estimators of $\bar{Y}$ and $\bar{X}$ respectively and $(k^{-1} - s^{-1})\Sigma(b_i - \bar{b})(\bar{x}_i - \bar{x})/(k - 1)$ is an unbiased estimator of $\text{Cov}(\bar{b},\bar{x})$ where $\bar{b} = Sb_i/k$, $\bar{x} = S\bar{x}_i/k$. Considering $\bar{y} + \bar{b}(\bar{X} - \bar{x})$ and its expectation $\bar{Y} - \text{Cov}(\bar{b},\bar{x})$, prove that an unbiased estimator of $\bar{Y}$ is given by $\bar{y} + \bar{b}(\bar{X} - \bar{x}) + (1 - n/N)\Sigma(b_i - \bar{b})(\bar{x}_i - \bar{x})/[k(k - 1)]$.

**38.** A wtr simple random sample of $n$ units is selected from a population of $N$ units. The first $a$ selections give a mean of $\bar{y}_a, \bar{x}_a$ for the characters $y$ and $x$, respectively. Given the first $a$ selections, the $(n - a)$ remaining selections form a random sample from the population of $N - a$ units. Thus, given the first $a$ selections, $(n\bar{x} - a\bar{x}_a)/(n - a)$ estimates $(N\bar{X} - a\bar{x}_a)/(N - a)$ and $(n\bar{y} - a\bar{y}_a)/(n - a)$ estimates $(N\bar{Y} - a\bar{y}_a)/(N - a)$. Denoting by $f(z_a)$ a function of the sample values obtained from the first $a$ selections, prove that, given the first $a$ selections, the expected value of

$$\frac{n\bar{y} - a\bar{y}_a}{n - a} - f(z_a)\left(\frac{n\bar{x} - a\bar{x}_a}{n - a} - \frac{N\bar{X} - a\bar{x}_a}{N - a}\right)$$

is given by $(N\bar{Y} - a\bar{y}_a)/(N - a)$. Hence prove that an unbiased estimator of $\bar{Y}$ is provided by

$$t(a) = \frac{N - a}{N}\frac{n}{n - a}[\bar{y} - f(z_a)(\bar{x} - \bar{X})] - \frac{(N - n)a}{N(n - a)}[\bar{y}_a - f(z_a)(\bar{x}_a - \bar{X})]$$

Give the forms of $t(a)$ for the particular cases when $f(z_a)$ is

(1)
$$\mathop{S}_{1}^{a} \frac{(y_i/x_i)}{a}$$

(2)
$$\frac{Sy_i}{Sx_i}$$

(3)
$$\frac{S(y_i - \bar{y}_a)(x_i - \bar{x}_a)}{S(x_i - \bar{x}_a)^2}$$

By forming $t(a)$ for all possible values of $a$ and averaging the results, what estimators do you get in situations (1) to (3) above?

**39.** A simple random sample $(y'_j, x_{1j}, \ldots, x_{pj})(j = 1, \ldots, n)$ is taken from a finite population. The proposed ratio estimate of $\bar{Y}$ is $\bar{y} = \sum^{p} w_i r_i \bar{X}_i$, where $r_i = \bar{y}'/\bar{x}_i$ and $\Sigma w_i = 1$. We shall denote by $V(\bar{y}|p)$ and $V(\bar{y}|p,q)$ the variances of $\bar{y}$ based on the auxiliary characters $x_1, \ldots, x_p$ and $x_1, \ldots, x_q$, $q > p$. If the allocation of the weights $w_i$ is optimum in either case, prove that $V(\bar{y}|p) \geq V(\bar{y}|p,q)$.

**40.** A population is divided into $L$ strata. One unit is selected from each stratum with certain probabilities and this gives rise to $\bar{y}$, $\bar{x}$ as estimates of $\bar{Y}$, $\bar{X}$ respectively. We take $k$ interpenetrating samples of this type, giving $\bar{y}_i$, $\bar{x}_i$ $(i = 1, \ldots, k)$. We shall use the notation:

$$\bar{y}_{st} = \sum \frac{\bar{y}_i}{k} \qquad \bar{x}_{st} = \sum \frac{\bar{x}_i}{k} \qquad \bar{r}_{st} = \sum \frac{(\bar{y}_i/\bar{x}_i)}{k} = \sum \frac{r_i}{k}$$

Prove that an unbiased estimator of $\bar{Y}$ is provided by

$$\bar{r}_{st}\bar{X} + \frac{\Sigma(r_i - \bar{r}_{st})(\bar{x}_i - \bar{x}_{st})}{k - 1} = \bar{r}_{st}\bar{X} + \frac{k(\bar{y}_{st} - \bar{r}_{st}\bar{x}_{st})}{k - 1}$$

Obtain the variance of this estimator.

**41.** Show that an estimate of the variance of the combined ratio estimator based on a stratified sampling design (Sec. 5.18) is given by

$$\Sigma N_h^2(1 - f_h)n_h^{-1}(s_{gh}^2 + \hat{R}^2 s_{xh}^2 - 2\hat{R}r_h s_{yh} s_{xh})$$

the relative variance being estimated by

$$\sum N_h^2(1 - f_h)n_h^{-1}\left(\frac{s_{yh}^2}{\hat{Y}^2} + \frac{s_{xh}^2}{\hat{X}^2} - 2\frac{r_h s_{yh} s_{xh}}{\hat{Y}\hat{X}}\right)$$

In case two units are selected from each stratum, show that

$$N_h{}^2 \frac{s_{yh}{}^2}{2\hat{Y}^2} = \left(\frac{N_h y_{h1} - N_h y_{h2}}{2\hat{Y}}\right)^2$$

$$N_h{}^2 \frac{s_{xh}{}^2}{2\hat{X}^2} = \left(\frac{N_h x_{h1} - N_h x_{h2}}{2\hat{X}}\right)^2$$

and
$$N_h{}^2 \frac{r_h s_{yh} s_{xh}}{2\hat{Y}\hat{X}} = \frac{N_h y_{h1} - N_h y_{h2}}{2\hat{Y}} \frac{N_h x_{h1} - N_h x_{h2}}{2\hat{X}}$$

Hence show that for $n_h = 2$ and $f_h = \bar{f}$, an unbiased estimate of the variance is given simply by

$$(1 - \bar{f}) \sum_h \left(\frac{N_h y_{h1} - N_h y_{h2}}{2\hat{Y}} - \frac{N_h x_{h1} - N_h x_{h2}}{2\hat{X}}\right)^2$$

**42.** For estimating the population ratio $R = E(y)/E(x)$, a random sample of size $n$ is split into two halves to give $r_1 = y_1/x_1$, $r_2 = y_2/x_2$, while the estimator based on the complete sample is $r = y/x = \frac{1}{2}(y_1 + y_2)/[\frac{1}{2}(x_1 + x_2)]$. (The $y_i$ and $x_i$ are actually the sample means.) We shall assume that the $x_i$ ($i = 1, 2$) are normally distributed with variance $2h$, which is $0(n^{-1})$, and that $y_i = a + bx_i + u_i$, where $E(u_i|x_i) = 0$, $E(u_i{}^2|x_i) = 2\delta$. Then $y = a + bx + u$, where $u = (u_1 + u_2)/2$. We shall choose the units of measurement such that $E(x) = 1$ and let $x = 1 - z$. Neglecting terms of order $n^{-4}$ or lower, show that $E(x^{-1}) = 1 + h + 3h^2 + 15h^3$, $E(x^{-2}) = 1 + 3h + 15h^2 + 105h^3$. Use these results to prove that the bias of $r$ for estimating $R$ is $a(h + 3h^2 + 15h^3)$, which is $0(n^{-1})$ and that $V(r) = a^2(h + 8h^2 + 69h^3) + \delta(1 + 3h + 15h^2 + 105h^3)$. On the other hand, if the estimator $t = 2r - (\frac{1}{2})(r_1 + r_2)$ (due to Quenouille) is used, its bias is $a(6h^2 + 90h^3)$, which is $0(n^{-2})$. Further $V(t) = a^2(h + 4h^2 + 12h^3) + \delta(1 + 2h + 8h^2 + 108h^3)$, which is smaller than $V(r)$.

## SAMPLING AND SUBSAMPLING OF CLUSTERS

**43.** A population consists of $N$ clusters each containing $M$ elements. A simple random sample of $n$ clusters is selected to estimate the population mean per element. An unbiased estimator would be $S\bar{y}_i/n$ with a variance of $S_b{}^2/(nM)$ where $S_b{}^2 = \Sigma M(\bar{Y}_i - \bar{Y})^2/(N - 1)$, and the finite population correction is ignored. Assuming $S_w{}^2$, the variance within clusters, to be given by $aM^g$, $g > 0$, and the cost function to be $C = c_1 M n + c_2 \sqrt{n}$, find the optimum size of the cluster for which the variance of the estimator is a minimum, given the total cost of the survey. Show that the optimum value of $M$ will be smaller if $c_1$ increases or $c_2$ decreases.

**44.**  In a two-stage design the number of second-stage units $M_i$ is known for each psu in the population.  A sample of $n$ different psu's is selected in the following manner.  The psu's are selected with replacement with pp to $M_i$.  Selection continues till $(n + 1)$ psu's are taken where the last psu to enter the sample does so at the $(r + 1)$st selection.  The last psu is rejected.  Every time the $i$th psu in the population is selected in the sample, the same random sample of $m_i$ second-stage units is taken.  Denoting by $r_i$ the number of times the $i$th psu occurs in the sample, show by the conditional argument that

$$E \frac{r_i}{r} = \frac{M_i}{M_0} \qquad E \frac{r_i(r_i - 1)}{r(r - 1)} = \frac{M_i^2}{M_0^2} \qquad E \frac{r_i r_j}{r(r - 1)} = \frac{M_i M_j}{M_0^2} \qquad M_0 = \Sigma M_i$$

Hence show that $\bar{y} = \Sigma r_i \bar{y}_i / r$ is an unbiased estimator of the population mean per subunit, the variance estimator being

$$\frac{\Sigma r_i(\bar{y}_i - \bar{y})^2}{r(r - 1)} + \sum \left[ r_i(r_i - 1) \left( 1 - \frac{m_i}{M_i} \right) \frac{s_i^2/m_i}{r(r - 1)} \right]$$

**45.**  We have a population consisting of $L$ strata, $N_h$ psu's in stratum $h$, and $M_{hi}$ second-stage units within psu $h_i$.  A simple random sample of $n_h$ psu's is selected from $N_h$ and a simple random sample of $m_{hi}$ second-stage units is taken from the $M_{hi}$.  Estimate from this design the ratio $R = Y/X$.  How will you estimate the variance of $\hat{R}$ and the within-psu and between-psu components of the variance?

**46.**  A stratum contains $N$ psu's from which $n$ are selected with replacement with probabilities $\pi_i = M_i/M_0$ $(i = 1, \ldots , N)$, where $M_i$ is the number of subunits in the $i$th psu and $\Sigma M_i = M_0$.  If a psu occurs in the sample $\lambda$ times, a wtr random sample of $m\lambda$ subunits is selected from it.  Prove that $t_1 = \sum\limits_{i=1}^{N} \lambda_i \bar{y}_i / n$ is an unbiased estimator of $\theta = \Sigma \pi_i \theta_i$, where $\theta_i$ is the mean per subunit in the $i$th psu and $\lambda_i$ is the frequency with which this psu occurs in the sample, $\bar{y}_i$ being defined as zero when no sample is taken from the psu.  Further prove that

$$V(t_1) = A + B - C \qquad \text{where } A = n^{-1} \sum \pi_i S_i^2 \left( \frac{1}{m} - \frac{1}{M_i} \right)$$

$$B = n^{-1} \Sigma \pi_i (\theta_i - \theta)^2$$

$$C = n^{-1}(n - 1) \sum \left( \frac{\pi_i^2 S_i^2}{M_i} \right)$$

$$S_i^2 = \sum_j \frac{(y_{ij} - \bar{Y}_i)^2}{M_i - 1}$$

If subsampling is carried out independently every time a psu enters the sample by taking a wtr random sample of $m$ subunits, prove that $t_2 = S\bar{y}_i/n$ is an unbiased estimator of $\theta$ and $V(t_2) = A + B$. Hence show that $V(t_1) < V(t_2)$. Show that in the first case

$$V(t_1) \cong \frac{\Sigma\lambda_i(\bar{y}_i - \bar{y})^2}{n(n-1)} - \frac{\Sigma s_i{}^2}{n(n-1)}\left[(n-1)\lambda_i\frac{\pi_i}{M_i} - \frac{\lambda_i - 1}{m}\right]$$

while in the second case

$$V(t_2) \cong \frac{S(\bar{y}_i - \bar{y})^2}{n(n-1)}$$

**47.** A population is divided up into $L$ strata, stratum $h$ containing $N_h$ psu's each having $M$ subunits. A simple random sample of $n_h$ psu's is selected from stratum $h$ ($h = 1, \ldots, L$) and a random sample of $m$ subunits is taken from each. Estimate from this sample the gain due to stratification by estimating the variance for an unstratified design in which $n = \Sigma n_h$ psu's are selected at random and $m$ subunits taken at random from each sample psu.

**48.** Consider a two-stage design in which a wtr random sample of psu's is taken and $m_i$ subunits are selected at random from the $i$th psu if in the sample. The expected number of subunits in the sample is then $E(Sm_i) = (n/N)\Sigma m_i = m_0$, which we shall call the expected cost of the survey. Show that, given cost, the minimum variance of the population total estimate $\hat{Y} = (N/n)SM_i\bar{y}_i$ would be

$$V_1 = N^2\left(\frac{1}{n} - \frac{1}{N}\right)\sigma^2 + \frac{1}{m_0}\left(\sum M_i\sigma_{wi}\right)^2 - \frac{N}{n}\sum M_i\sigma_{wi}{}^2$$

$$= N^2\left(\frac{1}{n} - \frac{1}{N}\right)\sigma^2 + \frac{\left(\sum\limits_s\sum\limits_i M_{is}\sigma_{wis}\right)^2}{m_0\left(\dfrac{N-1}{n-1}\right)^2} - \frac{N}{n}\frac{\sum\limits_s\sum\limits_i M_{is}\sigma_{wis}{}^2}{\left(\dfrac{N-1}{n-1}\right)}$$

where $\sum\limits_s$ denotes summation over all possible samples and $\sigma$, $\sigma_w$ stand for $S$, $S_w$ respectively. Consider now another situation in which $m_0$ is the number of subunits to be taken from each sample of psu's so that $m_{1s} + m_{2s} + \cdots + m_{ns} = m_0$ for all $s$. In this case, show that the minimum variance is

$$V_2 = N^2\left(\frac{1}{n} - \frac{1}{N}\right)\sigma^2 + \frac{1}{\left(\dfrac{N}{n}\right)}\frac{N^2}{n^2}\sum_s\frac{1}{m_0}\left(\sum_i M_{is}\sigma_{wis}\right)^2 - \frac{1}{\left(\dfrac{N}{n}\right)}\frac{N^2}{n^2}\sum_s\sum_i M_{is}\sigma_{wis}{}^2$$

Prove that $V_2 - V_1 > 0$, so that the sampling plan in which the sample size is a random variable gives a smaller variance.

**49.** In a two-stage design one subunit is selected with pp to $x$ from the entire population. If this happens to come from the $i$th psu, a wtr random sample of $m_i - 1$ subunits is taken from the $M_i - 1$ that remain in the psu. From the other $(N - 1)$ psu's a wtr random sample of $(n - 1)$ psu's is taken. Subsampling of the selected psu's is wtr simple random. Show that $\Sigma M_i \bar{y}_i / \Sigma M_i \bar{x}_i$ is an unbiased estimator of $R = Y/X$.

**50.** From a stratum containing $N$ psu's a sample of $n$ psu's is selected following the scheme of Sec. 3.17. Each psu is subsampled in a known manner. Let $T_i$ be an unbiased estimator of the psu total for $y$ based on subsampling. Defining $z'_n$ as $z'_n = [(N - 1)(N - 2) \cdots (N - n + 1)]^{-1} T_n / (p_{i1} p_{j2} \cdots p_{tn})$, prove that $Z' = \sum_{i=1}^{n} c_i z'_i$, $\sum c_i = 1$ is an unbiased estimator of the stratum total. Obtain the variance of $Z'$ and an unbiased estimator of the variance.

**51.** A stratum contains $N$ psu's with measures of size $X_i$ $(i = 1, \ldots, N)$. One psu is selected with pps and another with pps of the remaining units. Let $T_i$ $(i = 1, 2)$ be an unbiased estimator of the total of the $i$th sample psu, the estimator being based on subsampling from the psu. Then, prove that $Z_1 = T_1/p_1, Z_2 = T_1 + (1 - p_1)T_2/p_2$ are unbiased estimators of the stratum total and $V(Z_2) < V(Z_1)$.

**52.** Suppose a population consists of $N$ psu's out of which $n$ are selected so that the probability that a sample $s_n$ be selected is proportional to $Sx_i$, where $x_i$ is some measure of size of the psu. Suppose further that for the $i$th psu there is an estimator $T_i$ (based on sampling at the second and subsequent stages) of the total $Y_i$ of the psu such that $E_2(T_i) = Y_i$, $V_2(T_i) = \sigma_i^2 = E_2(s_i^2)$. Show that $\hat{Y} = X(ST_i)/(Sx_i)$ is an unbiased estimator of the population total. Obtain an expression for $V(\hat{Y})$ and an unbiased estimator of $V(\hat{Y})$.

**53.** Consider a population of four units with the variate-values $y_1, y_2, y_3$, and $y_4$ arranged in ascending order of magnitude. If the population is to be divided into clusters of two units each, there will be three ways of forming the clusters, one of the clusters being $(y_1, y_2)$ or $(y_1, y_3)$ or $(y_1, y_4)$ in the three situations. The object is to estimate the population total by selecting one cluster at random. If the absolute errors (of the estimate from the true value) are denoted by $e_1, e_2, e_3$, show that $e_3 \leq e_2 \leq e_1$. Hence show that, for loss functions which are monotonically increasing with $e$, the risk is a minimum for the third method of forming clusters. Generalize this result to populations containing an even number of units by proving that the best way of forming clusters of two units is to take units equidistant from either end.

**54.** Consider the following multistage generalization of the sample design described in Exercise 16(c). One psu is selected from each substratum with pp to $x$. Each sample psu is subsampled in a known manner. Based on subsampling, let $t_{ij}$ be an unbiased estimator of $Y_{ij}$, which is the total value of $y$ for $U_{ij}$, the $j$th psu belonging to the $i$th substratum. Given $U_{ij}$, let $V_3(t_{ij})$, $\hat{V}_3(t_{ij})$ stand for the variance of $t_{ij}$ and an unbiased estimator of it. Then show that

$$\hat{Y} = \sum_{i=1}^{n} \frac{t_{ij}}{p'_{ij}}$$

$$V(\hat{Y}) = \frac{\Sigma N_i^2 - N}{N(N-1)} \left( \sum \sum \frac{Y_{ij}^2}{p_{ij}} - Y^2 \right) + E \sum_i \frac{V_3(t_{ij})}{p'^2_{ij}}$$

Show further that

$$E \left[ \sum_i \frac{t_{ij}^2}{p_{ij}p'_{ij}} - \sum_i \frac{\hat{V}_3(t_{ij})}{p_{ij}p'_{ij}} \right] = \sum \sum \frac{Y_{ij}^2}{p_{ij}}$$

$$E(\hat{Y}^2 - v) = Y^2 \qquad E(v) = V(\hat{Y})$$

Hence $\quad v = \dfrac{\Sigma N_i^2 - N}{N^2 - \Sigma N_i^2} \left( \sum_i \dfrac{t_{ij}^2}{p_{ij}p'_{ij}} - \hat{Y}^2 \right) + \dfrac{N(N-1)}{N^2 - \Sigma N_i^2} \sum_i \dfrac{\hat{V}_3(t_{ij})}{p'^2_{ij}}$

$$- \frac{\Sigma N_i^2 - N}{N^2 - \Sigma N_i^2} \sum_i \frac{\hat{V}_3(t_{ij})}{p_{ij}p'_{ij}}$$

If, however, in samples of two psu's per stratum, a simpler variance estimator $u$ be used where $u = (t_{1j}/p'_{1j} - t_{2j}/p'_{2j})^2$, then $E(u) = V(\hat{Y}) + NS_y^2$ for $N_1 = N/2 = N_2$.

**55.** A population contains $N$ psu's, $M_i$ being the number of subunits in the $i$th psu. A sample of $n$ psu's is selected with replacement with probabilities $p_i$, $\Sigma p_i = 1$. If the $i$th psu occurs in the sample $\lambda_i$ times, $\lambda_i$ independent subsamples of $m_i$ subunits each are selected from it, sampling being wtr simple random for each subsample. Consider the following estimators of the population total $Y$:

$$\hat{Y} = \frac{1}{n} \overset{n}{\underset{1}{S}} \frac{M_i \bar{y}_i}{p_i} \qquad \hat{Y}' = \frac{1}{n} \sum_{1}^{N} \frac{\lambda_i M_i \bar{y}'_i}{p_i}$$

In the first case $\bar{y}_i$ is the mean per subunit based on a sample of $m_i \lambda_i$ subunits. In the latter case the mean $\bar{y}'_i$ is based on the distinct subunits in the sample of $m_i\lambda_i$ subunits. Show that $\hat{Y}'$ gives a smaller variance than $\hat{Y}$.

**56.** In a multistage design the psu's are selected without replacement and sampling is done independently in the psu's. Let $E(z_i|i) = Z_i$, where $z_i$ is an estimate made from the subsample drawn in the $i$th psu. Then show that $t = Sz_i$ is an unbiased estimate of $\Sigma\pi_iZ_i$ with a variance of $V(t) = V(\hat{Z}) + \Sigma\pi_i\sigma_i{}^2$ where

$$\hat{Z} = SZ_i \qquad \sigma_i{}^2 = E[(z_i - Z_i)^2|i]$$

And an unbiased estimate of $V(t)$ is provided by

$$\hat{V}(t) = [v(\hat{Z})]_{Z_i=z_i} + \Sigma\pi_i\hat{\sigma}_i{}^2$$

where $v(\hat{Z})$ is an unbiased estimated of $V(\hat{Z})$ in one-stage sampling and $\hat{\sigma}_i{}^2$ is an unbiased estimate of $\sigma_i{}^2$ based on sampling at the second and subsequent stages. Hence obtain the following rule for estimating the variance in multistage sampling.

*Based on one-stage sampling, get an unbiased estimate $v(\hat{Z})$ of $V(\hat{Z})$. In this replace $Z_i$ by $z_i$. To this add $\Sigma\pi_i\hat{\sigma}_i{}^2$ where $\hat{\sigma}_i{}^2$ is an unbiased estimate of the within psu variance of $z_i$.*

## DOUBLE SAMPLING AND REPETITIVE SURVEYS

**57.** When the initial random sample of size $n'$ is taken for purposes of stratification and the subsequent subsample for collecting information on $y$ within strata, show that an unbiased estimator of the variance of $\Sigma a_h\bar{y}_h$ (Sec. 7.8) is provided by

$$\frac{n'}{n'-1}\sum_h\left[\left(a_h{}^2 - \frac{a_h}{n'}\frac{N-n'}{N-1}\right)\frac{s_h{}^2}{n_h} + \frac{N-n'}{n'(N-1)}a_h\left(\bar{y}_h - \sum a_h\bar{y}_h\right)^2\right]$$

assuming that $n_h/N_h$ and $1/N$ are negligible as compared with unity. Show further that the estimator of variance reduces to $\Sigma(a_h{}^2s_h{}^2/n_h)$ if the $n_h$ are small as compared with $n'$.

**58.** A preliminary random sample of $n'$ units is taken from a population and information collected on $p$ variates $x_1, x_2, \ldots, x_p$. A random subsample of size $n$ is selected on which $y$ alone is measured. Show that an unbiased estimator of the population mean for $y$ is given by

$$\hat{M} = \sum_{i=1}^{p} w_iu_i$$

where $u_i = \bar{y} - k_i(\bar{x}_i - \bar{x}_i')$ and $\bar{y}$, $\bar{x}_i$ $(i = 1, \ldots, p)$ are the means for the subsample, $\bar{x}_i'$ is the mean of $x_i$ in the preliminary sample and $k_i$'s are some constants, $w_i$ being the weights adding up to unity. Show further that $V(\hat{M}) = n^{-1}\Sigma\Sigma w_i w_j b_{ij}$ where

$$b_{ij} = \left(1 - \frac{n}{N}\right) S_{00} + \left(1 - \frac{n}{n'}\right)(k_i k_j S_{ij} - k_i S_{0i} - k_j S_{0j})$$

and $S_{uv}$ is the covariance between $u$ and $v$ and $0, 1, \ldots, p$ stand for $y, x_1, x_2, \ldots, x_p$, respectively. Show that an unbiased estimator of $V(\hat{M})$ is given by

$$\left(\frac{1}{n'} - \frac{1}{N}\right)(n - 1)^{-1} \overset{n}{\underset{1}{S}} (y_j - \bar{y})^2$$

$$+ \left(\frac{1}{n} - \frac{1}{n'}\right)(n - 1)^{-1} S \left[y_j - \bar{y} - \sum_i w_i k_i (x_{ij} - \bar{x}_i)\right]^2$$

What would be the results if only one $x$-variate be used?

**59.** In order to estimate the total of a stratum for the character $y$, an initial sample of $n'$ psu's is selected at random for which information is collected inexpensively on a character $x$. Then a subsample of $n$ psu's is taken with replacement with pp to $x$. Let $T_i$ be an unbiased estimator of the $i$th psu total $Y_i$, based on subsampling at the second and subsequent stages. Show that $(N/n')(x'/n)S(T_i/x_i)$ is an unbiased estimator of the stratum total $Y$, where $N$ is the number of psu's in the stratum and $x'$ is the total of $x$ in the preliminary sample. Prove further that the variance of the estimator is given by

$$(N - 1)^{-1}N\left(1 - \frac{1}{n'}\right)n^{-1}\sum p_i \left(\frac{Y_i}{p_i} - Y\right)^2 + (n')^{-1}N(N - n')S_y^2$$

$$+ (N - 1)^{-1}N(nn')^{-1}\left[(N - n')\sum V(T_i) + (n' - 1)X\sum \frac{V(T_i)}{X_i}\right]$$

If the second sample is taken independently of the preliminary sample, show that the additional contribution to the variance due to subsampling is

$$\left[N^2\left(\frac{1}{n'} - \frac{1}{N}\right)S_x^2 + X^2\right](nX)^{-1}\sum \frac{V(T_i)}{X_i}$$

**60.** A random sample of $n'$ units is selected to observe the variate $x$ while a random subsample of size $n$ is taken to observe $y$. The object is to estimate the population mean $\bar{Y}$. Show that $u = \bar{x}'\bar{y}/\bar{x}$ and $v = \bar{r}\bar{x}' + n(n' - 1)[n'(n - 1)]^{-1}(\bar{y} - \bar{r}\bar{x})$ are competing estimators of $\bar{Y}$, where $\bar{r} = n^{-1}\overset{n}{\underset{1}{S}}(y_i/x_i)$. Calculate $V(u)$ and $V(v)$ and obtain the conditions under which $v$ is superior to $u$.

**61.** A population is sampled on two occasions. To use the notation of Sec. 7.9.2, an estimate of $M_1$ is provided by the mean $\bar{x} = \lambda \bar{x}' + \mu \bar{x}''$ of the sample on the first occasion. On the second occasion, when a proportion $\mu$ of the units is selected afresh, it is desired to make the best unbiased estimates of $M_2$ and the change $\Delta = M_2 - M_1$ in such a manner that $\hat{\Delta} = \hat{M}_2 - \bar{x}$. This means that $\hat{M}_2$ is of the form $(e + \lambda)\bar{x}' - (e + \lambda)\bar{x}'' + c\bar{y}' + (1 - c)\bar{y}''$, whereas $\hat{\Delta}$ is of the form $e\bar{x}' - (e + 1)\bar{x}'' + c\bar{y}' + (1 - c)\bar{y}''$. Determine the constants $e$ and $c$ such that $V(\hat{M}_2) + V(\hat{\Delta})$ is a minimum.

**62.** A survey is to be planned on two occasions to estimate $\theta = aM_1 + bM_2$ where $M_1$, $M_2$ are the means on the two occasions and $a,b$ are known constants. A sample of $n$ units will be taken on the first occasion. On the second occasion a subsample of $n_1$ units will be taken, as well as an independent sample of $n_2 = n - n_1$ units. If the total cost of the survey be represented by the function $C = c_0 + cn + c_1 n_1 + c_2 n_2$, obtain the best values of $n$ and $n_1$ so that for a specified cost the variance of the estimator is minimized.

**63.** A population is sampled over several occasions in the following manner. Each time an independent random sample of $n$ units is taken. During the enumeration each member of the sample provides data both for the current period and also for the previous period. Let $\bar{y}_h$ and $\bar{x}_{h-1}$ denote the sample means for the $h$th and $(h - 1)$st occasions based on the sample taken on occasion $h$. Then the best linear estimator $\hat{M}_h$ of the mean on occasion $h$ will be of the form

$$\hat{M}_h = \bar{y}_h - a_n \bar{x}_{h-1} + a_h \hat{M}_{h-1} \quad \text{with } a_1 = 0$$

and
$$\hat{M}_{h-1} = \bar{y}_{h-1} - a_{h-1} \bar{x}_{h-2} + a_{h-1} \hat{M}_{h-2}$$

In order that $\hat{M}_h$ have minimum variance, the condition is:

$$\text{Cov } (\bar{x}_{h-1}, \hat{M}_h) = \text{Cov } (\bar{y}_{h-1}, \hat{M}_h)$$

We shall assume that $V(\bar{y}_h) = \sigma^2/n$ on each occasion and that $\rho$ is the correlation coefficient between consecutive periods. Then

$$\text{Cov } (\bar{x}_{h-1}, \hat{M}_h) = (\rho - a_h)\sigma^2/n$$

$$\text{Cov } (\bar{y}_{h-1}, \hat{M}_h) = a_h \text{ Cov } (\bar{y}_{h-1}, \hat{M}_{h-1}) = a_h(1 - a_{h-1}\rho)\sigma^2/n$$

Hence show that $a_h = \rho/(2 - \rho a_{h-1})$ and $V(\hat{M}) = \text{Cov } (\bar{y}_h, \hat{M}_h) = (1 - \rho a_h)\sigma^2/n$. Show that the sequence $\{a_h\}$ converges with the limiting value $a = [1 - (1 - \rho^2)^{1/2}]/\rho$ and the limiting variance of $\hat{M}_h$ is $(1 - \rho^2)^{1/2}\sigma^2/n$.

**64.** A population containing $N$ units is sampled over time in this manner. At occasion $h$ a random sample of $n_h$ units is taken and each member of the sample provides data for the current period as well as for the previous period. To use the notation of Exercise 63, the best estimator of $\hat{M}_h$ will be of the form $\hat{M}_h = \bar{y}_h - a_h\bar{x}_{h-1} + a_h\hat{M}_{h-1}$. Show that the coefficient $a_h$ is given by $n_{h-1}\rho/(n_{h-1} + n_h - n_h a_{h-1}\rho)$ and $V(\hat{M}_h) = \sigma^2(1 - \rho a_h)/n_h$. Suppose it is desired to take sample sizes $n_h$ so that $V(\hat{M}_h) = \sigma^2/g$ is the same for each occasion. Show that in this case $n_1 = g$ and $n_h = g(1 - \rho^2)^{\frac{1}{2}}$ and $a_h$ are independent of $h$ for $h > 1$.

**65.** Consider the sampling procedure of Exercise 63. Suppose the mean at occasion $h$ is estimated after information on occasion $(h + 1)$ relating to occasion $h$ is assembled. Show that this situation is identical with Sec. 7.11, in which a sample of $2n$ units is selected every time, half of which is the old sample and the other half selected afresh. Denoting by $M'_h$ the estimate of the mean on occasion $h$, we have $M'_h = W_h\hat{M}_h + (1 - W_h)\bar{x}_h$, where $\hat{M}_h$ is defined in Exercise 63. We know that $V(\hat{M}_h) = (1 - \rho a_h)\sigma^2/n$, $V(\bar{x}_h) = \sigma^2/n$. The best values of $W_h$ and $1 - W_h$ would be quantities proportional to inverses of the variances of $\hat{M}_h$ and $\bar{x}_h$. Hence show that

$$M'_h = (2 - \rho a_h)^{-1}\hat{M}_h + (1 - \rho a_h)(2 - \rho a_h)^{-1}\bar{x}_h$$

and
$$V(M'_h) = \frac{\sigma^2}{n}(1 - \rho a_h)(2 - \rho a_h)^{-1}$$

**66.** From a universe of $N$ units, 12 random samples are selected independently, each of size $n$. One of the 12 samples is enumerated in the first month of each calendar year, a second in the second month of each calendar year and so on. During the enumeration, each member of the sample reports data for the current month as well as for the previous month. Denote by $y_h$ and $x_{h-1}$ the estimates of the population total for occasions $h$ and $h - 1$, respectively, based on information collected on occasion $h$. Show that an unbiased estimate of the population total $Y_h$ on occasion $h$ is given by

$$\hat{Y}_h = y_h - Kx_{h-1} + K\hat{Y}_{h-1} = z_h + K\hat{Y}_{h-1} = K^{h-1}y_1 + \sum_{i=2}^{h} K^{h-i}z_i$$

Assuming that $V(y_i) = V(x_i) = \sigma^2$ and that the monthly correlations are all $\rho$, show that $V(z_i) = (1 - 2K\rho + K^2)\sigma^2$ and Cov $(z_i, z_{i-12r}) = (1 - K)^2\rho_{12r}\sigma^2$. Ignoring the yearly correlations with $y_1$ and the terms involving 12th or higher powers of $K$, show that for large $h$, we have $V(\hat{Y}_h) = (1 - K^2)^{-1}(1 - 2K\rho + K^2)\sigma^2$. Further prove that the best value of $K$ is $[1 - (1 - \rho^2)^{\frac{1}{2}}]/\rho$ and $V(\hat{Y}_h)$ then is given as $\sigma^2(1 - \rho^2)^{\frac{1}{2}}$.

**67.** Consider the following procedure recommended for use when the sample contains unexpectedly large units which will otherwise inflate the sampling variance. A 1 percent sample is selected from a universe every month from January to December, 1966, and information is collected on $y$. A suitable cutoff is set at $Y_0$, and all sample units found to be above this cutoff in all the months are assigned to one stratum (called the surprise stratum). A new sample is selected for the month of January, 1967, and information collected on $y$. Any unit in this sample which is above the cutoff is assigned to the surprise stratum. Information is collected on all units in the surprise stratum and their weight is diminished by the number of months involved (13 in this case). The procedure is repeated month after month. Using the fact that the sample units in the surprise stratum form a random sample from that stratum, show how this procedure may help in reducing the variance of the estimate for each month beginning January, 1967. How will you determine the point of cutoff?

How will you modify this procedure if the technique is to be made operative right from the second month of the survey?

### NONSAMPLING ERRORS

**68.** The measurement technique is such that observations $y_i$ are subject to a constant bias of $u$, that is, $y_i = z_i + u$, where $z_i$ is the true value of the unit. Show that the mean based on a wtr simple random sample will be subject to a bias of $u$. What is the effect of this bias on the variance of $\bar{y}$ and on the variance estimator? If measurements on an auxiliary variate $x$ are subject to a constant bias of $v$, discuss its effect on the three estimators $\bar{y} + k(\bar{X} - \bar{x})$, $\bar{y} + b(\bar{X} - \bar{x})$ and $\bar{X}\bar{y}/\bar{x}$.

**69.** The object is to estimate the true proportion $P$ of units in a population belonging to a class $A$, by drawing a wtr random sample of $n$ units. Due to errors of measurement some units get misclassified. Let $P_i$ be the probability that the unit $U_i$ is classified as belonging to $A$. Let the model be $y_{ia} = M'_i + e_{ia}$ so that given $U_i$, $E_2(y_{ia}) = M'_i = P_i$ and $V_2(y_{ia}) = P_iQ_i$. Assume that the errors of measurement are uncorrelated from unit to unit and that they average to zero over the whole population that is, $\sum_1^N P_i/N = P$. Then prove that the variance of the sample proportion $p$ would be given by

$$V(p) = \frac{1 - f}{n} \frac{\Sigma(P_i - P)^2}{N - 1} + \frac{1}{nN} \sum P_iQ_i < \frac{1}{n} \frac{N}{N - 1} PQ$$

**70.** In order to estimate the mean of a population a random sample of $n$ units is randomly and equally distributed among $m$ enumerators chosen out of an infinite supply. Assume that $y_{ij}$, the observation taken by enumerator $i$ on unit $j$ can be expressed as $y_{ij} = M_j + a_i + e_{ijk}$ where $E(e_{ijk}|i,j) = 0$, $V(e_{ijk}|i,j) = S_c^2$ and $e_{ijk}$ is uncorrelated with $e_{ij'k'}$. Then obtain the expected value and the variance of the sample mean. Assuming the cost of the survey to be represented by $C = c_1 n + c_2 m + c_3 (nm)^{1/2}$, find the optimum number of enumerators for which the variance of the sample mean will be a minimum for fixed cost. Discuss the special case $c_3 = 0$.

**71.** A population containing $N$ units is divided up into $L$ groups with $N_h$ units in the $h$th group. There are $M_h$ interviewers available to interview the units in group $h$. A random sample of $n$ units is selected from the entire population giving rise to $n_h$ (a random variable) sample units from group $h$. Let $\bar{n}_h$ be the number of units to be assigned to an interviewer in group $h$, there being $m_h$ (a random variable) interviewers required for the sample. Assume that the $m_h$ interviewers are selected at random from the $M_h$ and allocated at random to the sets of $\bar{n}_h$ units made from the sample. Assume further that the response $x_{hijk}$ obtained by interviewer $i$ on unit $j$ in group $h$ is a random variable and the responses obtained are independent if both the interviewer and respondent are different. Then examine the estimator $\sum_h S_i S_j x_{hijk}/n$ for its bias and MSE.

**72.** We shall denote by $N_{ij}$ the number of units in the population belonging to the class $(i,j)$, $i$ being 1 if the unit is available for interview and 0 otherwise, and $j$ being 1 if the unit will answer "yes" and 0 if "no." The same notation applies to sample numbers $n_{ij}$, a dot (.) denoting summation over the variable. The object is to estimate $P = (N_{11} + N_{01})/N$, the proportion responding "yes" in the population. A wr random sample of $n$ units produces $n_{11}$ available and responding "yes" out of $n_1$, the total number available for interview. Show that $n_{11}/n_1$ is a biased estimator of $P$, the bias being $(N_{0.}/N)(N_{11}/N_1 - N_{01}/N_{0.})$. Obtain conservative bounds for this bias, using the fact that $N_{01}/N_0$ lies between 0 and 1. Further show that the variance of $n_{11}/n_1$ is approximately given by $(N_{11}/N_1)(N_{10}/N_1)[(n+1)N_1/N]^{-1}$. Denoting $H = n_{11}/n_1 - P$, show that the sample size $n$ required so that $Pr(|H| \leq \delta) \geq 1 - \alpha$ is given by

$$n \geq \frac{t_a^2}{4\delta(N_1/N)[\delta - (N_0/N)]} - 1$$

where $t_a$ is the normal deviate corresponding to the risk $\alpha$ that the error $H$ exceeds $\delta$.

**73.** A population is supposed to be divided up into $(m + 1)$ strata, the $i$th stratum consisting of units that will respond at the $i$th call. Let $P_{i1}$, $M_{i1}$ and $S_{i1}^2$ $(i = 1, \ldots, m)$ represent the relative weight, mean and variance of stratum $i$, the corresponding quantities for the last stratum being $P_{m2}, M_{m2}$ and $S_{m2}{}^2$. Questionnaires are mailed to a random sample of $n_1$ units leading to $n_{11}$ responses and $n_{12}$ nonresponses. A subsample of $k_2 n_{12}$ units is taken and contacted in a second mail attempt giving $n_{21}$ responses and $n_{22}$ nonresponses. A subsample $k_3 n_{22}$ is chosen at random for the third attempt and so on. At the $(m + 1)$st step a random sample of $w n_{m2}$ units is taken and information collected on it. Show that $E(n_{11}/n_1) = P_{11}$, $E[n_{21}/(k_2 n_1)] = P_{21}$, and so on. Hence prove that an unbiased estimator of the population mean $M = \sum\limits_{i}^{m} M_{i1} P_{i1} + P_{m2} M_{m2}$ is given by

$$\frac{1}{n_1}\left[ y_1 + k_2^{-1} y_2 + k_2^{-1} k_3^{-1} y_3 + \cdots + \left(\prod_i^m k_i\right)^{-1} y_m + (w\Pi k_i)^{-1} y_{m+1}\right]$$

where $y_j$ is the total of the characteristic $y$ for the respondents at the $j$th attempt. Derive the variance of this estimator.

**74.** From a population containing $N$ persons a simple random sample of $n$ persons is selected and $s$ random calls are made on each sample person. Information on the variate $y$ is collected from those persons who are available at least once. Denoting by $p_i$ the probability that a specified person will be found at home, the chance that he is available at least once in $s$ calls is $1 - q_i{}^s$ where $q_i = 1 - p_i$. Prove that the expected value of the sample mean would be $\Sigma y_i(1 - q_i{}^s)/N$. Compare this and the variance of the sample mean with the corresponding quantities obtained when the plan of Politz and Simmons (Sec. 8.12) is followed.

**75.** There is a population of $N$ bank accounts $A_j$ $(j = 1, 2, \ldots, N)$, with $Y_j$ being the true balance of $A_j$. A wr simple random sample of $n$ account holders is selected, and information regarding their balance is collected from them. Let $x_j$ be the balance reported by the $j$th account holder in the sample. The reported balance is matched against the one shown in the bank records, and the difference is called the response error $e_j$. Because of the presence of matching errors, however, $x_j$ may not always be matched against $y_j$. Let $x_j$ be matched against $y_j$, with probability $p$, and against $y_k$ $(k \neq j)$, with probability $q$, so that $p + (N - 1)q = 1$. Show that, under this model, the mean response error $\bar{e} = S e_i/n$ is an unbiased estimator of the true value $\bar{R} = \bar{X} - \bar{Y}$ even though matching errors are present.

Show further that

$$V(e_j) = \frac{\Sigma(e_j - \Sigma e_j/N)^2}{N} + 2q\Sigma(X_j - \bar{X})(Y_j - \bar{Y})$$

Hence obtain the variance of $\bar{e}$ and show that an unbiased estimator of $V(\bar{e})$ is provided by $S(e_i - \bar{e})^2/[n(n - 1)]$.

**76.** In Exercise 75, given that the reported balance is $x_j$, the balance against which it is matched is denoted by $z_j$ where

$$z_j = y_j \quad \text{with probability } p$$
$$= y_k \quad (k \neq j) \text{ with probability } q$$

and $$p + (N - 1)q = 1$$

In random samples of $n$ accounts selected with replacement, show that

$$E(z) = \bar{Y} \quad V(z) = V(y)$$
$$\text{Cov } (x,z) = (p - q) \text{ Cov } (x,y)$$
$$\text{Cov } (e,y) = \text{Cov } (x,y) - (p - q)V(y)$$
$$\text{Cov } (e,z) = (p - q) \text{ Cov } (x,y) - V(y)$$

How will you interpret these results?

**77.** A survey $t$ is conducted to estimate the proportion $P$ of units belonging to a certain class $C$. A simple random sample gives $p_t = Sx_{jt}/n$ as an estimate of $P$, where $x_{jt} = 1$ with probability $P_j$ and 0 otherwise. The survey $t'$ is repeated on the same sample units under improved essential conditions, and the estimate obtained is $p_{t'} = Sx_{jt'}/n$. Show that, under certain conditions (to be carefully stated), the quantity $S(x_{jt} - x_{jt'})^2/n^2$ may be used as an estimator of $V(p_t - p_{t'})$.

**78.** The object is to estimate $P$, the proportion of a population belonging to the group $A$. A wr sample of $n$ units is selected and each unit is classified to group $A$ or $\bar{A}$ (not $A$) on the basis of an observation which is subject to error. The survey is repeated on the same units independently with the following results.

|            |           | Survey 1 |         |         |
| :--------- | :-------: | :------: | :-----: | :-----: |
|            |           | $A$      | $\bar{A}$ |         |
| Survey 2   | $A$       | $a$      | $b$     | $a + b$ |
|            | $\bar{A}$ | $c$      | $d$     | $c + d$ |
|            |           | $a + c$  | $b + d$ | $n$     |

Let $p_{i1}$, $q_{i1}$ $(i = 1, 2)$ denote the probabilities that a unit belonging to $A$ is correctly classified and incorrectly classified respectively at the $i$th survey. The corresponding probabilities for a unit belonging to $\bar{A}$ are $p_{i2}$, $q_{i2}$ $(i = 1, 2)$. Thus the chance that a unit selected at random is misclassified in survey 1 is $\bar{q}_1 = Pq_{11} + Qq_{12}$, and the corresponding probability in survey 2 is $\bar{q}_2 = Pq_{21} + Qq_{22}$. Let $\bar{q} = (\bar{q}_1 + \bar{q}_2)/2$. Show that

$$\hat{P} = \frac{a}{n} + \frac{b+c}{2n}$$

is a biased estimator of $P$ and

$$\frac{\text{Bias}(\hat{P})}{P} = \frac{\bar{q} - (q_{11} + q_{21})E(\hat{P})}{E(\hat{P}) - \bar{q}}$$

Obtain upper and lower limits for the bias in $\hat{P}$.

**79.**  It is desired to estimate the total area under wheat in a region containing $N$ parcels of land. A sample of $n$ parcels is selected with replacement with pp to $x$, area of the parcels. The area devoted to wheat in a parcel is determined by eye-estimation. Let $x_{jt}$ be the observation on the $j$th parcel at trial $t$. For a given parcel $j$, let $E(x_{jt}) = X_j$, $\Sigma X_j = X$. Defining $d_{jt} = (x_{jt} - X_j)/p_j$ as the response deviation, $\delta_j = X_j/p_j - X$ as the sampling deviation, and $B = X - Y$ as the bias, show that the mean square error of the estimate $\hat{Y} = n^{-1}S(x_{jt}/p_j)$ about $Y$ is given by

$$V\frac{Sd_{jt}}{n} + V\frac{S\delta_j}{n} + 2\,\text{Cov}\left(\frac{Sd_{jt}}{n}, \frac{S\delta_j}{n}\right) + B^2$$

$$= \text{(response variance)} + \text{(sampling variance)} + 2\,\text{(covariance}$$
$$\text{between sampling and response deviations)} + \text{(bias)}^2$$

Give explicit expressions for these terms.

**80.**  A random sample of households is staggered uniformly over the year and information collected on the number of births occurring during the year preceding the date of enquiry (which may be taken as the first of each month) along with the month of occurrence of the birth. Since this procedure involves a recall period of one year, it is feared that the estimated number of births over the year will be subject to considerable response bias due to recall lapse. The following method is used for diminishing the effect of recall lapse. Let $x_{ik}$ be the number of births reported in the $i$th month of the survey to have occurred in the $k$th preceding month ($k = 1, 2, \ldots, 12$). Assume that $x_{ik} = y + b_k + e_{ik}$, where $y$ is the true number of births, $b_k$ = recall bias which is supposed to be a function of $k$, and $e_{ik}$ = random error with zero expectation and variance $\sigma^2$. Then $\sum_i x_{ik}$ is the number of births based on the $k$th pre-

ceding month, and $t_k = \sum_{r=1}^{k} \sum_{i=1}^{12} x_{ir}/k$ will give the average monthly number of births based on a recall period up to and including the $k$th month. A curve of the form $y = y_0 \exp(-ak^2)$ is fitted to the points $(k, t_k)$,

$k = 1, \ldots, 12$, and the value of $y_0$ determined which gives the average number of births per month with no recall lapse ($k = 0$). Comment on this procedure of eliminating response bias, showing how the model proposed is actually used. How will you proceed to attach a margin of error to the adjusted sample estimate?

## MISCELLANEOUS

**81.** From a random sample of $n$ units a random subsample of $n_1$ units is taken and added to the original sample. Show that the mean based on the $(n + n_1)$ observations is an unbiased estimate of the population mean but its variance is greater than the variance of the mean based on the original $n$ units by the approximate factor

$$\left(1 + 3\frac{n_1}{n}\right)\left(1 + \frac{n_1}{n}\right)^{-2}$$

**82.** Let $t$ be an unbiased estimator of $\theta$ with $V(t) = k\theta^2$, $k$ being known. Let the loss function be $\lambda(\theta)(t - \theta)^2$ where $\lambda(\theta) > 0$. Prove then that the risk associated with $t$ will be greater than that of $t/(k + 1)$. Use this result to show that $S(y_i - \bar{y})^2/(n + 1)$ is a better estimator of the variance of the normal population than $S(y_i - \bar{y})^2/(n - 1)$.

**83.** Let $v^2$ be an unbiased estimator of $S_y^2$. Then $E(v - S_y)^2 = 2S_y[S_y - E(v)] \geq 0$. Hence prove that $E(v) \leq S_y$.

**84.** Let $x$ and $y$ be two random variables. Let $\Delta x = x - \bar{X}, \Delta y = y - \bar{Y}$, $\delta x = \Delta x/\bar{X}$, $\delta y = \Delta y/\bar{Y}$, $D_{ij} = E[(\delta x)^i(\delta y)^j]$, and $E_{ij} = E[(\Delta x)^i(\Delta y)^j]$. Show that $xy - E(xy) = \bar{X}\bar{Y}(\delta x + \delta y + \delta x\delta y - D_{11})$. Hence prove that

$$V(xy) = (\bar{X})^2 V(y) + (\bar{Y})^2 V(x) + 2\bar{X}\bar{Y}E_{11}$$
$$+ 2\bar{X}E_{12} + 2\bar{Y}E_{21} + E_{22} - E_{11}^2$$

Based on a random sample of $n$ observations $(x_i, y_i)$, show that $w = (n\bar{x}\bar{y} - \Sigma x_i y_i/n)/(n - 1)$ is an unbiased estimator of $\bar{X}\bar{Y}$. Obtain the variance of $w$.

**85.** We shall define a sampling scheme as a procedure of selecting units one by one from a finite population with predetermined sets of probabilities of selection for the units at each of the selections. By a sample design we shall mean an arbitrary collection of samples $s$ with a probability $p(s)$ for each sample, $\Sigma p(s) = 1$. It is clear that any sampling scheme generates a unique sample design. By introducing the null unit in the population (the occurrence of which at a draw means the absence of selection of any unit then) and by augmenting samples by the null unit suitably, prove that for any given sample design $D$ we can find a sampling scheme uniquely which results in $D$.

**86.** Suppose the sample estimator $Sa_iy_i$ is unbiased for the population total $Y$. Instead of the $n$ weights $a_i$, we wish to use just $k$ (considerably smaller than $n$) rounded-off multipliers $b_1 < b_2 < \cdots < b_k$ such that $E(Sr_iy_i) = Sa_iy_i$ and $V(Sr_iy_i)$ is a minimum, where $r_i$ is a random variable taking the values $b_1, b_2, \ldots, b_k$ with certain probabilities. If the range of the rounded-off multipliers includes the range of the $a_i$, show that $E(r_i) = a_i$ and $V(r_i)$ is a minimum if $r_i$ takes the values $b_j$, $b_{j+1}$ nearest to $a_i$ on both sides of it $(b_j \leq a_i \leq b_{j+1})$, with probabilities $(b_{j+1} - a_i)/(b_{j+1} - b_j)$ and $(a_i - b_j)/(b_{j+1} - b_j)$, respectively.

**87.** There are two long lists containing $N$ and $M$ names with $D$ names common to them. Samples of sizes $n$ and $m$ are selected at random without replacement from the two lists and $d$ names are observed to be common to the two samples. Show that an unbiased estimate of $D$ is given by $\hat{D} = NMd/(nm)$, the variance of $\hat{D}$ being $V(\hat{D}) = NMD(nm)^{-1}[1 + (n-1)(m-1)(D-1)(N-1)^{-1}(M-1)^{-1}] - D^2$. Show further that an unbiased estimator of $V(\hat{D})$ may be taken as

$$\hat{D}\left[\frac{(N-1)(M-1)}{(n-1)(m-1)} - 1\right] + \hat{D}^2\left[1 - \frac{nm(N-1)(M-1)}{(n-1)(m-1)NM}\right]$$

Given the cost function $C = c_0(n + m) + c_1nm$, show that the values of $n$ and $m$ which minimize $V(\hat{D})$ for a specified $C$ are given by $n = m$ if $D < 1 + c_0(N-1)(M-1)(C - c_0)^{-1}$.

**88.** There are two lists of names merged into one with $R$ names. A wtr random sample of $r$ names is selected and the names in the sample are classified as those belonging to the first list or to the second. Let $d$ be the observed number of names common to the two lists. Define the random variable $\delta_j$ $(j = 1, \ldots, R - D)$ associated with the $j$th distinct name as follows: $\delta_j = 1$ if the name occurs in both samples and 0 otherwise. Show that $d = \Sigma\delta_j$ and $E(d) = D\binom{r}{2}\Big/\binom{R}{2}$. Hence show that an unbiased estimate of $D$ is provided by $\hat{D} = R(R-1)d/[r(r-1)]$, the variance of $\hat{D}$ being

$$\frac{R(R-1)}{r(r-1)}D\left[1 + (D-1)\frac{(r-2)(r-3)}{(R-2)(R-3)}\right] - D^2$$

Consider the special case when the two lists are of the same size $W$. A wtr sample of size $u$ is selected from either list when the lists are separated and let $V_1(\hat{D})$ be the variance of the estimator. In the other situation the lists are merged into one, and a random sample of $2u$ names is taken to find out the number of names common to the lists. Let $V_2(\hat{D})$ be the variance of the estimator in this case. Show that $V_1(\hat{D}) - V_2(\hat{D}) < 0$ provided that $D - 1 < c_0(W - 1)^2(C - c_0)^{-1}$.

**89.** There are two frames $A$ and $B$, with a known degree of coverage and overlap, available for a population, it being assumed that every unit in the population belongs to at least one of the frames. Let $N_a$ units belong to $A$ only (domain $a$), $N_b$ to $B$ only (domain $b$), and $N_{ab}$ to both $A$ and $B$ (domain $ab$). The unit $U_i$ possessing the value $y_i$ will be given the value $py_i$ if it is in $A$ and belongs to $ab$ and given the value $(1 - p)y_i = qy_i$ if it is in $B$ and belongs to $ab$. Thus the population total $Y = Y_a + pY_{ab} + (1 - p)Y_{ab} + Y_b$. Simple random samples of $n_A$ and $n_B$ units are selected from the two frames and the population total is estimated by $\hat{Y} = N_a\bar{y}_a + N_{ab}(p\bar{y}'_{ab} + q\bar{y}''_{ab}) + N_b\bar{y}_b$.

Show that the variance of $\hat{Y}$ is given approximately by

$$V(\hat{Y}) = \frac{N_A{}^2}{n_A}[S_a{}^2(1 - \alpha) + p^2\alpha S_{ab}{}^2] + \frac{N_B{}^2}{n_B}[S_b{}^2(1 - \beta) + q^2\beta S_{ab}{}^2]$$

where $\alpha = N_{ab}/N_A$, $\beta = N_{ab}/N_B$, fpc's being ignored. Assuming a linear cost function $C = c_A n_A + c_B n_B$, find expressions for the values of $p$, $n_A$ and $n_B$ such that for a given cost, the variance of $\hat{Y}$ is made a minimum. For the special case in which the frame $A$ has 100 percent coverage so that $N_{ab} = N_B$, $\beta = 1$, $S_b{}^2 = S_{ab}{}^2$, show that the best value of $p$ is given by

$$p^2 = \frac{S_a{}^2}{S_b{}^2} \frac{1 - N_B/N_A}{c_A/c_B - N_B/N_A}$$

**90.** The coefficient of variation $\sigma(y)/\mu$ for a population is known to be $k$ and it is proposed to use this for estimating the population mean $\mu$. Show that in wr simple random sampling, $\hat{\mu} = nw\bar{y}$ has a mean square error of $nw^2\sigma^2 + \mu^2(1 - nw)^2$. Hence prove that MSE$(\hat{\mu})$ is a minimum when $w = 1/(n + k^2)$. And for this value of $w$,

$$\text{MSE}(\hat{\mu}) = \sigma^2/(n + k^2) < V(\bar{y})$$

**91.** A sample of two units is selected with unequal probabilities without replacement at each draw. To estimate the population total $Y$, the estimator used is $Sc_r y_r$ where $c_r$ is a constant attached to the $r$th draw. Let $p_{ir}$ be the probability of selecting the $i$th unit in the population at the $r$th draw. Prove that the condition that the estimator be unbiased is $\sum c_r p_{ir} = 1$ for every $i$. Hence show that no unbiased estimator exists for this general sampling system. Prove further that there does exist an unbiased estimator if the sampling scheme consists in selecting the first element of the sample with probabilities $p_i$ and the second with equal probabilities.

**92.** A population consists of five units with selection probabilities $p_i$, proportional to $x_i$, as given below:

| Unit | $p_i$ |
| --- | --- |
| $U_1$ | 0.33 |
| $U_2$ | 0.19 |
| $U_3$ | 0.18 |
| $U_4$ | 0.16 |
| $U_5$ | 0.14 |

The problem is to estimate the population total $Y$ by selecting a sample of two units so that the selection probabilities $\pi_i = 2p_i$ are preserved. Further, the probability of selecting each of the nonpreferred samples $(u_2,u_4)$, $(u_2,u_5)$, $(u_3,u_4)$, $(u_3,u_5)$, and $(u_4,u_5)$ is to be made as small as 0.02. What would be the probabilities of selecting the other five preferred samples?

**93.** A sample of $n$ different units is to be selected from a population of $N$ units. It is considered desirable that the probability of the selection of $m = \binom{N}{n} - \binom{N}{2}$ nonpreferred samples be made as small as $\alpha/m$ each. The sampling scheme should be such that each unit in the population has a probability $\pi_i = n/N$ of being selected in the sample. To effect this solution, $\pi_{ij}$ is set equal to $n(n-1)/[N(N-1)]$. This will give $\binom{N}{2}$ linear equations in the $P_i$, where $P_i$ is the probability of selecting the $i$th sample. Obtain the conditions under which this system of equations will produce a meaningful solution. Assuming the conditions to hold, how will you estimate the population total and the variance of the estimate?

**94.** A survey is planned to estimate the proportion of a population belonging to the group $C$. It is, however, feared that respondents will not cooperate in answering the question involved, which is very personal. Thus the following procedure, in which the respondent furnishes information on a probability basis only, is adopted. The respondent is given a spinner with a face marked so that the spinner points to the letter $C$ with probability $p$ (known) and to $\bar{C}$ (not $C$) with probability $q = 1 - p$. The respondent is required to spin the spinner unobserved by the interviewer and report only whether or not the spinner points to the letter representing the group to which he belongs.

A wr simple random sample of $n$ respondents is selected to estimate $P$. Let $x_{jt}$ be the response obtained from the $j$th individual where $x_{jt}$ takes on the values 0 (no) and 1 (yes) only.

Then $\qquad Pr(x_{jt} = 1) = Pp + (1 - P)q$

$\qquad\qquad\quad Pr(x_{jt} = 0) = P(1 - p) + (1 - P)p$

Show that $\qquad E(x_{jt}) = P(p - q) + q = E(x_{jt}^2)$

Hence show that $\hat{P} = (Sx_{jt}/n - q)/(p - q)$ is unbiased for estimating $P$ and

$$V(\hat{P}) = \frac{1}{n}\left[\frac{1}{16}\left(p - \frac{1}{2}\right)^{-2} - \left(P - \frac{1}{2}\right)^{2}\right]$$

**95.** Two samples will be said to be equivalent if they contain the same units irrespective of their frequency of occurrence. If the sample space (set of all possible samples) generated by a sampling scheme can be partitioned into subsets containing equivalent samples, the partition will be called sufficient. By defining a statistic $t$ we induce a partition of the sample space into subsets each containing samples with a particular value of $t$. If this partition is sufficient, the statistic $t$ will be said to be sufficient.

Use these definitions to answer the following.

**a.** A population contains $N$ units $U_1$, $U_2$, . . . , $U_N$ where $j$ is the index of the unit $U_j$. The different units in a sample of $n$ are arranged in ascending order of their indices and the set $(u_{(1)}, u_{(2)}, . . .)$ obtained is called the order statistic. Show that the order statistic is sufficient.

**b.** Let $t$ be an unbiased estimator of the population total $Y$ based on a sample of size $n$. Let $t' = E(t|T)$, where $T$ is a sufficient statistic. Show that $t'$ is unbiased for $Y$ and

$$V(t') = V(t) - E(t - t')^2$$

so that $t'$ has a smaller variance. (This is the Rao-Blackwell theorem.)

**c.** Suppose a population is sampled with replacement with probabilities $p_i\,(i = 1, 2, . . . , N)$, $\Sigma p_i = 1$, until two distinct units have been selected. Then $t = y/p$ is an unbiased estimator of $Y$ where $(y,p)$ relate to the unit selected first. Let the two distinct units forming the sample $s$ be $i$ and $j$. Then the probability that the sample $s$ contains $i$ and $j$ and $i$ is the first selection $= p_i p_j/(1 - p_i)$ and, similarly, the probability that $j$ is selected first $= p_i p_j/(1 - p_j)$. Hence $Pr(s) = p_i p_j\,[1/(1 - p_i) + 1/(1 - p_j)]$. Thus the conditional probability that the first selection is $i$ (given the sample $s$) $= (1 - p_j)/(2 - p_i - p_j)$. Considering $s(i,j)$ as the sufficient statistic $T$, show that:

$$t' = E(t|T) = \frac{(y_i/p_i)(1 - p_j) + (y_j/p_j)(1 - p_i)}{2 - p_i - p_j}$$

has a smaller variance than $t$ and that

$$V(t') = \frac{1}{2} \sum \sum \left( \frac{y_i}{p_i} - \frac{y_j}{p_j} \right)^2 p_i p_j \frac{1 - p_i - p_j}{2 - p_i - p_j}$$

and an unbiased estimator of $V(t')$ is provided by

$$\hat{V}(t') = \left( \frac{y_i}{p_i} - \frac{y_j}{p_j} \right)^2 \frac{(1 - p_i)(1 - p_j)(1 - p_i - p_j)}{(2 - p_i - p_j)^2}$$

$$< \frac{1}{4} \left( \frac{y_i}{p_i} - \frac{y_j}{p_j} \right)^2 (1 - p_i - p_j)$$

**d.** A sample of $n$ units is selected with replacement with equal probabilities from the population $U_1, U_2, \ldots, U_N$. The distinct units in the sample are arranged in increasing order of their indices and their value for $y$ ascertained. Show that the order statistic $t$ $(y_{(1)}, \ldots)$ is sufficient and that $E(\bar{y}|t) = Sy_i/\nu$ where $\bar{y} = Sy_i/n$ and $\nu$ is the number of distinct units. Hence use the Rao-Blackwell theorem to prove that the estimator based on distinct units is superior to the one based on all units in the sample.

**96.** **a.** There is an incomplete list available of the units forming a target population and a sample is selected from it. This sample is supplemented by an area sample to take in units not on the list. Let $N = N_1 + N_2 + N_3$ where

$N_1 =$ number of units accessible only through list sampling
$N_2 =$ number of units accessible only through area sampling
$N_3 =$ number of units accessible through both list and area sampling

Let $Y = Y_1 + Y_2 + Y_3$. Based on the list sample, we have $\hat{Y}_L = \hat{Y}_{L1} + \hat{Y}_{L3}$ as an unbiased estimate of $Y_1 + Y_3$. Similarly, we have $\hat{Y}_A = \hat{Y}_{A2} + \hat{Y}_{A3}$ as an unbiased estimate of $Y_2 + Y_3$ from the area sample. Show that

$$\hat{Y} = \hat{Y}_{L1} + \hat{Y}_{A2} + \lambda \hat{Y}_{L3} + (1 - \lambda) \hat{Y}_{A3} \qquad 0 \le \lambda \le 1$$

is an unbiased estimate of $Y$. How will you obtain the best value of $\lambda$? Interpret the case when $\lambda = 1$.

**b.** The various units in a population are considered to be ordered geographically so that it is possible to determine unambiguously the successor of each unit. There is a list (possibly incomplete) of the units in the population. A simple random sample of units is selected from the list and the following method is used to take in units not on the list. For each unit in the sample, determine its successor to see if it is on the list. If the successor is on the list, discard it. If it is not on the list, include it in the sample; then identify its successor and proceed in the same way until a successor is found to be on the list. How will you analyze the data thus obtained?

**97.** There is a population containing three units $u_1$, $u_2$, and $u_3$. The object is to estimate the population total $Y = y_1 + y_2 + y_3$ by selecting a sample of two units. Let the sampling and estimation procedures be as follows:

| Sample($s$) | Pr($s$) | Linear estimator $t$ | Quadratic estimator $t'$ |
|---|---|---|---|
| $(u_1, u_2)$ | $\frac{1}{2}$ | $y_1 + 2y_2$ | $y_1 + 2y_2 + y_1{}^2$ |
| $(u_1, u_3)$ | $\frac{1}{2}$ | $y_1 + 2y_3$ | $y_1 + 2y_3 - y_1{}^2$ |

Prove that the admissible estimator $t$ and the quadratic estimator $t'$ are unbiased and that

$$V(t) = \frac{1}{2} \left[ (y_1 + 2y_2)^2 + (y_1 + 2y_3)^2 \right] - Y^2$$
$$V(t') = V(t) + y_1{}^2(y_1{}^2 + 2y_2 - 2y_3)$$

Thus $V(t') < V(t)$ for some values of the $y$'s. Hence show that there does not exist a linear estimator of the population total which is uniformly better than the quadratic estimator $t'$.

**98.** There is a skew population containing $N$ units with their values arranged in ascending order of magnitude as $x_1$, $x_2$, . . . , $x_N$. The $i$ largest units are taken in the sample with certainty and a wtr simple random sample of $n - i$ units is selected from the rest. An unbiased estimate of the population mean $\mu$ is given by

$$\hat{\mu} = \frac{[(N - i)\bar{x}_{(n-i)} + i\mu_{(i)}]}{N}$$

with
$$V(\hat{\mu}) = \left( \frac{N - i}{N} \right)^2 \frac{1}{n - i} \frac{N - n}{N - i - 1} \sigma^2_{(N-i)}$$

where $\sigma^2_{(N-i)}$ is the variance of the $N - i$ units from which the sample is selected and similar remarks apply to $\mu_{(i)}$. The problem is to determine the cutoff point $X'$ and the associated number of units $m$ beyond which to take the sample with certainty. Using the necessary condition that $V(\hat{\mu})$ with $i = m - 1$ and with $i = m + 1$ should exceed $V(\hat{\mu})$ with $i = m$, show that

$$X' = \mu_{(N-m)} + \sqrt{\frac{N - m}{n - m}} \, \sigma_{(N-m)}$$

and an upper limit for $X'$ is given by

$$X' < \mu + \sigma \sqrt{\frac{N}{n}}$$

where $\mu$ and $\sigma$ are respectively the mean and the standard deviation of the population. Suppose the rule is followed that as many units as can be identified to exceed $\mu + k\sigma$ are included in the sample with certainty. What would be the value of $k$?

**99.** It is desired to estimate the mean consumption of cigarettes in a certain area for which lists of households and of individuals are available. The following procedure is adopted in order to give the subgroup of heavy smokers increased numerical representation in the sample (which a random sample of individuals will not do). Select a random sample of households. In each selected household select all individuals who are heavy smokers (e.g., smoke more than 20 cigarettes per day) and at random one individual who is not a heavy smoker. Thus the procedure involves two-stage sampling with stratification at the second stage and 100 percent sampling of subgroup members.

How will you calculate an unbiased estimate of the population mean and its variance? Under what conditions is this procedure better than taking a simple random sample of individuals?

**100.** There is a finite area $S$ in which $m$ points are located at random. We can trace a continuous path among the $m$ points by starting at some point and connecting the points by line segments. The points can be connected in any order giving rise to $m!$ possible paths along with their associated distances. Denoting by $L$ the length of the shortest path, show that a lower bound for the expected value of $L$ is given by

$$E(L) \geq \frac{1}{2} \sqrt{A} \, \frac{m-1}{\sqrt{m}}$$

where $A$ is the measure of the area $S$ in which the $m$ random points are located.

**101.** A bag contains $N$ balls of various colors, but the number of colors is not known. The object is to estimate the number of colors $K$ present in the bag by taking a wtr simple random sample of $n$ balls from it. Let $x_i$ be the number of colors with $i$ balls in the sample. Assuming that $n$ is not less than the maximum number $q$ of balls of any color in the bag, show that

$$E(x_i) = \sum_{j=i}^{q} \frac{\binom{j}{i}\binom{N-j}{n-i}}{\binom{N}{n}} K_j$$

where $K_j$ is the number of colors with $j$ balls in the bag. Hence show that an unbiased estimate of $K$ is given by

$$\hat{K} = \sum_{i=1}^{n} A_i x_i$$

where $\qquad A_i = 1 - (-1)^i \dfrac{(N - n + i - 1)^{(i)}}{n^{(i)}}$

and $\qquad a^{(t)} = a(a - 1)(a - 2) \cdots (a - t + 1) \qquad a^{(0)} = 1$

Give the status of the estimators:

(a) $\displaystyle\sum_{1}^{n} x_i$
$\qquad\qquad\qquad\qquad$ (b) $\dfrac{N}{n} \displaystyle\sum_{1}^{n} x_i$

(c) $\hat{K}' = N - \dfrac{N(N - 1)}{n(n - 1)} x_2 = a \qquad$ if $a' \geq \Sigma x_i$

$\quad\ \ \hat{K}' = \Sigma x_i \qquad\qquad\qquad\qquad$ if $a' < \Sigma x_i$

**102.** A wtr sample of two units is selected from a stratum of $N$ units in the following manner. The first unit $u_i$ is selected with probabilities $p_i$ based on measures of size $x_i$ ($i = 1, 2, \ldots, N$). The second unit $u_j$ is selected with probabilities

$$\frac{1}{1 + A} p_j \left( \frac{1}{1 - 2p_i} + \frac{1}{1 - 2p_j} \right) \qquad j \neq i$$

where $\qquad\qquad\qquad A = \displaystyle\sum_{k=1}^{N} \frac{p_k}{1 - 2p_k}$

Show that

$$\pi_{ij} = \frac{2p_i p_j}{1 + A} \left( \frac{1}{1 - 2p_i} + \frac{1}{1 - 2p_j} \right)$$

Hence prove that the probability $\pi_i$ that the unit $U_i$ is selected in the sample is proportional to its measure of size $x_i$.

Consider an alternative scheme in which the first unit is selected with probabilities proportional to $p_i(1 - p_i)/(1 - 2p_i)$ and the second with probabilities proportional to $p_j$ ($j \neq i$). Show that this scheme gives the same $\pi_{ij}$ as the first one. Comment on the two schemes.

**103.** There is a population of $N$ vouchers where $N$ is very large. It is proposed to accept or reject the population on the basis of a single sampling inspection plan. The probability of rejecting the population should not exceed $\alpha$ if the proportion of incorrect vouchers is $P_1$ or less and that of accepting the population should be less than $\beta$ if the proportion of incorrect vouchers is $P_2$ or higher. Assuming that the number of incorrect vouchers, $d$, in random samples of $n$, follows $(a)$ the normal distribution, $(b)$ the Poisson distribution, determine the sample size $n$ and the acceptance number $c$.

**104.** The purpose is to devise a single sampling inspection plan for a product being received in lots of $N$ items. The expected quality is known to be $\bar{P}$ in terms of the proportion of defective items. The plan should ensure a specified value of the average outgoing quality limit (AOQL) at minimum cost of inspection. Assuming that the number of defective items $d$ in random samples of $n$ items follows the Poisson distribution, show that the maximum proportion defective in the outgoing quality after inspection occurs for $p = p_1$ when

$$\sum_{d=0}^{c} \frac{e^{-z}z^d}{d!} = \frac{e^{-z}z^{c+1}}{c!} \qquad z = np_1$$

and

$$\text{AOQL} = \left(\frac{1}{n} - \frac{1}{N}\right)\frac{e^{-z}z^{c+2}}{c!}$$

The cost of inspection will be given by

$$C(\bar{P}) = N - (N - n) \sum_{d=0}^{c} \frac{e^{-n\bar{P}}(n\bar{P})^d}{d!}$$

Find the sample size $n$ and the acceptance number $c$ which minimize the cost of inspection for a specified value of the AOQL.

**105.** Show that the variance of the product of two random variables $X$ and $Y$ is given approximately as

$$V(XY) \doteq (\bar{X}\bar{Y})^2 \left[\frac{V(X)}{\bar{X}^2} + \frac{V(Y)}{\bar{Y}^2} + 2\frac{\text{Cov}(X,Y)}{\bar{X}\bar{Y}}\right]$$

Use this result to find the variance of the product estimator $\bar{x}\bar{y}/\bar{X}$ calculated from a random sample of size $n$ for estimating the population mean $\bar{Y}$. Show that the product estimator has a smaller variance than the sample mean $\bar{y}$ when $\rho < -(1/2)CV(X)/CV(Y)$.

**106.** It is intended to estimate the population mean $\bar{Y}$ by taking a wtr random sample. It is found that auxiliary information on $p + q$ variates $x_i, x_2, \ldots, x_p, x_{p+1}, \ldots, x_{p+q}$ is already available but the variates $x_{p+1}, x_{p+2}, \ldots, x_{p+q}$ are negatively correlated with $y$. Show that the bias in the estimator

$$\hat{\mu} = \sum_1^p w_i \frac{\bar{X}_i}{\bar{x}_i} \bar{y} + \sum_{p+1}^{p+q} w_i \frac{\bar{x}_i}{X_i} \bar{y} \qquad \Sigma w_i = 1$$

is given by

$$B(\hat{\mu}) = -\sum_1^p w_i \operatorname{Cov}\left(\frac{\bar{y}}{\bar{x}_i}, \bar{x}_i\right) + \sum_{p+1}^{p+q} \frac{w_i}{\bar{X}_i} \operatorname{Cov}(\bar{y}, \bar{x}_i)$$

Find a large sample approximation to the variance of $\hat{\mu}$.

**107.** There is a sampling scheme which permits unbiased estimation of $Y$ and $X$. Denoting the estimators by $\hat{Y}$ and $\hat{X}$ respectively, show that the bias of the ratio estimator $\hat{R} = \hat{Y}/\hat{X}$ satisfies the relation

$$\frac{B(\hat{R})}{\sigma(\hat{R})} \leq CV(\hat{X})$$

Further, an approximate expression for $B(\hat{R})$ is given by

$$B(\hat{R}) \doteq RCV(\hat{X})[CV(\hat{X}) - \rho(\hat{R}, \hat{X})CV(\hat{Y})]$$

and $\qquad E(\hat{R} - R)^2 \doteq \frac{1}{X^2}[V(\hat{Y}) + R^2 V(\hat{X}) - 2R \operatorname{Cov}(\hat{X}, \hat{Y})]$

# REFERENCES TO EXERCISES
# WITH REMARKS

## JOURNAL ABBREVIATIONS

*AISM:* Annals of the Institute of Statistical Mathematics
*AMS:* Annals of Mathematical Statistics
*BISI:* Bulletin of the International Statistical Institute
*JASA:* Journal of the American Statistical Association
*JISAS:* Journal of the Indian Society of Agricultural Statistics
*JRSS:* Journal of the Royal Statistical Society
*RISI:* Review of the International Statistical Institute

**1.** Raj, D. and S. H. Khamis (1958), *AMS*, 29. Basu, D. (1958), *Sankhya*, 20. This shows that it is better to exclude repetitions than to include them.

**2.** It always pays to possess information on some units in the population.

**3.** Roy, J. and I. M. Chakravarti (1960), *AMS*, 31. It is shown that an estimator with variance proportional to the population variance is linearly invariant and that there exists a lower bound for its variance.

**4.** Raj, D. (1954), *Ganita*, 5. The condition for pps sampling to be superior to equal probability sampling is given.

**5.** Raj, D. (1958), *JASA*, 53. Another condition for pps sampling to produce lower variance than equal probability sampling is stated.

**6.** Durbin, J. (1953), *JRSS*, B15. Gives the bias of the variance estimator appropriate to with-replacement pps sampling when sampling is wtr with unequal probabilities.

**7.** Sen, A. R. (1955), *JISAS*, 5. Raj, D. (1956), *JASA*, 51. Gives a situation in which Yates and Grundy's variance estimator is positive.

**8.** Raj, D. (1956), *Sankhya*, 17. Here is a method of selecting a wtr sample of two units from a stratum when there is linearity between $y$ and $x$.

**9.** *a.* Sen, A. R. (1955), *JISAS*, 5. Raj, D. (1956), *JASA*, 51. Singh, D. (1954), *JISAS*, 6. *b.* Rao, J. N. K. (1961), *AISM*, 13. Some situations are presented in which Yates and Grundy's variance estimator is positive.

**10.** Fellegi, I. P. (1963), *JASA*, 58. Here is a situation in which the variance of the wtr pps scheme is smaller than the variance of the associated wr pps scheme.

**11.** Durbin, J. (1953), *JRSS*, B 15. Shows the status of some simpler estimators when sampling is with unequal probabilities without replacement.

**12.** Das, A. C. (1951), *BISI*, 33. Raj, D. (1956), *JASA*, 51. An alternative estimator in wtr sampling with unequal probabilities.

**13.** Murthy, M. N. (1957), *Sankhya*, 18. A method is given by which an estimator based on an ordered sample can be improved.

**14.** Yates, F. (1953), "Sampling Methods for Censuses and Surveys." This brings out the superiority of taking complementary random starts in systematic sampling.

**15.** Madow, W. G. (1953), *AMS*, 24. Proves that for monotone populations centered systematic sampling is better than random start systematic sampling.

**16.** A simple method of obtaining an unbiased estimator of the variance in certain situations.

**17.** Seth, G. R. and J. N. K. Rao (1964), *Sankhya*, A26. Compares simple random sampling with and without replacement for equivalent costs.

**18.** Pathak, P. K. (1964), *Biometrika*, 51. Shows that the method of inverse sampling with unequal probabilities is, in a sense, equivalent to selecting the first unit with pps, the second with pps of the remaining units, and so on.

**19.** Pathak, P. K. (1964), *Biometrika*, 51. Compares two estimators of the population total in inverse sampling with unequal probabilities.

**20.** Ross, A. (1961), *JASA*, 56. Allocates the sample to strata for minimizing the variance of the variance estimator.

**21.** Raj, D. (1957), *Sankhya*, 17. Gives theory when not one but many linear functions of strata means are to be estimated.

22. Stephan, F. F. (1945), *AMS*, 16. This paper gives $E(1/n_h)$. The result shows that stratification after selection is about equal to proportionate allocation.

23. Cochran, W. G. (1953), "Sampling Techniques." Shows that small deviations from the optimum allocation ordinarily do not bring about much loss in precision.

24. The variance falls off inversely to the square of the number of strata when the distribution within strata is uniform.

25. Raj, D. (1964), *JASA*, 59. Raj, D. (1953), *Ganita*, 4. An example of the use of truncated distributions in stratification problems.

26. Raj, D. (1954), *JISAS*, 6. Gives an unbiased estimator of a ratio in stratified sampling.

27. Raj, D. (1958), *JASA*, 53. Compares unstratified pps with stratified sampling under a mathematical model.

28. Nanjamma, N. S., et al. (1959), *Sankhya*, 21. Gives a sampling system providing unbiased ratio estimators.

29. Ghosh, S. P. (1963), *AMS*, 34. An extension of stratification problems to two variables.

30. Folks, J. L. and C. E. Antle (1965), *JASA*, 60. A complete set of efficient allocations to strata is given when several characteristics are of interest.

31. Williams, W. H. (1962, 1964), *JASA*, 57, 59. How to improve precision by using strata weights when the sample selected is simple random from the entire population is shown here.

32. Raj, D. (1964), *JASA*, 59. Gives a condition for the usual approximation for the variance of a ratio estimate to be an understatement.

33. This is an unbiased ratio-type estimator based on interpenetrating subsamples.

34. Goodman, L. A. and H. O. Hartley (1958), *JASA*, 53. Here is a situation in which the usual ratio estimator is better than the ratio-type estimator.

35. Murthy, M. N. and N. S. Nanjamma (1959), *Sankhya*, 21. Quenouille, M. H. (1949), *JRSS*, B11. Provides an almost unbiased ratio estimator of $R$.

36. Hansen, M. H., et al. (1953), "Sample Survey Methods and Theory." This is an alternative derivation of the variance of the regression estimator.

37. Williams, W. H. (1962), *JASA*, 57. This gives a general method of generating unbiased ratio and regression estimators.

38. Mickey, M. R. (1959), *JASA*, 54. This is another method of generating unbiased ratio and regression estimators.

39. Olkin, I. (1958), *Biometrika*, 45. This shows that it is always better to include an additional variate in multivariate ratio estimation.

40. De Pascual, J. N. (1961), *JASA*, 56. This is a form of a combined unbiased ratio estimator in stratified sampling.

**41.** Keyfitz, N. (1957), *JASA*, 52. Provides a short cut to the computation of variance when two units are selected from a stratum.

**42.** Durbin, J. (1959), *Biometrika*, 46. If $x$ is normally distributed and the regression of $y$ on $x$ is linear, Quenouille's ratio estimator reduces not only the bias but also the variance.

**43.** Cochran, W. G. (1963), "Sampling Techniques." This is an excellent demonstration of the fact that the optimum size of the cluster is not a fixed characteristic of the population but depends on the cost structure of the survey.

**44.** Sampford, M. R. (1962), *Biometrika*, 49. A method of taking $n$ distinct psu's with probability proportionate to size.

**45.** Estimation of between- and within-psu components of the variance.

**46.** Sukhatme, P. V. and R. D. Narain (1952), *JISAS*, 4. Raj, D. (1954), *Ganita*, 5. A method by which subunits within psu's do not repeat in the sample, although psu's do.

**47.** Sukhatme, P. V. (1950), *JISAS*, 2. Estimates the gain due to stratification from a subsampling design.

**48.** Godambe, V. P. (1951), *JRSS*, B13. Shows that a two-stage design in which the number of subunits is a random variable is better than another in which this number is fixed at the expected value calculated in the former case.

**49.** Nanjamma, N. S., et al. (1959), *Sankhya*, 21. Gives a method of obtaining an unbiased estimator of a ratio in multistage designs.

**50.** Raj, D. (1956), *JASA*, 51. This is an extension of the estimator of Exercise 12 to multistage sampling.

**51.** Raj, D. (1966), *Ganita*, 17. Gives a method of forming estimates in multistage sampling making use of conditional probabilities of selection only.

**52.** Raj, D. (1954), *JISAS*, 6. Gives another method of making unbiased estimates of ratios in multistage sampling.

**53.** Sethi, V. K. (1965), *Sankhya*, B27. Gives the best way of forming clusters of two units when information on $y$ is available.

**54.** Raj, D. (1966), *JASA*, 61. Gives an unbiased variance estimator when the psu's in the stratum are split at random into $n$ substrata and one psu is selected from each substratum with pp to $x$.

**55.** The estimator based on distinct subunits is superior when psu's are selected with replacement with pp to $x$ and every selection is subsampled independently.

**56.** Durbin, J. (1953), *JRSS*, B15. A rule for estimating the variance in multistage designs.

**57.** A variance estimator in double sampling for stratification is obtained.

**58.** Raj, D. (1964), *JASA*, 59. This is a method of using multiauxiliary information in double-sampling designs.

**59.** Raj, D. (1964), *AMS*, 35. This is an application of double sampling for pps estimation when the initial sample is a sample of psu's.

**60.** Sukhatme, B. V. (1962), $JASA$, 57.   This is a generalization of the unbiased ratio-type estimator to double-sampling designs.

**61.** Hansen et al. (1953), "Sample Survey Methods and Theory," vol. 2.   The mean at the second occasion and the change between the two periods are estimated such that the change is the difference between the estimates for the two periods.

**62.** Kulldorff, G. (1963), $RISI$, 31.   The sample size on the first occasion and the subsampling fraction at the second occasion are determined so that the variance of the estimated sum is minimized.

**63.** Eckler, A. R. (1955), $AMS$, 26.   Gives the best estimate of the mean at occasion $h$ when information is collected from independent samples for the current period as well as for the previous period.

**64.** Eckler, A. R. (1955), $AMS$, 26.   This is a generalization of Exercise 63 to the situation in which differential sample sizes are used on different occasions.

**65.**   This shows how problems of 50 percent overlapping samples can be solved by the method of Exercise 63.

**66.** Hansen, et al. (1953), "Sample Survey Methods and Theory."   Discusses a method of making monthly estimates when information is collected on the previous month, too.

**67.** Woodruff, R. S. (1963), $JASA$, 58.   Gives a procedure of reducing the variance due to the presence of unusually large observations when information is to be collected over time.

**68.**   When observations are subject to a constant bias, its effect on the simple average, ratio, regression and difference estimators is studied.

**69.** Hansen, et al. (1961), $BISI$, 38.   This shows that the variance of the sample proportion in the presence of uncorrelated response errors is smaller than the variance $PQ/n$ normally used.

**70.** Sukhatme, P. V. (1953), "Sampling Theory of Surveys with Applications." This is an analysis of uncorrelated response errors under a specific model.

**71.** Hansen, M. H., et al. (1953), "Sample Survey Methods and Theory." Extends the analysis of response errors to the situation in which a random sample taken from the entire population is allocated to strata.

**72.** Birnbaum, Z. W. and M. G. Sirken (1950), $JASA$, 45.   This gives bounds on the bias due to noninterview.   The sample size $n$ is found such that the total error is small at a given probability level.

**73.** El Badry, M. A. (1956), $JASA$, 51.   This is a generalization of the technique which involves one mail attempt followed by a personal interview of a sample of the nonrespondents.

**74.**   An offshoot of the plan of Politz and Simmons in which the not-at-homes are brought into the sample without call backs.

**75.** Neter, J., E. S. Maynes, and R. Ramanathan (1965), $JASA$, 60.   Studies the effect of matching errors on the measurement of response bias under a certain model.

**76.** Neter, J., E. S. Maynes, and R. Ramanathan (1965), *JASA*, 60. Presents correlations between the reported values, the values matched, the response errors, and the true values for the problem considered in Exercise 75.

**77.** Hansen, M. H., W. N. Hurwitz, and L. Pritzker (1964), "Contributions to Statistics," *Calcutta*. The net difference rate is estimated when observations are subject to errors of response.

**78.** Bryson, M. R. (1965), *JASA*, 60. Upper and lower limits, for the bias of an estimate of the proportion of a population, are obtained when there are errors of classification and the survey is repeated on an identical sample.

**79.** A useful way of exhibiting the total error in terms of response and sampling variances and associated terms.

**80.** Som, R. K. (1966), "Recall Lapse in Demographic Enquiries." This is how demographers propose to diminish the response bias arising from recall lapse.

**81.** Gives the effect of duplicating some units in order to keep the sample size as originally planned.

**82.** Goodman, L. A. (1953), *AMS*, 24. This gives a simple method of improving estimators in certain situations.

**83.** This shows that an unbiased estimator of the variance gives a biased estimator of the standard deviation, the bias being negative.

**84.** Goodman, L. A. (1960), *JASA*, 55. Here is a formula for the variance of the product of two random variables which are not necessarily independent.

**85.** Hanurav, T. V. (1962), *Sankhya*, A24. A sampling scheme generates a unique sample design. The converse is proved here.

**86.** Murthy, M. N. and V. K. Sethi (1961), *JASA*, 56. Discusses a method of simplifying calculations by reducing the number of multipliers.

**87.** Deming, W. E. and G. J. Glasser (1959), *JASA*, 54. Raj, D. (1961), *JASA*, 56. Theory is given for estimating by sampling methods the number of names common to two lists.

**88.** Raj, D. (1961), *JASA*, 56. Extends the theory of Exercise 87 to the case where the two lists are found to be merged into one.

**89.** Hartley, H. O. (1962), *Proc. Soc. St. Sec., ASA*. Gives theory for the case in which two frames are used for sampling a population. As a particular case, the second frame may be a list of the very large establishments in a survey of establishments.

**90.** Searls, D. T. (1964), *JASA*, 59. Presents an estimator superior to the sample mean when the coefficient of variation is known.

**91.** Ajgaonkar, S. G. P. (1965), *JASA*, 60. Gives an example showing that not a single unbiased estimator exists in the general wtr sampling scheme with unequal probabilities when a particular class of estimators is considered.

**92.** Sukhatme, B. V. and M. S. Avadhani (1965), *AISM*, 17. A method of selecting a sample of two different units such that the probability of selecting some nonpreferred samples is reduced to a desired level.  In this example the probabilities $\pi_{ij}$ are given as:

|  | $U_1$ | $U_2$ | $U_3$ | $U_4$ | $U_5$ | $\pi_i$ |
|---|---|---|---|---|---|---|
| $U_1$ | $\cdots$ | 0.10 | 0.08 | 0.26 | 0.22 | 0.66 |
| $U_2$ | 0.10 | $\cdots$ | 0.24 | 0.02 | 0.02 | 0.38 |
| $U_3$ | 0.08 | 0.24 | $\cdots$ | 0.02 | 0.02 | 0.36 |
| $U_4$ | 0.26 | 0.02 | 0.02 | $\cdots$ | 0.02 | 0.32 |
| $U_5$ | 0.22 | 0.02 | 0.02 | 0.02 | $\cdots$ | 0.28 |
| $\pi_i$ | 0.66 | 0.38 | 0.36 | 0.32 | 0.28 | 2.0 |

**93.**  Avadhani, M. S. and B. V. Sukhatme (1965), *JISAS*, 17.  A method of selecting a sample of $n \geq 3$ units under which the probability of selecting some nonpreferred samples is reduced to a desired level.

**94.**  Warner, S. L. (1965), *JASA*, 60.  Presents a method by which respondents furnish information on a probability basis only when they do not want to confide to the interviewer the correct answer to a certain question.

**95.**  Hajek, J. (1959), *Casopis Post. Mat.*, 84.  Pathak, P. K. (1964), *AMS*, 35. The concept of sufficiency is introduced and the Rao-Blackwell theorem used for improving estimators.  A situation covered is that in which sampling with pps is continued till two different units are obtained.

**96.**  Hansen, M. H., W. N. Hurwitz, and T. B. Jabine (1963), *BISI*, XL.  Some problems are considered when the lists used for sample selection are found to be imperfect.

**97.**  Godambe, V. P. and V. M. Joshi (1965), *AMS*, 36.  An example is given showing that corresponding to a nonlinear estimator of the population total, there does not exist a linear estimator which is uniformly better.

**98.**  Glasser, G. J. (1962), *RISI*, 30.  Gives a rule for determining the points of cutoff for sampling skew populations.

**99.**  Tulse, R. (1957), *Appl. Stat.*, 6.  A simple method of selecting the sample when greater representation is to be given to the subgroup of main interest.

**100.**  Marks, E. S. (1948), *AMS*, 19.  Gives a lower bound for the expected travel among $m$ random points.

**101.**  Goodman, L. A. (1949), *AMS*, 20.  Here is a method of estimating the number of classes in a population by examining a random sample selected from it.

**102.**  Durbin, J. (1967), *Appl. Stat.*, 16.  Brewer, K. R. W. (1963), *Austr. J. Stat.*, 5.  A method of selecting two units from a stratum such that the probability of inclusion of a unit is strictly proportionate to its size.

**103.**  The parameters $n$ and $c$ of a single sampling plan are determined when the lot tolerance proportion defective and the acceptable quality level are given.

**104.** Dodge, H. F. and H. G. Romig (1944), *Sampling Inspection Tables.* A procedure of obtaining a single sampling inspection plan by which the cost of inspection is minimized for a specified value of the average outgoing quality limit.

**105.** The product estimator is used when the correlation between $y$ and $x$ is negative.

**106.** Rao, P. S. R. S. and G. S. Mudholkar (1967), *JASA*, 62. A generalization of the ratio and product estimators when auxiliary information on several $x$-variates is available.

**107.** Approximate expressions for the bias and the mean square error of the ratio estimator are obtained for a general sample design.

# REPORT ON AN ACTUAL SAMPLE SURVEY

## A.1 GENERAL

In order to illustrate some of the sampling principles presented in this book, a description of an actual survey will now be given.[1]  This survey was conducted in Greece in April, 1962, as a part of a continuing series of surveys of employment and unemployment in the country.  The object was to produce reliable national estimates of the number of persons unemployed, duration of their unemployment, the number employed by branch of economic activity, etc., and the changes occurring in the size and composition of the components of the labor force since the population census of March, 1961.  The data collected related to the week ending April 8, 1962.  Interviewers filled out questionnaires, specially designed for the purpose, pertaining to members of the sample households aged 10 or more

[1] The survey was carried out by the National Statistical Service of Greece (NSSG) with Mr. B. Helger and the author as UN consultants.  Thanks are due to Mr. P. Couvelis, Director-General, NSSG, for permission to draw on the draft report prepared for the use of the Government.

at the time of the survey. All civilians who passed the night of April 8, 1962, in a private household were the persons covered by the survey. Thus institutional households—hotels, boarding houses, etc.—were outside the jurisdiction of the enquiry and they formed about 3.4 percent of the total population in March, 1961.

### A.2  ADMINISTRATIVE REQUIREMENTS

The sample for the survey was designed under certain administrative requirements. Except for Greater Athens the staff required for making out lists of dwellings for sample selection and for supervision of the work of interviewers was very limited. And the area to be covered by a supervisor had to be kept small for adequate supervision and effective control of the various operations involved. This meant that no more than about 60 primary sampling units (psu's) could be selected in the sample from the countryside.

### A.3  PRINCIPAL RESOURCES AND MATERIALS

A study was made of the material that was available to help make an efficient design. All that the 1961 census provided at that time was the number of persons in each commune or municipality in the country. This data was available by block in Greater Athens and other cities with a population of 10,000 or more, and by ED (enumeration district) in the rural areas. Sketches made at the time of the 1961 census for the ED's and for the blocks were available for possible use in the survey. For other types of information, such as the proportion of population dependent on agriculture, industry, the Population Census of 1951 had to be used.

### A.4  SAMPLE DESIGN

The first step was to divide the country into the three principal strata of Greater Athens, other urban areas with 1961 population exceeding ten thousand, and the rest of the country (semiurban and rural areas, called "rural areas" for brevity). This stratification is important because the rural and urban parts of the country differ widely with respect to labor-force characteristics. In the rural areas the psu used was an eparchie (an administrative unit containing about 33,000 persons). The considerations involved in its choice were the following. It is fairly heterogeneous in character; it generally contains both semiurban and rural population;

it is quite often partly plain and partly mountainous; it is agricultural and somewhat industrial as well.   And, administratively, it is the single largest unit which could be effectively supervised by one survey supervisor.

## SAMPLING IN THE RURAL AREAS

There were 147 eparchies in the country and they differed markedly in their populations.   Some of the eparchies were too small to be efficient psu's.   For this reason twelve of these were amalgamated with neighboring ones to form 135 reasonably efficient psu's.   The next step was to stratify the psu's in order to reduce the between-psu component of the variance. The variables used for purposes of stratification were: 1961 population of the eparchie (excluding the urban part); proportion of the population dependent on agriculture/industry; and per capita cultivated area.   Since about 40 supervisors were available for this part of the sample and each supervisor could work in just one psu, the total number of psu's to be taken into the sample was automatically fixed at about 40.   In order to get valid estimates of sampling error there should be at least two psu's in the sample from each stratum.   Thus in all 20 strata were formed. One of the strata contained the two largest psu's and another psu believed to be highly variable with respect to employment.   All three psu's in this stratum were selected with certainty.   The other 19 strata were made of about equal population of 240,000.   This was particularly con-venient and somewhat efficient.   From each of these strata two psu's were selected in the sample.   The selection in each stratum was made systematically with probability proportionate to size (1961 population) after arranging the psu's at random.   The reason for using pps sampling was that the eparchies differed considerably in size even after stratifica-tion.   Since the estimation of totals was of primary importance, the variability in the size of psu had to be controlled.   With regard to sub-sampling from selected psu's, it was considered desirable to introduce some kind of stratification in view of the considerable diversity within psu's. The second-stage units were the communes which were arranged by alti-tude within each sample psu.   (Previous studies had shown that the employment pattern in mountainous areas was different from that in plain areas.)   Two independent samples, each containing two communes, were selected systematically with probability proportionate to population from each sample psu.   There were thus a total of 164 communes in the sample. The maps showing the ED boundaries for the sample communes were examined.   Within a sample commune the ED's shown on the map were listed along with their 1961 populations (in private households).   From each commune a systematic sample of four ED's was selected with proba-bility proportionate to population.   If the commune contained four or fewer ED's, all ED's in the commune were included in the sample. The supervisor of the psu made a list of all properties (called ekodomies) in the selected ED's by visiting all places there. A sample of properties was selected systematically with equal probabilities. The sampling fractions were worked out at headquarters in order to achieve a self-weighting sample for an expected sampling fraction of 0.5 percent. All households in the sample properties became the subject of further investigation by enumerators trained for the purpose.

### GREATER ATHENS

In Greater Athens, which represents roughly one-fourth of the population of Greece, there was no need to select the sample in large clusters. This is the seat of the National Statistical Service of Greece, which could easily spare a number of its trained employees to work for the survey for a day or two. As a result, the sample here was spread well over the entire area. On the basis of geographic contiguity, the 57 municipalities and communes in Greater Athens were allocated to 20 strata. The strata were made of about equal size (size being judged by 1961 population-census figures). Within a stratum a list was made of all census blocks arranged in a serpentine fashion along with the number of persons in private households in each block. The very small blocks were amalgamated with neighboring ones to form block-clusters of a reasonable size. From each stratum two independent samples, each consisting of seven block-clusters, were taken. In each sample the block-clusters were selected systematically with probability proportionate to the number of persons enumerated in private households during the 1961 census. A list was prepared of all dwelling units in the sample blocks. The sampling interval for dwelling units within block-clusters was so chosen that the sample became self-weighting for an expected sampling fraction of 0.5 percent. The households in the sample dwelling units became the object of further study.

### OTHER URBAN AREAS

The 62 municipalities and communes comprising the other urban areas were stratified on the basis of the proportion of population dependent on agriculture/industry and the rate of population growth (during the last decade). In all nine strata were formed, each stratum containing about 200,000 persons. From each stratum a sample of two municipalities or communes was selected systematically with probability proportionate to the number of persons enumerated in private households during the 1961 Census. Before sample selection the psu's within strata were arranged at random. For each sample psu the census records were used to make a list of all blocks, together with the number of persons enumerated in private households in them. The very small blocks were clustered with neighboring ones. From each sample psu two independent samples, each containing seven block-clusters, were selected systematically with probability proportional to the number of persons in private households. The supervisor of the area went from door to door in order to make a list of dwelling units in each sample block. A systematic sample of dwelling units was taken from each block-cluster, the sampling interval being so determined that the entire sample became self-weighting for an expected sampling fraction of 0.5 percent.

## A.5 PERSONNEL AND EQUIPMENT

The supervisory staff of the survey were the chiefs of the various field offices of the National Statistical Service of Greece. They are men with considerable experience in collecting data in different fields. They were given thorough training at headquarters in the purposes of the survey, the procedures of listing, and the methods of measurement. They in turn trained the interviewers of the survey, who were local school teachers with previous experience consisting of the collection of labor-force data at the time of the census of 1961. While in the field, the supervisors checked the filled-in schedules for obvious inconsistencies, missing entries, etc. When the schedules arrived in Athens, a specially trained staff scrutinized them thoroughly according to instructions prepared beforehand and coded the relevant entries. The data were then transferred to punched cards and the tables produced.

## A.6 STATISTICAL ANALYSIS AND COMPUTATIONAL PROCEDURES

Since the sample was made self-weighting with an expected sampling fraction of 0.5 percent, the estimation of population totals was simply made by multiplying the sample totals by 200. The sampling errors were based on the differences within strata of the two subsamples (eparchies in the rural areas, block-clusters in Greater Athens, and municipalities in other urban areas). This quick method of calculation of sampling errors may not be considered entirely appropriate as far as the rural and other urban areas are concerned, where the psu's were selected without replacement. In order to study this quick procedure as compared with the unbiased, but difficult, procedure outlined in Sec. 6.4, calculations were made for a few selected items using both procedures. Table A.1 gives

**Table A.1   Ratio of the biased to the unbiased estimates
of variance for selected items**

| Item number | Item | Males | Females | Persons |
|---|---|---|---|---|
| 1 | population of all ages | 1.254 | 0.949 | 1.114 |
| 2 | population aged 10 and more | 1.155 | 0.780 | 1.001 |
| 3 | the active | 1.178 | 1.138 | 1.086 |
| 4 | the employed | 1.202 | 1.162 | 1.116 |
| 5 | the unemployed: total | 1.185 | 1.274 | 1.195 |
| 6 | the unempolyed: inexperienced | 1.473 | 1.130 | 1.513 |
| 7 | population not active | 1.140 | 1.230 | 1.144 |

the ratio of the estimated variances in the two cases.   It will be seen that
by and large the biased estimator overestimated the variance, the average
overestimation being of the order of about 16 percent.   To this extent
the estimator is conservative and safe to use (Raj, 1964).

## A.7   PRECISION OF THE SURVEY

Based on the quick estimator of variance, which slightly overestimates the
true variance, sampling errors of a large number of items were calculated.
Table A.2 gives the coefficients of variation of a few selected estimates of

**Table A.2   Relative sampling errors of selected items, percent**

| | All ages | Aged 10 or more | Active | Employed | Total unem- ployed | New unem- ployed | Non- active |
|---|---|---|---|---|---|---|---|
| | | | *All Greece* | | | | |
| Males | 1.7 | 1.7 | 2.1 | 2.2 | 6.7 | 12.8 | 2.8 |
| Females | 1.1 | 1.0 | 3.0 | 3.3 | 7.3 | 7.5 | 2.1 |
| Persons | 1.3 | 1.3 | 1.9 | 2.2 | 5.8 | 7.4 | 1.9 |
| | | | *Greater Athens* | | | | |
| Males | 2.0 | 2.2 | 2.2 | 2.1 | 7.6 | 17.1 | 3.9 |
| Females | 1.7 | 1.8 | 3.2 | 3.1 | 7.1 | 9.3 | 2.0 |
| Persons | 1.6 | 1.7 | 1.8 | 1.8 | 5.6 | 9.1 | 1.9 |
| | | | *Other urban areas* | | | | |
| Males | 4.0 | 3.8 | 3.4 | 3.0 | 12.3 | 25.6 | 5.5 |
| Females | 3.0 | 2.8 | 9.5 | 10.1 | 16.3 | 9.8 | 3.0 |
| Persons | 3.5 | 3.2 | 4.6 | 4.3 | 12.2 | 10.2 | 3.2 |
| | | | *Rural areas* | | | | |
| Males | 2.4 | 2.6 | 3.2 | 3.4 | 16.4 | 25.2 | 4.8 |
| Females | 1.5 | 1.2 | 3.7 | 3.9 | 18.2 | 28.6 | 4.4 |
| Persons | 1.8 | 1.8 | 2.5 | 3.0 | 14.6 | 22.9 | 3.6 |

the population of Greece classified according to activeness or nonactiveness. It will be found that except for the inexperienced unemployed (a very small subclass) most of the other estimates were subject to small sampling errors.

## A.8 QUALITY OF RESULTS

Some indication of the quality of the results obtained from the survey can be had by making a comparison with the census data. The census was taken at about the same time 1 year ago. Table A.3 gives comparative estimates from the two sources, the census figures being based on a 2 percent sample taken for making advance estimates. The comparison is

**Table A.3 Population by activity status, as estimated by April, 1962, survey and 1961 census sample, with sampling errors of differences (all Greece)[1]**

| Item | April 1962, sample (000) | March 1961, sample (000) | Difference (d) (000) | Standard error of difference (s) (000) | (d/s) |
|---|---|---|---|---|---|
| *Males* | | | | | |
| Population aged 10 or more | 3127.8 | 3103.5 | 24.3 | 55.3 | 0.44 |
| Active | 2465.2 | 2390.3 | 74.9 | 52.2 | 1.43 |
| Employed | 2345.2 | 2266.8 | 78.4 | 53.0 | 1.45 |
| Unemployed: total | 120.0 | 123.5 | −3.5 | 8.3 | −0.42 |
| Unemployed: inexperienced | 24.6 | 41.4 | −16.8 | 3.4 | −4.94** |
| Not active | 662.6 | 713.2 | −50.6 | 19.6 | −2.58* |
| Population of all ages | 3940.8 | 3867.3 | 73.5 | 66.6 | 1.10 |
| *Females* | | | | | |
| Population aged 10 or more | 3623.4 | 3509.6 | 113.8 | 36.7 | 3.10** |
| Active | 1618.2 | 1189.9 | 428.3 | 49.5 | 8.62** |
| Employed | 1517.0 | 1076.2 | 440.8 | 50.1 | 8.80** |
| Unemployed: total | 101.2 | 113.8 | −12.6 | 7.7 | −1.64 |
| Unemployed: inexperienced | 51.8 | 46.2 | 5.6 | 4.1 | 1.36 |
| Not active | 2005.2 | 2319.8 | −314.6 | 42.5 | −7.40** |
| Population of all ages | 4365.4 | 4238.1 | 127.3 | 48.5 | 2.62* |
| *All persons* | | | | | |
| Population aged 10 or more | 6751.2 | 6613.1 | 138.1 | 84.7 | 1.63 |
| Active | 4083.4 | 3580.2 | 503.2 | 76.8 | 6.55** |
| Employed | 3862.2 | 3343.0 | 519.2 | 85.9 | 6.04** |
| Unemployed: total | 221.2 | 237.2 | −16.0 | 13.2 | −1.21 |
| Unemployed: inexperienced | 76.4 | 87.5 | −11.1 | 6.0 | −1.85 |
| Not active | 2667.8 | 3033.0 | −365.2 | 50.8 | −7.19** |
| Population of all ages | 8306.2 | 8105.4 | 200.8 | 109.1 | 1.84 |

[1] These figures are not official and are given here for illustrative purposes only.
* Significant at 5 percent level.     ** Significant at 1 percent level.

revealing. The survey gave a far higher rate of labor-force participation than the census. The explanation seems to lie in the fact that "employment" is an elusive character. For many persons (especially women) attachment to the labor force is not a fixed fact but an attitude that may vary considerably according to the manner the questions are asked and the circumstances prevailing at the time of interview. The more careful and detailed procedures of the survey helped in classifying such persons better than the general census.

## A.9  EFFICIENCY IN RELATION TO OTHER SAMPLING DESIGNS

The results of a survey often provide information on the efficiency of the sample design actually used in relation to other sampling designs which might have been used. Based on the present survey, a comparison was made with the following alternative methods of selection of two psu's per stratum in the principal strata of other urban areas and the rural areas.

Scheme *A*   Selection of psu's with replacement with pp to population
Scheme *B*   Selection of a sample of two psu's with probability proportionate to the aggregate population of the sample psu's
Scheme *C*   Selection of the first sample psu with pp to population and the second with pp to the population of the remaining psu's

In all cases subsampling was assumed to have been done according to the plan actually followed.

### COMPARISON WITH SCHEME *A*

Using the formulas given in Sec. 6.6, the amount of gain in precision attained through the without-replacement scheme of the survey as compared with with-replacement pps sampling was calculated for a few selected items. The results are given in Table A.4.

It will be seen that the relative gain in precision averaged about 8 percent, the range being −11 percent to 26 percent. Since the within-psu component of the variance is the same in either case, it would be more useful to see by how much the between-psu component gets reduced in the case of without-replacement sampling. Table A.5 provides data on this point.

The average reduction turned out to be about 21 percent. Thus, as compared to the overall relative gain in precision of 8 percent, the reduction in the between-psu component was more than twice as high. The reason that the reduction in the total variance was low was that the within-psu component (Table A.6) was generally more important than the between-psu component. This was because the psu's had been sub-sampled at a very low rate.

**Table A.4  Ratio of the estimates of variance based on with-replacement sampling to without-replacement sampling**

| Item number | Item | Males | Females | Persons |
|---|---|---|---|---|
| 1 | population of all ages | 1.127 | 0.974 | 1.057 |
| 2 | population aged 10 and more | 1.078 | 0.890 | 1.001 |
| 3 | the active | 1.089 | 1.069 | 1.043 |
| 4 | the employed | 1.101 | 1.081 | 1.058 |
| 5 | the unempolyed: total | 1.092 | 1.137 | 1.097 |
| 6 | the unemployed: inexperienced | 1.236 | 1.065 | 1.256 |
| 7 | population not active | 1.070 | 1.115 | 1.072 |

**Table A.5  Percent reduction in the between-psu component of variance (base: estimated between-psu variance for wr sampling)**

| Item number | Item | Males | Females | Persons |
|---|---|---|---|---|
| 1 | population of all ages | 20 | −12 | 12 |
| 2 | population aged 10 and more | 14 | * | 0.2 |
| 3 | the active | 16 | 17 | 10 |
| 4 | the employed | 17 | 19 | 12 |
| 5 | the unemployed: total | 18 | 20 | 16 |
| 6 | the unemployed: inexperienced | 36 | 86 | 51 |
| 7 | population not active | 13 | 34 | 20 |

* Base zero.

**Table A.6  Estimated between- and within-psu contributions to the total relative variances (coefficients of variation squared)**

| Item number | Males | | Females | | All persons | |
|---|---|---|---|---|---|---|
| | Between | Within | Between | Within | Between | Within |
| 1 | 0.00017 | 0.00017 | 0.000046 | 0.00015 | 0.00010 | 0.00014 |
| 2 | 0.00018 | 0.00021 | 0.0000061 | 0.00016 | 0.000073 | 0.00016 |
| 3 | 0.00026 | 0.00029 | 0.00035 | 0.00068 | 0.00023 | 0.00035 |
| 4 | 0.00030 | 0.00031 | 0.00039 | 0.00075 | 0.00026 | 0.00038 |
| 5 | 0.0034 | 0.0049 | 0.0068 | 0.0055 | 0.0038 | 0.0035 |
| 6 | 0.010 | 0.014 | 0.00014 | 0.013 | 0.0026 | 0.0079 |
| 7 | 0.00052 | 0.00063 | 0.00014 | 0.00050 | 0.00017 | 0.00042 |

## COMPARISON WITH SCHEME *B*

Suppose that two psu's are selected from each stratum with probability proportionate to aggregate size. Let $T_i$ be an unbiased estimator of the $i$th psu total $Y_i$, the estimator being based on subsampling. Let $V(T_i) = \sigma_i^2$ and $\hat{\sigma}_i^2$ denote an unbiased estimator of $\sigma_i^2$. Then an unbiased estimator of the stratum total would be

$$\hat{Y} = X \frac{ST_i}{Sx_i}$$

with a variance of

$$V(\hat{Y}) = \frac{X}{N-1} \sum' (y_i + y_j) \left( \frac{y_i + y_j}{x_i + x_j} - R \right) + \frac{X}{N-1} \sum' \frac{\sigma_i^2 + \sigma_j^2}{x_i + x_j}$$

Let $\pi_{ij}$ be the probability with which psu's $i$ and $j$ are actually selected in the sample. Then an unbiased estimator of $V(\hat{Y})$ based on the present survey would be given by

$$\frac{1}{(N-1)\pi_{ij}} \left[ \left( \frac{X}{x_i + x_j} - 1 \right) (T_i^2 + T_j^2) \right.$$

$$\left. - 2 \left( N - 1 - \frac{X}{x_i + x_j} \right) T_i T_j + \hat{\sigma}_i^2 + \hat{\sigma}_j^2 \right]$$

Table A.7 presents some comparisons between ppas sampling and other techniques including ep (equal probability) sampling. It is clear that

**Table A.7  Comparison of ppas sampling with other techniques**

| Item | Total variance | | | Between-psu variance |
|---|---|---|---|---|
| | ep/pps | ep/ppas | ppas/pps | ppas/pps |
| Males of all ages | 8.5 | 3.2 | 2.7 | 3.9 |
| Males aged 10 or more | 8.0 | 2.4 | 3.3 | 5.3 |
| Number active | 6.8 | 2.3 | 3.0 | 4.6 |
| Number employed | 5.8 | 2.0 | 2.9 | 4.3 |
| Number not active | 3.3 | 2.4 | 1.4 | 1.8 |
| Unemployed: total | 1.6 | 1.7 | 0.95 | 0.66 |
| Unemployed: inexperienced | 1.0 | 1.1 | 0.90 | 0.75 |

for most items ppas sampling was found to be intermediate between equal probability sampling and pps sampling. This could possibly be traced to the fact that ppas sampling is equivalent to the selection of the first psu with pps and the second with equal probability.

## COMPARISON WITH SCHEME C

Now let the first psu be selected with pps and the second with pp to the sizes of the remaining units.   If $\pi_{ij}$ be the probability with which psu's $i$ and $j$ are actually selected in the survey, it is fairly simple to see that an unbiased estimator of the between-psu contribution to the variance would be

$$\frac{1}{\pi_{ij}} \left( 1 - \frac{p_i + p_j}{2} \right) \frac{p_i p_j}{2} \left[ \left( \frac{T_i}{p_i} - \frac{T_j}{p_j} \right)^2 - \left( \frac{\hat{\sigma}_i^2}{p_i^2} + \frac{\hat{\sigma}_j^2}{p_j^2} \right) \right]$$

This formula was used to obtain entries in Table A.8.   The average

**Table A.8   Percent reduction in the between-psu variance**
**(base: estimated variance for with-replacement pps sampling)**

| Item | Males | Females | Persons |
|------|-------|---------|---------|
| Population of all ages | 14.0 | .... | 5.1 |
| Population aged 10 or more | 11.9 | .... | 5.2 |
| The active | 13.1 | 15.4 | 11.4 |
| The employed | 13.4 | 16.3 | 12.6 |
| The unemployed | 10.7 | 13.0 | 10.5 |
| Population not active | 10.8 | 20.1 | 16.4 |

reduction in the between-psu variance worked out to be about 11 percent.

**Further reading**   Raj, D. (1964).   The use of systematic sampling with probability proportionate to size in a large scale survey.   *J. Am. Stat. Assoc.*, 59.

# PRINCIPAL NOTATION USED

Wherever the notation used is not explained, it should ordinarily have the following meaning.

| | |
|---|---|
| $(a_{ij})$ | the matrix of coefficients $a_{ij}$ |
| $B$ or $\beta$ | population regression coefficient |
| $b$ | sample regression coefficient |
| $B(\hat{R})$ | bias in the estimator $\hat{R}$ |
| $\beta_2$ | the fourth moment divided by the square of the second moment |
| $C_2(U,W)$ | conditional covariance of $U$ and $W$ given $H_j$ |
| $C_1(U,W)$ | covariance of $U$ and $W$ over all $H_j$ |
| Cov | covariance |
| CV | coefficient of variation |
| $E$ | expected value |
| $E_2(U)$ | conditional expected value of $U$ given $H_j$ |
| $E_1(U)$ | expected value of $U$ over all $H_j$ |
| ep | equal probability sampling |

| | |
|---|---|
| $\cong$ | is estimated by |
| $\doteq$ | approximately equal to |
| $f$ | sampling fraction |
| $h$ | stratum $h$ |
| MSE | mean square error |
| MVU | minimum variance unbiased |
| $N$ | number of units in the population |
| $n$ | number of units in the sample |
| $\binom{N}{n}$ | number of combinations of $N$ things taken $n$ at a time |
| $P$ | population proportion |
| $p$ | sample proportion |
| pp | probability proportional |
| pps | probability proportional to size |
| ppas | probability proportional to aggregate size |
| $Pr$ | probability |
| psu | primary sampling unit |
| $\pi_i$ | probability that the unit $U_i$ is selected in the sample |
| $\pi_{ij}$ | probability that $U_i$ and $U_j$ are both included in the sample |
| $R = Y/X$ | population ratio of $y$ to $x$ |
| $\rho$ | correlation coefficient |
| $S$ | summation over all units in the sample |
| $S'$ | summation over all different pairs of units in the sample |
| $S_y^2$ | $\Sigma(Y_i - \bar{Y})^2/(N - 1)$ |
| $s_y^2$ | $S(y_i - \bar{y})^2/(n - 1)$ |
| $\sigma$ | positive square root of variance |
| $\sigma_y^2$ | $\Sigma(Y_i - \bar{Y})^2/N$ |
| $\Sigma$ | summation over all units in the population |
| $\Sigma'$ | summation over all different pairs of units in the population |
| $U\|H_j$ | $U$ given $H_j$ |
| $V$ | variance |
| $V_2(U)$ | conditional variance of $U$ given $H_j$ |
| $V_1(U)$ | variance of $U$ over all $H_j$ |
| wr | with replacement |
| wtr | without replacement |
| $W_h = N_h/N$ | weight of stratum $h$ |
| $\bar{x}'$ | mean of the preliminary sample of size $n'$ |
| $Y$ | population total for the character $y$ |
| $\bar{Y}, M, \mu$ | population mean for $y$ |
| $\bar{y}$ | sample mean for $y$ |
| $\hat{Y}$ | an estimator of $Y$ |

APPENDIX THREE

# RANDOM NUMBERS

| 01 | 02 | 03 | 04 | 05 | 06 | 07 | 08 | 09 | 10 | 11 | 12 | 13 | 14 | 15 |
|----|----|----|----|----|----|----|----|----|----|----|----|----|----|----|
| 25 | 19 | 17 | 50 | 50 | 46 | 26 | 92 | 62 | 41 | 27 | 66 | 85 | 60 | 70 |
| 54 | 61 | 41 | 41 | 91 | 88 | 83 | 30 | 32 | 75 | 59 | 03 | 58 | 58 | 83 |
| 97 | 50 | 71 | 35 | 65 | 67 | 15 | 45 | 73 | 09 | 17 | 60 | 68 | 38 | 05 |
| 96 | 17 | 27 | 35 | 82 | 80 | 77 | 28 | 97 | 11 | 26 | 72 | 02 | 88 | 96 |
| 21 | 48 | 84 | 49 | 72 | 93 | 48 | 66 | 75 | 82 | 36 | 33 | 77 | 97 | 35 |
|    |    |    |    |    |    |    |    |    |    |    |    |    |    |    |
| 85 | 12 | 09 | 36 | 72 | 81 | 06 | 73 | 04 | 02 | 03 | 10 | 81 | 34 | 44 |
| 49 | 57 | 40 | 54 | 64 | 88 | 97 | 69 | 03 | 12 | 94 | 45 | 86 | 74 | 66 |
| 07 | 43 | 79 | 37 | 60 | 96 | 75 | 39 | 46 | 33 | 42 | 41 | 29 | 83 | 73 |
| 80 | 07 | 51 | 15 | 59 | 55 | 24 | 80 | 49 | 12 | 61 | 68 | 00 | 44 | 58 |
| 40 | 71 | 81 | 93 | 03 | 03 | 60 | 02 | 42 | 53 | 38 | 35 | 05 | 67 | 73 |
|    |    |    |    |    |    |    |    |    |    |    |    |    |    |    |
| 50 | 24 | 44 | 84 | 14 | 02 | 13 | 95 | 71 | 17 | 46 | 16 | 45 | 72 | 36 |
| 51 | 36 | 08 | 02 | 99 | 65 | 46 | 51 | 84 | 51 | 20 | 85 | 22 | 94 | 38 |
| 62 | 81 | 28 | 56 | 90 | 81 | 19 | 95 | 58 | 41 | 50 | 80 | 91 | 11 | 62 |
| 83 | 33 | 85 | 65 | 91 | 68 | 33 | 17 | 85 | 77 | 15 | 53 | 18 | 87 | 75 |
| 24 | 05 | 75 | 46 | 93 | 05 | 64 | 39 | 09 | 20 | 73 | 52 | 84 | 82 | 81 |
|    |    |    |    |    |    |    |    |    |    |    |    |    |    |    |
| 28 | 40 | 31 | 45 | 53 | 96 | 36 | 84 | 57 | 60 | 99 | 82 | 84 | 93 | 66 |
| 21 | 23 | 47 | 38 | 68 | 53 | 19 | 50 | 06 | 54 | 28 | 00 | 56 | 78 | 63 |
| 00 | 78 | 78 | 51 | 53 | 72 | 74 | 90 | 79 | 03 | 63 | 27 | 02 | 60 | 44 |
| 66 | 96 | 71 | 70 | 61 | 05 | 98 | 64 | 67 | 41 | 35 | 00 | 84 | 20 | 51 |
| 46 | 24 | 17 | 92 | 11 | 04 | 92 | 17 | 17 | 89 | 52 | 52 | 65 | 59 | 36 |
|    |    |    |    |    |    |    |    |    |    |    |    |    |    |    |
| 55 | 69 | 47 | 19 | 10 | 36 | 47 | 63 | 23 | 35 | 15 | 03 | 79 | 56 | 48 |
| 75 | 17 | 81 | 21 | 31 | 84 | 98 | 99 | 77 | 96 | 71 | 72 | 67 | 99 | 24 |
| 35 | 04 | 66 | 64 | 83 | 34 | 75 | 18 | 40 | 58 | 65 | 35 | 98 | 48 | 02 |
| 05 | 83 | 68 | 55 | 63 | 72 | 35 | 53 | 51 | 48 | 26 | 41 | 11 | 16 | 45 |
| 45 | 48 | 17 | 48 | 46 | 21 | 44 | 18 | 99 | 41 | 51 | 94 | 64 | 83 | 03 |
|    |    |    |    |    |    |    |    |    |    |    |    |    |    |    |
| 88 | 44 | 33 | 02 | 47 | 97 | 47 | 04 | 12 | 38 | 93 | 25 | 03 | 29 | 72 |
| 49 | 91 | 93 | 73 | 14 | 15 | 01 | 47 | 02 | 70 | 30 | 96 | 01 | 06 | 30 |
| 45 | 42 | 46 | 06 | 93 | 60 | 41 | 09 | 31 | 29 | 52 | 49 | 68 | 82 | 39 |
| 50 | 69 | 74 | 10 | 51 | 89 | 66 | 51 | 57 | 21 | 54 | 95 | 58 | 76 | 46 |
| 18 | 56 | 73 | 16 | 02 | 87 | 41 | 05 | 13 | 87 | 13 | 61 | 08 | 73 | 29 |
|    |    |    |    |    |    |    |    |    |    |    |    |    |    |    |
| 43 | 73 | 70 | 73 | 19 | 41 | 04 | 60 | 25 | 42 | 09 | 50 | 42 | 45 | 01 |
| 52 | 69 | 34 | 01 | 65 | 33 | 19 | 62 | 22 | 41 | 29 | 65 | 24 | 43 | 22 |
| 01 | 15 | 92 | 69 | 53 | 78 | 68 | 58 | 74 | 08 | 05 | 11 | 38 | 94 | 28 |
| 94 | 46 | 83 | 72 | 49 | 19 | 98 | 09 | 56 | 83 | 25 | 40 | 01 | 22 | 61 |
| 44 | 42 | 06 | 32 | 95 | 17 | 32 | 67 | 80 | 84 | 09 | 69 | 57 | 52 | 92 |

| 16 | 17 | 18 | 19 | 20 | 21 | 22 | 23 | 24 | 25 | 26 | 27 | 28 | 29 | 30 |
|----|----|----|----|----|----|----|----|----|----|----|----|----|----|----|
| 81 | 58 | 85 | 33 | 16 | 11 | 87 | 12 | 17 | 39 | 12 | 11 | 07 | 72 | 20 |
| 60 | 25 | 84 | 42 | 22 | 94 | 38 | 96 | 52 | 03 | 38 | 97 | 12 | 87 | 15 |
| 53 | 12 | 75 | 59 | 76 | 42 | 73 | 48 | 95 | 57 | 51 | 31 | 12 | 50 | 82 |
| 02 | 68 | 01 | 17 | 09 | 00 | 38 | 12 | 31 | 52 | 22 | 24 | 73 | 89 | 09 |
| 95 | 68 | 53 | 92 | 82 | 11 | 96 | 03 | 47 | 31 | 35 | 59 | 02 | 23 | 84 |
| 00 | 32 | 10 | 43 | 45 | 44 | 48 | 02 | 29 | 03 | 71 | 82 | 60 | 44 | 48 |
| 67 | 16 | 84 | 57 | 42 | 18 | 97 | 25 | 03 | 16 | 56 | 57 | 02 | 46 | 13 |
| 11 | 23 | 91 | 28 | 97 | 34 | 06 | 48 | 44 | 87 | 56 | 80 | 11 | 02 | 46 |
| 75 | 25 | 43 | 39 | 13 | 14 | 29 | 63 | 79 | 33 | 69 | 90 | 40 | 59 | 83 |
| 16 | 67 | 93 | 59 | 86 | 81 | 53 | 07 | 69 | 33 | 47 | 40 | 14 | 70 | 07 |
| 25 | 81 | 18 | 46 | 46 | 96 | 68 | 34 | 08 | 88 | 78 | 35 | 34 | 55 | 49 |
| 80 | 49 | 70 | 27 | 17 | 99 | 43 | 11 | 36 | 95 | 04 | 05 | 19 | 52 | 40 |
| 44 | 44 | 96 | 11 | 09 | 82 | 38 | 91 | 73 | 62 | 44 | 72 | 30 | 09 | 91 |
| 46 | 90 | 22 | 50 | 50 | 53 | 83 | 95 | 82 | 13 | 26 | 25 | 16 | 55 | 89 |
| 35 | 48 | 16 | 10 | 07 | 10 | 67 | 28 | 66 | 79 | 16 | 26 | 74 | 55 | 78 |
| 50 | 01 | 66 | 62 | 10 | 38 | 47 | 86 | 17 | 59 | 64 | 26 | 02 | 36 | 17 |
| 13 | 35 | 98 | 13 | 29 | 61 | 37 | 85 | 44 | 14 | 96 | 63 | 98 | 71 | 28 |
| 68 | 37 | 23 | 74 | 77 | 92 | 37 | 14 | 25 | 88 | 78 | 96 | 90 | 90 | 00 |
| 40 | 43 | 78 | 99 | 64 | 47 | 23 | 89 | 80 | 49 | 91 | 95 | 59 | 60 | 06 |
| 90 | 37 | 63 | 74 | 14 | 30 | 64 | 66 | 72 | 38 | 19 | 28 | 01 | 63 | 44 |
| 04 | 84 | 87 | 41 | 64 | 03 | 89 | 57 | 82 | 34 | 07 | 71 | 33 | 49 | 80 |
| 43 | 95 | 90 | 88 | 46 | 27 | 34 | 43 | 61 | 52 | 24 | 53 | 09 | 84 | 27 |
| 94 | 20 | 01 | 52 | 38 | 82 | 74 | 59 | 52 | 76 | 29 | 85 | 59 | 84 | 16 |
| 64 | 04 | 67 | 90 | 38 | 25 | 44 | 69 | 32 | 35 | 04 | 27 | 03 | 98 | 84 |
| 91 | 89 | 73 | 11 | 07 | 29 | 69 | 79 | 89 | 36 | 79 | 99 | 56 | 05 | 63 |
| 24 | 43 | 43 | 01 | 91 | 48 | 33 | 23 | 60 | 63 | 87 | 15 | 15 | 27 | 59 |
| 77 | 67 | 34 | 95 | 86 | 99 | 27 | 54 | 40 | 61 | 32 | 54 | 74 | 63 | 89 |
| 09 | 91 | 95 | 96 | 96 | 59 | 13 | 33 | 76 | 69 | 65 | 15 | 88 | 82 | 08 |
| 36 | 59 | 12 | 33 | 44 | 28 | 85 | 77 | 72 | 84 | 23 | 05 | 57 | 14 | 43 |
| 67 | 03 | 48 | 83 | 77 | 15 | 39 | 38 | 60 | 87 | 93 | 20 | 89 | 37 | 55 |
| 87 | 07 | 87 | 94 | 15 | 70 | 33 | 87 | 92 | 20 | 44 | 52 | 85 | 28 | 63 |
| 70 | 83 | 47 | 08 | 44 | 92 | 03 | 01 | 69 | 36 | 54 | 02 | 85 | 92 | 92 |
| 35 | 61 | 24 | 35 | 08 | 63 | 55 | 43 | 88 | 72 | 23 | 80 | 06 | 83 | 24 |
| 33 | 90 | 47 | 53 | 07 | 64 | 57 | 02 | 75 | 91 | 23 | 41 | 95 | 06 | 18 |
| 10 | 86 | 00 | 20 | 21 | 25 | 38 | 66 | 72 | 50 | 88 | 21 | 00 | 24 | 82 |

# INDEX

Numbers in *italics* indicate Exercises and are followed by their respective page references.